Maths for the future

JIM MILLER

*Deputy Head, Redewood School, Newcastle upon Tyne
and Principal Examiner in GCSE KS4 Mathematics*

GRAHAM NEWMAN

*Head of Mathematics, Prestwich High School, Bury,
Moderator and Chief Examiner in GCSE KS4 Mathematics*

Nelson

Thomas Nelson and Sons Ltd
Nelson House Mayfield Road
Walton-on-Thames Surrey
KT12 5PL UK

Nelson Blackie
Wester Cleddens Road
Bishopbriggs
Glasgow
G64 2NZ UK

Thomas Nelson Australia
102 Dodds Street
South Melbourne
Victoria 3205 Australia

Nelson Canada
1120 Birchmount Road
Scarborough Ontario
MIK 5G4 Canada

First published by Thomas Nelson and Sons Ltd 1994

I(T)P Thomas Nelson is an International Thomson Publishing Company
I(T)P is used under licence

ISBN 0-17-438536-6
NPN 9 8 7 6 5 4 3 2

Printed in the United Kingdom by Hobbs the Printers of Southampton

Acknowledgements

The authors and publishers would like to acknowledge with thanks:
The Guinness Book of Records (Guinness Publishing Ltd) and *The Kingfisher Science
Encyclopedia* (Kingfisher Books) as sources for the interesting facts throughout this
book;
Barclays Bank, Midland Bank and NatWest for permission to use their logos;
*Isle of Man map extract reproduced with kind permission of Michelin from their Road
Atlas of Great Britain, 1993 edition. Authorisation no 93–887.*

The authors and publishers would like to thank the following Examination Groups
and Boards for permission to reproduce the questions included in this book:
University of London Examination and Assessment Council [ULEAC, formerly
LEAG]
Midlands Examining Group [MEG]
Northern Examinations and Assessment Board [NEAB, formerly NEA and NREB]
Southern Examining Group [SEG]
*Pre-1992 questions were not written to address the statements of attainment of the
National Curriculum and must be seen therefore as a guide and not as specimen
questions approved by the Examination Boards. The answers are the sole responsibility
of the authors and have not been provided by any Examination Group or Board.*

The authors and publishers would like to acknowledge with thanks the following
photographic sources: Mike Sturley and Rex Features.

CONTENTS

PREFACE

Mathematics is an essential part of our lives. You may need mathematics for your employment or as part of a search for better qualifications, or perhaps you are interested in exploring the applications and uses of mathematics. This book is designed to guide you and give you a better appreciation of what mathematics can do for you.

This book is written specifically to correspond to the Mathematics GCSE Criteria, and hence to the National Curriculum for Mathematics, up to level 8. In particular, it is aimed at those students who wish to continue to study mathematics up to GCSE level 8, perhaps in search of a better GCSE grade. However, it also offers ample opportunity for practice in mathematics which is used in a range of applications, and is therefore suited to RSA, City and Guilds, and other vocational numeracy and mathematics courses.

To make it easy to use, the book is divided into four sections, each of three chapters, which broadly cover Number, Algebra, Shape and Space, and Handling Data, which are four of the Attainment Targets of the National Curriculum. To enable you to use the book for reference there is both a contents list and an index.

Each chapter is divided into clear sections, providing you with ample worked examples and graded exercises, some of which include questions from GCSE examination papers. Each chapter closes with a few ideas for investigations, which could assist you to meet the coursework requirements of GCSE which relate to the Attainment Target Ma1: Using and Applying Mathematics. Answers to all questions are included at the end of the book.

Maths for the future

USING **1** NUMBERS

Numbers have been used to pass on information for many thousands of years. Prehistoric man has left some records which show they counted using, primarily, the fingers on one hand: that is, in fives. Throughout history numbers have been used in calculations to combine information. Numbers also summarise information. There are many different ways of doing calculations, but they are usually grouped into three methods:

1 Mental mathematics. All the calculations are done in your head; only the answer is written down. Mental mathematics is also used in estimating the accuracy of answers calculated by other means.

2 Pen and paper methods. Calculations are done without the aid of a calculator. Calculations are broken down into easier steps, and written out on paper. This makes it easier to do the problems.

3 Calculator methods. Using the power of today's modern calculators.

1.1 **Mental Mathematics**

In doing calculations mentally it sometimes helps to see the problem 'in your head'. You would then do it in the same way as you would do it on paper. You can also use the value of the numbers, and number patterns, to help you work out the problems more easily.

Example $345 + 173$

Add the units first:	$5 + 3 = 8$
Add the tens next:	$4 + 7 = 11$
Add the hundreds:	$3 + 1 + 1 = 5$
Answer:	518

That is 1 ten and 1 hundred.

Example $5 + 17 + 36 + 3 + 15$

Units:	$(7 + 3) + (5 + 5) + 6 = 10 + 10 + 6 = 26$
Tens:	$1 + 3 + 1 + 2 = 7$
Answer:	76

Use the patterns in the numbers.

Example $7000 \div 20$

$7000 \div 20$

$= 700 \div 2$

$= 350$

Divide each number by 10.

Example 30×0.04

$30 \times 0.\underline{04}$ **There are two digits behind the decimal point.**

$30 \times 4 = 120$ **Ignore the decimal point at first.**

Answer: $1.20 = 1.2$ **Then put the point back in, two places from the end.**

Exercise 1

You must only write down the answers. All working out needs to be done in your head.

1 What do the even numbers less than 10 add up to? *20*

2 A 90-minute video tape is used for a programme of 55 minutes' duration. How much time is left on the tape? *35*

3 There are 41 houses on one side of the street, and 28 houses on the other side. How many houses are there altogether? *69*

4 The hours Jenny worked each day in one week are: 8, 5, 7, 6, 5, 3. How many hours did she work altogether? *34*

5 How much longer is 723 mm than 589 mm? *134 mm*

6 Find the total of £435, £274, and £309. *1018*

7 There are 86 eggs that are to be packed into boxes of six. How many eggs will be left over? *2*

8 How many minutes are there in seven hours? *420 mins*

Exercise 2

1 There are 6000 people who have each paid £20 to attend a concert. How much money is this altogether? *£12 000*

2 A radio charity show asks 4000 people to donate 50p each. How much will this amount to? *£20000*

3 An outing for 200 students will cost £4000. What is the cost for each student? *£2.00*

4 There are 9000 company shares that are to be divided among 30 people. How many shares will each person receive? *30*

5 A box contains 8000 microchips. Each microchip weighs 0.2 g. What is the total weight of the microchips?

6 A 200 kg bag of powder is to be divided into sachets containing 0.05 g. How many sachets will there be?

7 A bottle of oil contains 0.8 litres. How many litres will there be in 50 bottles?

8 How many 20p coins can you get in exchange for £70?

1.2 Pen and paper methods

There are many times in real life when we need to do a calculation without a calculator. It is useful, then, to write the problem out.

Example $600 - 45$

First borrow using the six:

$$\begin{array}{r} {}^{5}\!6^{1}0\ 0 \\ -\ 4\ 5 \\ \hline \end{array}$$

Then using the ten:

$$\begin{array}{r} {}^{5}\!6^{1}9^{\,}0\ {}^{1}0 \\ -\ 4\ 5 \\ \hline \end{array}$$

Then subtract:

$$\begin{array}{r} {}^{5}\!6^{1}9^{\,}0\ {}^{1}0 \\ -\ 4\ 5 \\ \hline 5\ 5\ 5 \end{array}$$

Example 438×27

This is $(438 \times 7) + (438 \times 20)$
  or $(438 \times 7) + (438 \times 2 \times 10)$

$$\begin{array}{r} 4\ 3\ 8 \\ \times\ 7 \\ {}_{2}\ {}_{5} \\ \hline 3\ 0\ 6\ 6 \end{array}$$

$$\begin{array}{r} 4\ 3\ 8 \\ \times\ 2 \\ {}_{1} \\ \hline 8\ 7\ 6 \end{array} \times 10 = 8760$$

Which can be done in one sum:

$$\begin{array}{r} 438 \\ \times\ 27 \\ \hline 3066 \\ 8760 \\ \hline 11826 \end{array}$$

So $438 \times 27 = 3066 + 8760 = 11826$.

Example $672 \div 8$

$$8\,)\,\overline{6\,7^{3}2}\quad \overset{8\ 4}{}$$

The remainder ($67 - 64 = 3$) is carried on to the next digit.

Example $1056 \div 42$

$$42\,)\,\overline{1\,0\,5\,6}$$

$$42\,)\,\overline{1\,0\,5^{21}6}\quad \overset{2}{}$$

$105 \div 42 = 2\ r21$

$$42\,)\,\overline{1\,0\,5\,6}\quad \overset{2\ 5\ r6}{}$$

$216 \div 42 = 5\ r6$

So $1056 \div 42 = 25$ with remainder 6.

When doing division with large numbers it is sometimes useful to write out a times table.

1 × 42 = 42
2 × 42 = 84
3 × 42 = 126
4 × 42 = 168
5 × 42 = 210
6 × 42 = 252
7 × 42 = 294
8 × 42 = 336
9 × 42 = 378
10 × 42 = 420

Exercise 3

Do not use a calculator with these questions. You may use pen and paper to work them out. Set out your calculations clearly.

1 A piece of wood of length 700 mm has 135 mm cut off. What length remains?

2 In a college there are 1435 male students and 1473 female students. How many students attend the college?

3 A workshop takes delivery of 196 tyres. How many cars can have their four tyres changed?

4 There are 12 items in one dozen. How many make 25 dozen?

5 A football pool's win of £1312 is to be divided amongst 16 workers. How much will each receive?

6 A coach has 42 seats; 165 students are expected on a field trip. How many coaches are needed?

7 A lorry is delivering 318 boxes of crisps. There are 48 packets of crisps in each box. How many packets are there altogether?

8 How many felt-tip pens are needed to fill 244 boxes?

This method of calculation was used in India during the twelfth century. To do 456 × 34 set the digits around the outside of the grid. Multiply each pair of digits together, placing the answers inside the grid. Then add along the diagonals, starting from the right; this gives the answer around the outside: 15 504!

1.3 Calculator methods

Many people believe that using a calculator has made mathematics easier. Calculators may have made calculations easier to do, but we still have to understand which buttons to press to get the correct answer, and in which order.

Example A telephone bill is made up of:
(a) a call charge of 110 units at 5.5p per unit
(b) a rental line charge of £25.80.

What is the total bill?

The first telephone was invented by Alexander Graham Bell in 1876.

(a) $110 \times 5.5 = 605$ ◄———— *This answer is in pence. We need to write this*
(b) £6.05 + £25.80 = £31.85   *as £6.05 before adding the rental charge.*

Example Jenny has a basic pay rate of £3.10 per hour. She gets 'time and a half' for overtime. In one week Jenny works 36 hours, plus five hours overtime. What is her total wage for the week?

Normal rate:	$36 \times £3.10 =$	£111.60
Overtime rate:	$5 \times 1.5 \times £3.10 =$	£ 23.25
		£134.85

Time-and-a-half rate is 1.5 × normal rate.

Exercise 4

1 What is the total cost of four rulers at 65p each, and three pens at £1.20 each?

2 An adult ticket for an amusement park is £5.60. Children pay half the adult price. What is the total entry fee for five adults and three children?

3 A video club will give one video free for every six bought. How many videos will be *bought* out of a stock of 105?

4 A car uses one litre of petrol every six miles. Petrol costs 44p per litre. How much will it cost, in petrol, to make a journey of 300 miles?

5 Remi buys a video recorder. The deposit is £80. The 24 monthly payments are £11.25 each. What is the total cost of Remi's video recorder?

6 The maximum mortgage a couple can obtain is (larger salary $\times$ $2\frac{1}{2}$) + (smaller salary $\times$ 1). A couple earn £12 800 and £6000. What is the maximum mortgage they can obtain?

The first gas light was put into a house in Cornwall, in 1972. London received its first gas street-lighting 15 years later.

7 Building insurance is £2.50 per £1000 value; house contents insurance is £6.50 per £1000 value. What is the total cost of insuring a house valued at £80 000, with contents estimated at a value of £30 000?

8 Stanley's gas bill is made up of a quarterly charge of £8.83 plus 44.3 pence per therm. He uses 160 therms in the quarter. What is Stanley's total bill?

Exercise 5

Each of these questions is slightly longer. Remember to write down all your working out, even the calculations you do on the calculator.

1 An apprentice earns £1.70 per hour for a basic week of 35 hours. Overtime is paid at 'time and a half'. Calcuate his total weekly wage if he works the following hours:

Mon. 7 h	Tue. 6 h	Wed. $7\frac{1}{2}$ h	Thu. 8 h	Fri. $6\frac{1}{2}$ h	Sat. (overtime) 5 h

2 What will be the date in exactly 40 weeks from March 3rd?

3 An electronics supplier has the following delivery charges: an initial charge of £5.30 plus 15p for each of the first 50 items, 10p for each of the next 50 items, and 5p for each item thereafter. What would be the delivery charge on (a) 30 items (b) 75 items (c) 118 items?

Present	Previous
72248E	71118

4 These are the readings from an electricity meter over a quarterly period. The cost of each unit used is 6.6 pence. To this should be added a quarterly charge of £8.83.

(a) What is the total bill?

(b) The present reading is an estimate. It should have been 72008. What should the total bill have been?

5 Martin is booking an adventure holiday for a group of families. There are seven adults and nine children: two under 5, one aged 6, one aged 8, two aged 9, two aged 12, and one aged 13.

The cost of the holiday is advertised as follows:

Adult rates	Week 1	Week 2	Children
2 nights	£56	£52	Under 5: free
Each additional night	£25	£23	5–9 years: $\frac{1}{2}$ price
7 nights	£180	£165	10–13 years: $\frac{2}{3}$ price

Martin needs to book seven nights the first week, and five nights the second week. Calculate the total bill for the group.

1.4 Number size

The Egyptians were excellent mathematicians for their time; they used a system not unlike our own:

one ten 100 1000 10 000

So 12 343 would be written:

When dealing with whole numbers we need to have an understanding of the size of numbers. The number 342604523857 has 12 digits, which can be grouped in threes:

342	604	523	857
billions	millions	thousands	hundreds/tens/units

Example Write in figures the number 'forty-two million, four thousand and fourteen'.

Forty-two million =	42 000 000
Four thousand =	4 000
Fourteen =	14
	42 004 014

The usual convention nowadays is that one billion is a thousand million. However, in some cases, one billion is taken to be a million million, which is the old UK meaning.

Example Add a quarter of a million to three-quarters of a thousand.

One million is 1 000 000. One quarter is 1 000 000 ÷ 4 = 250 000
One thousand is 1000. Three-quarters is 1000 ÷ 4 × 3 = 750

250 750

Exercise 6

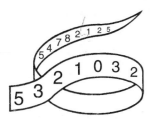

Write the following numbers in figures:

1 One hundred thousand and ten.

2 Three million, one hundred and five thousand, four hundred.

3 One million, thirty thousand, two hundred and fifty.

4 Four hundred and ten thousand, and six.

5 Five million, two thousand, five hundred and nine.

6 Four million, eight hundred and five thousand, and seventy-eight.

Write the following numbers in words, as in questions 1–6:

7 205 103	8 4 030 120	9 990 009
10 8 750 003	11 7 006 207	12 5 100 550

13 Rearrange these cheque numbers into numerical order, smallest first:

605431   650547   649531   631427   650001   609495

14 Rearrange these file reference numbers into order of size, largest first:

2435721   2404321   3571453   3600005
2314373   2450401   2837431

15 Add a quarter of a thousand and half a million.

16 What is twice half a million?

17 Write in figures the number which is three-quarters of a million.

18 Five people share £$\frac{1}{4}$ million equally. How much will each receive?

19 A salary is described as '£22$\frac{3}{4}$K', where K is 1000. Write the salary as a 5-digit number.

20 A company is bought out for £35$\frac{3}{4}$ million. Write this amount in figures.

The highest bid in a corporation take-over was $21 billion for RJR Nabisco Inc. in 1988. The largest company in 1993 was General Motors, with assets of $180 billion.

1.5 Indices

Repeated multiplication is something that occurs in mathematics:

$$2 \times 2 \times 2 \times 2 \times 2 = 32$$

Rather than write out these long problems there is a shorthand way of writing them:

$2 \times 2 \times 2 \times 2 \times 2$ is written as $2^5 = 32$ *index number*

The **index** tells us how many of these numbers we need to multiply together:

$$2^3 = 8, \; 2^2 = 4, \; 2^1 = 2$$

We also have **negative** indices:

$$2^{-1} = \tfrac{1}{2}, \; 2^{-2} = \tfrac{1}{4}, \; \text{etc.}$$

A negative index is another shorthand code to tell us to put 'one over' the answer, that is to write down the inverse. For 2^{-5}:

First work out $2^5 = 2 \times 2 \times 2 \times 2 \times 2 = 32$.

Then write it as $\tfrac{1}{32}$. So $2^{-5} = \tfrac{1}{32}$.

A **zero** index always gives an answer of 1: $2^0 = 1, \; 3^0 = 1, \; 100^0 = 1$

Example Work out (a) 4^3 (b) 2^6 (c) 3^{-2}

(a) $4^3 = 4 \times 4 \times 4 = 64$

(b) $2^6 = 2 \times 2 \times 2 \times 2 \times 2 \times 2 = 64$

(c) $3^{-2} = \tfrac{1}{3^2} = \tfrac{1}{9}$ *The negative index tells us to put 'one over' the answer.*

The largest named number is the centillion, which is a hundredth power of a million, or 1 followed by 600 noughts. A googol is 10^{100}.

To save us some time there is a button on some scientific calculators to help us work out indices: $\boxed{y^x}$

To work out 2^5 press: $\boxed{2}$ $\boxed{y^x}$ $\boxed{5}$ $\boxed{=}$

To work out 2^{-5} press: $\boxed{2}$ $\boxed{y^x}$ $\boxed{5}$ $\boxed{\pm}$ $\boxed{=}$

Note: A scientific calculator will give a negative index calculation as a decimal, not a fraction.

Exercise 7

Work out each of the following:

1 3^4	**2** 4^4	**3** 2^3	**4** 0^2	**5** 5^3
6 1^4	**7** 3^6	**8** 5^5	**9** 8^2	**10** 15^3
11 13^2	**12** 7^0	**13** 2^1	**14** 3^2	**15** 6^4
16 2^4	**17** 9^4	**18** 5^6	**19** 7^4	**20** 3^0
21 2^{-3}	**22** 6^{-1}	**23** 3^{-4}	**24** 10^{-3}	**25** 1^{-1}
26 7^{-2}	**27** 3^{-5}	**28** 8^{-2}	**29** 3^{-3}	**30** 4^0

Find the missing index:

31 $3^? = 27$ **32** $10^? = 1000$ **33** $4^? = 4096$ **34** $11^? = 1331$

35 $2^? = 32$ **36** $9^? = 729$ **37** $6^? = 216$ **38** $5^? = 125$

39 $2^? = 1024$ **40** $12^? = 1728$

Example Work out (a) 2×3^2 (b) $5^2 \times 4^3$ (c) $4^4 \div 2^3$

(a) $2 \times 3^2 = 2 \times 3 \times 3 = 2 \times 9 = 18$

(b) $5^2 \times 4^3 = 5 \times 5 \times 4 \times 4 \times 4 = 25 \times 64 = 1600$

(c) $4^4 \div 2^3 = 256 \div 8 = 32$

Exercise 8 Work out each of the following:

1 $2^4 \times 2^2$ **2** $4^3 \div 2^2$ **3** $4^2 \times 2^4$ **4** $3^2 \times 2^3$ **5** $8^4 \div 4^4$

6 5×6^2 **7** 3×5^3 **8** $4^5 \times 3^4$ **9** $6^3 \times 8^2$ **10** $5^4 \div 5^2$

1.6 Equivalent fractions

Fractions are parts of a whole.

The Egyptians also used fractions in hieroglyphics: they represented a number as a fraction by giving it a 'halo'.

$\frac{1}{4}$ $\frac{1}{24}$

This fraction is represented by 4 out of the 12 rectangles, that is $\frac{4}{12}$. It is also $\frac{2}{6}$, and $\frac{1}{3}$ of the whole shape.

$\frac{1}{3} = \frac{2}{6} = \frac{4}{12}$

These fractions are **equivalent** fractions, they have the same value.

There are many other fractions which are equivalent to these, for example: $\frac{10}{30} = \frac{200}{600} = \frac{16}{48}$

Example Find three fractions equivalent to $\frac{3}{7}$.

(a) $\frac{3}{7} = \frac{6}{14}$ (b) $\frac{3}{7} = \frac{9}{21}$ (c) $\frac{3}{7} = \frac{12}{28}$

Example Complete these equivalent fractions:

(a) $\frac{2}{5} = \frac{?}{10}$ (b) $\frac{7}{10} = \frac{84}{?}$ (c) $\frac{12}{15} = \frac{?}{5}$

We do this by first finding the link between the equivalent fractions.

(a) $\frac{2}{5} = \frac{?}{10}$ ***The link is: ×2 (since 10 ÷ 5 = 2).***

$$\frac{2}{5} \overset{\times 2}{\underset{\times 2}{=}} \frac{4}{10}$$

(b) $\frac{7}{10} = \frac{84}{?}$ ***The link is: ×12 (since 84 ÷ 7 = 12).***

$$\frac{7}{10} \overset{\times 12}{\underset{\times 12}{=}} \frac{84}{120}$$

(c) $\frac{12}{15} = \frac{?}{5}$ ***The link is: ÷ 3 (since 15 ÷ 5 = 3).***

$$\frac{12}{15} \overset{\div 3}{\underset{\div 3}{=}} \frac{4}{5}$$

Exercise 9

Write down a fraction representing the shaded part of each diagram:

1

2

3

4

Complete the equivalent fractions:

5 $\frac{2}{3} = \frac{6}{}$ **6** $\frac{2}{5} = \frac{}{20}$ **7** $\frac{1}{2} = \frac{}{4}$ **8** $\frac{7}{10} = \frac{70}{}$

9 $\frac{90}{100} = \frac{}{10}$ **10** $\frac{15}{9} = \frac{}{81}$ **11** $\frac{18}{21} = \frac{6}{}$ **12** $\frac{4}{3} = \frac{}{12}$

13 $\frac{24}{36} = \frac{6}{}$ **14** $\frac{3}{8} = \frac{}{240}$ **15** $\frac{7}{12} = \frac{84}{}$ **16** $\frac{2}{3} = \frac{}{24}$

1.7 Mixed and improper fractions

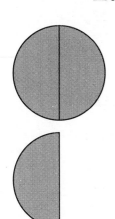

This is the fraction $\frac{3}{2}$ or three halves. This is called an **improper** fraction. It is also one whole circle and one half, i.e. $1\frac{1}{2}$. This is called a **mixed** fraction. When doing fraction calculations we sometimes need to change between mixed and improper fractions.

Example   Change $2\frac{3}{4}$ to to an improper fraction.

$$2\frac{3}{4} = (2 \times \frac{4}{4}) + \frac{3}{4} = \frac{8}{4} + \frac{3}{4} = \frac{11}{4}$$

$\frac{4}{4}$ is the same as one whole.

Example   Change into mixed fractions: (a) $\frac{20}{3}$ (b) $\frac{52}{7}$

(a) $3\overline{)20}$ 6 r2   Answer: $6\frac{2}{3}$ (b) $7\overline{)52}$ 7 r3   Answer: $7\frac{3}{7}$

Exercise 10   Change into improper fractions:

1   $1\frac{5}{6}$ 2 $6\frac{2}{3}$ 3 $7\frac{5}{6}$ 4 $2\frac{1}{6}$ 5 $8\frac{1}{5}$

6   $7\frac{2}{3}$ 7 $8\frac{3}{5}$ 8 $5\frac{7}{10}$ 9 $5\frac{5}{9}$ 10 $3\frac{7}{8}$

Exercise 11   Change into mixed numbers:

1   $\frac{49}{8}$ 2 $\frac{53}{6}$ 3 $\frac{33}{10}$ 4 $\frac{77}{9}$ 5 $\frac{23}{4}$

6   $\frac{84}{11}$ 7 $\frac{29}{5}$ 8 $\frac{60}{11}$ 9 $\frac{59}{12}$ 10 $\frac{40}{7}$

1.8 Cancelling fractions

When doing fraction calculations it is usually helpful to write the answer 'in its simplest form'. This means we need to reduce the numbers in the fraction, wherever possible.

Example   Write these fractions in their simplest form:

(a) $\frac{5}{20}$ (b) $\frac{84}{10}$

(a) $\frac{5}{20} = \frac{1}{4}$ ÷5 ÷5   *Divide by the largest number which is a factor of both numbers: 5.*

(b) $\frac{84}{10} = 8\frac{4}{10}$ *Write this as a mixed fraction.*

      $= 8\frac{2}{5}$ *Simplify the fraction part.*

Exercise 12   Write each fraction in its simplest form:

1 $\frac{6}{15}$ 2 $\frac{21}{28}$ 3 $\frac{16}{24}$ 4 $\frac{3}{18}$ 5 $\frac{22}{55}$

6 $\frac{36}{84}$ 7 $\frac{30}{45}$ 8 $\frac{18}{24}$ 9 $\frac{20}{32}$ 10 $\frac{24}{60}$

1.9 Simple addition and subtraction of fractions

The most common fractions are those with multiples of 2 in the denominators: $\frac{1}{2}$, $\frac{1}{4}$, $\frac{1}{8}$, $\frac{1}{16}$. An imperial ruler divides inches into these fractions: they are easy to change between when measuring inches.

When adding or subtracting fractions with the same denominators (lower numbers) we do not need to change the fractions.

Example   Work out (a) $\frac{5}{6} - \frac{1}{6}$ (b) $\frac{7}{10} + \frac{9}{10}$

(a) $\frac{5}{6} - \frac{1}{6} = \frac{4}{6}$ *Simply subtract one-sixth from five-sixths.*

$= \frac{2}{3}$ *Simplify your answer if possible.*

(b) $\frac{5}{10} + \frac{9}{10} = \frac{14}{10}$ *As we have the same denominator we can add.*

$= 1\frac{4}{10}$ *Write as a mixed fraction where possible.*

$= 1\frac{2}{5}$ *Simplify.*

When using fractions with *different* denominators we need to change the fractions, so that they will each have the same denominator, before we can add or subtract.

Example $\frac{1}{4} + \frac{3}{16}$

$\frac{1}{4} = \frac{4}{16}$ (×4, ×4)   *Change $\frac{1}{4}$ into $\frac{?}{16}$: the link is ×4.*

So $\frac{1}{4} + \frac{3}{16} = \frac{4}{16} + \frac{3}{16} = \frac{7}{16}$

Example $\frac{2}{3} - \frac{1}{4}$

We cannot change thirds into quarters, or quarters into thirds.
We can change them *both* into twelfths, since 3 and 4 both divide into 12.

$\frac{2}{3} = \frac{?}{12}$, $\frac{2}{3} = \frac{8}{12}$ (×4, ×4)

$\frac{1}{4} = \frac{?}{12}$, $\frac{1}{4} = \frac{3}{12}$ (×3, ×3)   So $\frac{8}{12} - \frac{3}{12} = \frac{5}{12}$.

Example $1\frac{1}{2} + 5\frac{1}{4}$

When we are adding or subtracting mixed numbers, we deal with the whole numbers first, and then the fractions:

$$1 + 5 = 6 \quad \text{and} \quad \frac{1}{2} + \frac{1}{4} = \frac{3}{4}$$
$$\text{So } 1\frac{1}{2} + 5\frac{1}{4} = 6\frac{3}{4}.$$

Exercise 13

It is only since the mid 1980s that calculators have been able to do fraction calculations. For many years they were only able to calculate using decimals.

1 $\frac{1}{3} + \frac{1}{3}$ 2 $\frac{5}{10} - \frac{3}{10}$ 3 $\frac{1}{5} + \frac{3}{5}$ 4 $\frac{3}{8} - \frac{1}{8}$

5 $\frac{9}{10} + \frac{7}{10}$ 6 $\frac{5}{7} + \frac{5}{7}$ 7 $\frac{1}{8} + \frac{1}{16}$ 8 $1\frac{1}{2} - 1\frac{1}{4}$

9 $\frac{3}{4} + \frac{3}{16}$ 10 $\frac{1}{6} + \frac{11}{12}$ 11 $\frac{1}{4} + \frac{7}{8}$ 12 $1\frac{3}{8} - \frac{11}{16}$

13 $9\frac{3}{4} - 1\frac{2}{3}$ 14 $6\frac{5}{8} - 3\frac{1}{2}$ 15 $5\frac{3}{16} + 2\frac{1}{4}$ 16 $5\frac{5}{16} + 2\frac{1}{4}$

1.10 Simple multiplication and division of fractions

Example   (a) $\frac{1}{3} \times \frac{6}{7}$ (b) $3\frac{1}{3} \times 4\frac{2}{5}$

(a) $\frac{1}{3} \times \frac{6}{7} = \frac{1 \times 6}{3 \times 7} = \frac{6}{21} = \frac{2}{7}$ *Multiply the numerators, and then the denominators.*

(b) $3\frac{1}{3} \times 4\frac{2}{5}$

$\quad = \frac{10}{3} \times \frac{22}{5}$ *When multiplying mixed fractions first change them into improper fractions.*

$\quad = \frac{220}{15}$ *Then multiply,*

$\quad = 14\frac{10}{15}$ *re-write as a mixed number,*

$\quad = 14\frac{2}{3}$ *and finally simplify.*

Exercise 14

1 $\frac{1}{7} \times \frac{7}{10}$ 2 $\frac{7}{8} \times \frac{5}{7}$ 3 $\frac{2}{15} \times \frac{1}{2}$

4 $\frac{14}{15} \times \frac{2}{7}$ 5 $\frac{4}{5} \times \frac{1}{16}$ 6 $\frac{3}{4} \times \frac{1}{12}$

7 $\frac{6}{7} \times \frac{2}{3}$ 8 $\frac{5}{11} \times \frac{22}{35}$ 9 $\frac{7}{12} \times 4\frac{4}{5}$

10 $2\frac{2}{5} \times \frac{1}{2}$ 11 $\frac{1}{11} \times 8\frac{1}{4}$ 12 $4\frac{4}{5} \times 6\frac{1}{4}$

Example   (a) $\frac{5}{9} \div \frac{2}{3}$ (b) $3\frac{1}{2} \div 1\frac{3}{4}$

We change division problems into multiplication problems by writing down the inverse of the divisor. We then work them out in the same way as the problems in the previous exercise.

(a) $\frac{5}{9} \div \frac{2}{3} = \frac{5}{9} \times \frac{3}{2}$ ***Invert the second fraction.***
Leave the first fraction as written.

$= \frac{15}{18} = \frac{5}{6}$

(b) $3\frac{1}{2} \div 1\frac{3}{4} = \frac{7}{2} \div \frac{7}{4}$ ***Change to improper fractions before***
inverting the second fraction.

$= \frac{7}{2} \times \frac{4}{7} = \frac{28}{14} = 2$

Exercise 15

1 $\frac{9}{16} \div \frac{3}{4}$ 2 $\frac{2}{3} \div \frac{4}{9}$ 3 $\frac{3}{4} \div \frac{5}{8}$ 4 $\frac{5}{9} \div \frac{2}{3}$

5 $\frac{5}{6} \div \frac{1}{8}$ 6 $3\frac{1}{2} \div \frac{3}{4}$ 7 $4\frac{1}{3} \div \frac{1}{4}$ 8 $4\frac{1}{8} \div 2\frac{1}{4}$

9 $4\frac{1}{5} \div 1\frac{1}{3}$ 10 $4\frac{7}{8} \div 2\frac{3}{5}$ 11 $3\frac{1}{7} \div 2\frac{4}{9}$ 12 $10\frac{2}{3} \div 3\frac{1}{3}$

1.11   Using fractions

Now we have the skills to use fractions in problems. To find a fraction *of* a quantity we *multiply* by that fraction.

Example   How many minutes are there in $\frac{2}{3}$ of 2 hours?

2 hours = 120 minutes

$\frac{2}{3}$ of 2 hours $= \frac{2}{3} \times 120 = \frac{2 \times 120}{3} = \frac{240}{3} = 80$ minutes

Example   A train carried 273 passengers; of these $\frac{2}{7}$ travelled first class. How many passengers travelled first class?

$\frac{2}{7}$ of 273 $= \frac{2}{7} \times 273 = \frac{546}{7} = 78$ passengers

Example   A student has £86. He spends £24 on an evening meal. What fraction of the original amount has he left?

Amount left = £86 − £24 = £62.

Fraction is $\frac{62}{86} = \frac{31}{43}$.

Some calculators can do fraction calculations. If you have such a calculator do each question by pen and paper method first, then use your calculator to check your answer.

Exercise 16

Write out each question as a fraction problem. Find the answer, giving any fractions in their simplest form.

1. What is the value of $\frac{1}{12}$ of 180?

2. There are 48 chocolates in a box. Of these $\frac{5}{12}$ have hard centres. How many chocolates have hard centres?

3. A student spends, on average, £24 per week. Of this $\frac{3}{16}$ is spent on bus fares, and $\frac{1}{8}$ on lunches. What is the actual amount spent on (a) bus fares (b) lunches?

4. Which is the larger weight: $\frac{3}{5}$ of 18 kg or $\frac{2}{3}$ of 15 kg?

5. Of 144 rail passengers who were surveyed, 16 claimed their train was regularly late. What is this, as a fraction of the total number of passengers in the survey?

6. During a 30-week holiday season, $\frac{3}{7}$ of the days were wet. How many dry days were there?

7. A salesman had 144 brushes. He sold $\frac{5}{12}$ at 60p each, and $\frac{4}{7}$ of the remainder at 30p each. How much money did he take?

8. Of 204 imported cars, $\frac{7}{12}$ were Japanese. How many imported cars were *not* Japanese?

Example How many bricks will be needed to build a wall that is eight bricks high?

$$8 \times 3\tfrac{3}{4} = \frac{8}{1} \times \frac{15}{4} = \frac{120}{4} = 30 \text{ bricks}$$

Example The cylinder has a diameter of $3\tfrac{1}{8}$ in.
The hole has a diameter of $5\tfrac{3}{4}$ in.
What is the maximum width of the gap between the two?

$$5\tfrac{3}{4} - 3\tfrac{1}{8} = 2\tfrac{6}{8} - \tfrac{1}{8} = 2\tfrac{5}{8} \text{ in}$$ — *Change the denominator.*

3¾ bricks

In the past, the sign " was used to mean inches, but this is no longer very common, e.g. $3\tfrac{1}{8}$".

Exercise 17

1. Two pipes, of lengths $3\tfrac{1}{4}$ ft and $4\tfrac{3}{8}$ ft, are put end to end. What is their total length?

2. If $2\tfrac{1}{4}$ bags of compost are needed for each hanging basket, how many bags are needed for 12 hanging baskets?

3. What is the length of the perimeter of this photograph?

4. A path is to be laid which is $9\tfrac{2}{3}$ slabs long, and $2\tfrac{1}{2}$ slabs wide. How many paving slabs will need to be bought, assuming there is no waste? (Paving slabs can be cut to size.)

5 A glass rod, $5\frac{7}{8}$ in long, has a length of $1\frac{3}{16}$ in cut off. What length is left?

6 Maclad, a stallion, is $14\frac{3}{4}$ hands high. Millady, a filly, is $10\frac{3}{8}$ hands high. What is the difference in their heights?

7 A recipe requires $1\frac{1}{4}$ cucumbers. How many cucumbers are needed to make six times the quantity stated?

8 A mechanic can fit a car tow-bar in $1\frac{1}{3}$ hours. He has 14 tow-bars to fit. How long will it take him?

1.12 Using decimals

The decimals similar to those we use today originated 2000 years ago in China. In using the abacus, it was easy to add extra wires for the decimal parts.

We have already used some decimals in the earlier part of this chapter. Decimals are like fractions; they show parts of a whole.

$$\begin{array}{ccc} \frac{1}{10} & \frac{1}{100} & \frac{1}{1000} \\ 0. \quad 4 & 6 & 5 \end{array} = \frac{4}{10} + \frac{6}{100} + \frac{5}{1000}$$

$$12.7 = 12\frac{7}{10}$$

They are easier to use than fractions, because all decimal numbers are a fraction or multiple of some power of **ten**.

Most decimal calculations are done on a calculator. In this section you will be reminded of the pen and paper methods for doing decimal calculations.

$$\frac{1}{10} \quad \frac{1}{100} \quad \frac{1}{1000}$$

Example (a) $3.1 + 45 + 0.001$ (b) $8 - 0.004$

(a)
$$\begin{array}{r} 3.1 \\ 45.0 \\ + \quad 0.001 \\ \hline 48.101 \end{array}$$

Write out the addition problem vertically. Make sure you keep the decimal points in a line underneath each other (45 can be written as 45.0).

Get the point?

(b)
$$\begin{array}{r} 8.0\,0\,0 \\ - \quad 0.0\,0\,4 \end{array}$$

Write 8 as 8.0 to begin with. Then add as many 0s as you need to make the two decimals the same length.

$$\begin{array}{r} 7\!\!\!/8.\cancel{9}\cancel{0}\cancel{0}{}^{1}0 \\ - \quad 0.\,0\,0\,4 \\ \hline 7.\,9\,9\,6 \end{array}$$

Exercise 18

1 $0.9 + 4.7$

2 $4.2 + 0.8 + 3.5$

3 $4.1 - 2.7$

4 $20.01 - 3.6$

5 $12.03 + 96.6 + 9.1$

6 $9.9 - 1.07$

7 $36 - 0.36$

8 $7.57 + 29.05 + 103.6$

9 $15 + 1.34 + 0.21$

10 $0.9 + 672.3 + 83.21$

Example (a) 3×0.03 (b) 0.651×2.4

(a) $3 \times 0.\underline{03}$ (b) $0.\underline{651} \times 2.\underline{4}$

First count how many digits there are after the decimal point.

Number of digits: 2   Number of digits: $3 + 1 = 4$

$3 \times 3 = 9$

$$
\begin{array}{r}
651 \\
\times 24 \\
\hline
2604 \\
13020 \\
\hline
15624
\end{array}
$$

Ignore the decimal point, and do the multiplication.

On the Continent the decimal point is represented by a comma, and not a dot, as it is in this country.

Answer: 0.09   Answer: 1.5624

Make sure there are the same number of digits after the decimal point as there were at the start.

Example (a) $120 \div 0.004$ (b) $1.25 \div 5$

(a) $120 \div 0.004$

$$= \frac{120}{0.004} \times \frac{\times 1000}{\times 1000} = \frac{120\,000}{4}$$

First multiply by 1000, to change 0.004 into a whole number; multiply both numerator and denominator.

$$4\overline{)120\,000} = 30\,000$$

Then divide as normal.

Answer: 30 000

The first person to use a decimal point was Francesco Pellos, in the year that Columbus discovered America, 1492.

(b) $5\overline{)1.2^25}$ = 0.25

If you are dividing by a whole number there is no need to multiply.

Answer: 0.25

Exercise 19

1 1.2×0.4	**2** 6×1.23	**3** $14 \div 0.8$	**4** $238 \div 0.7$
5 $16.94 \div 1.4$	**6** $42 \div 0.03$	**7** 6.03×11	**8** $6.82 \div 1.1$
9 311×0.12	**10** $0.252 \div 2.1$	**11** 0.81×16	**12** 0.72×48.7

Are you as quick as a calculator?

In 1980 Mrs Shakuntala Devi of India took 28 seconds to work out mentally:

$$7686369774870 \times 2465099945779$$

Her correct answer was: 18947668177995426773730!!!

1.13 Using a calculator

Throughout this book you will be shown sensible ways of using calculators. Calculators and indices were discussed earlier in this chapter. The use of brackets and memory will be looked at in detail in Chapter 5.

In using calculators we have to make sure we enter the numbers in the correct order.

$5 + 6 \times 3$
$\boxed{5}\ \boxed{+}\ \boxed{6}\ \boxed{=}\ \boxed{\times}\ \boxed{3}\ \boxed{=}$
gives 33

$5 + 6 \times 3$
$\boxed{5}\ \boxed{+}\ \boxed{6}\ \boxed{\times}\ \boxed{3}\ \boxed{=}$
gives 23

Which answer is correct?

Mathematicians have agreed a correct order for doing calculations. All $\times$ or $\div$ calculations are done first, from left to right. Then $+$ or $-$ calculations are done, from left to right.

Be careful! Some calculators do this automatically for you, others do not.

Check: $2 + 3 \times 5 - 4 \times 2$

Enter: $\boxed{2}\ \boxed{+}\ \boxed{3}\ \boxed{\times}\ \boxed{5}\ \boxed{-}\ \boxed{4}\ \boxed{\times}\ \boxed{2}\ \boxed{=}$

If your calculator follows the correct order you should get the correct answer of 9. If not, you will need to help it: $2 + 3 \times 5 - 4 \times 2$

$$= \boxed{2}\ \boxed{+}\ \boxed{15}\ \boxed{-}\ \boxed{8}\ \boxed{=}\ \boxed{9}$$

Exercise 20

Work out these calculations:

1 $8 - 6 \div 2$	**2** $12 + 9 \div 3$	**3** $18 \div 9 + 9$
4 $36 \div 9 \times 3$	**5** $6 \div 3 \times 8$	**6** $33 - 27 \div 3$
7 $35 - 6 \times 4$	**8** $3 + 4 \times 5$	**9** $18 \div 9 + 6$
10 $27 - 9 \div 3$	**11** $7 \times 2 - 2 \times 6$	**12** $10 + 3 \times 4 - 17$

1.14 Rounding

ATHLETICS ATTENDENCE

132, 863

Numbers are rounded off to make them easier to handle and compare.

This headline is rarely seen in newspapers. The figures are normally rounded off.

This attendance figure has been rounded off to the nearest thousand.

We round *up* if the number is halfway or more to the next rounding number. We round *down* if the number is less than halfway to the next rounding number.

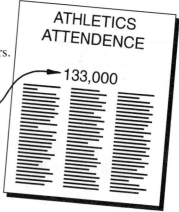

ATHLETICS ATTENDENCE

133,000

Example Round these three numbers, 2345, 2606, 2750: (a) to the nearest 1000 (b) to the nearest 100.

2000 2100 2200 2300 2400 2500 2600 2700 2800 2900 3000

2345   2660

Rounded to the nearest hundred million light-years, the most distant heavenly body is a quasar, at 13 200 million light-years.

(a) If we need to round these numbers to the nearest thousand:
2345 is *less* than half way (2500), so 2345 is rounded *down* to 2000.
2660 is *more* than halfway (2500), so 2660 is rounded *up* to 3000.
2750 is also rounded to 3000.

(b) Rounding to the nearest hundred is done in the same way:
2345 → 2300; 2660 → 2700
But 2750 is halfway between 2600 and 2700, so we round up to 2700.

Exercise 21

Round off each of the numbers (a) to the nearest 1000 (b) to the nearest 100.

1 41 341	**2** 5750	**3** 84 210
4 66 666	**5** 7586	**6** 3050
7 43 216	**8** 5131.5	**9** 47 198
10 1005.9	**11** 1175.6	**12** 1088.8

13 One summer the number of visitors to a museum was 23 893. Write this figure to the nearest thousand.

14 The attendance at a football match was 12 846. Write this figure to the nearest 100.

15 A house extension is estimated to cost £18 986. Write this quotation to the nearest £100.

Example Jenny needs 16 litres of paint, which is sold in 5-litre tins. How many tins will she buy?

To the nearest 5, 16 rounds off to 15 (three tins), but this will not leave her with enough paint. We need to round up in this type of situation. She will need four tins (20 litres).

Example Derek has £85 in £1 coins. He wants to change the coins for £10 notes. For how many notes will he exchange the coins?

£85 rounds up to £90, but Derek hasn't got £90! He will round down to £80, i.e. eight £10 notes.

Exercise 22

1 Tom has £2.59. He needs 20p coins. How many 20p coins will he get for £2.59?

2 Barbara needs 61 tiles for a bathroom wall. The tiles come in boxes of five. How many boxes will she need?

3 A taxi will carry a maximum of five persons. How many similar taxis are needed to take 71 disabled youngsters on a day's outing?

4 An empty tank has a capacity of 85 litres. How many 8-litre containers can you empty into the tank before it overflows?

85 Litres

5 A college orders pens in boxes of ten. It needs three pens for each of its 144 members of staff. How many boxes will need to be ordered?

6 Potting compost is sold in 4-kg bags. If 22 kg are needed for new plants, how many bags will need to be bought?

7 Eggs are sold in boxes of six. If 89 eggs have been laid, how many full boxes will be sold?

8 The number of people allowed in a lift is ten. How many trips will the lift need to make to transport (a) 48 people (b) 62 people?

1.15 Decimal places

Decimal places (d.p.) tell us how to round off numbers.

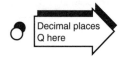

Decimal places
Q here

$$3\,2\,.\,0\quad 3\quad 2$$
$$\uparrow\quad\uparrow\quad\uparrow$$
1st 2nd 3rd decimal place

Example 23.147 Round this number off to (a) 2 d.p. (b) 1 d.p.

(a) 23.15 *The 5 is in the 2nd decimal place. As 7 is more than halfway to the next digit we have rounded up.*

(b) 23.1 *Since in the original number the 4 is less than halfway to the next digit we round down.*

Exercise 23 Round these numbers off to (a) 2 d.p. (b) 3 d.p.

1 3.8597 **2** 9.4185 **3** 29.8314 **4** 0.013 79 **5** 0.9753

6 6.4074 **7** 50.9137 **8** 4.8864 **9** 36.057 57 **10** 9.094

Round off to the number of decimal places given in brackets:

11 7.215 (2) **12** 95.786 (1) **13** 68.89 (1) **14** 29.971 (2) **15** 0.78567 (4)

1.16 Significant figures

Significant figures (s.f.) also tell us how to round off numbers. We can round off either whole numbers or decimals.

```
3   5 . 0   2   7
↑   ↑   ↑   ↑   ↑
1st 2nd 3rd 4th 5th
```

To round off decimals to significant figures we do almost the same as when rounding to decimal places.

Example Round off 35.027 to (a) 3 s.f, (b) 4 s.f.

```
3   5 . 0   2   7        (a) 3 5 . 0      (b) 3 5 . 0 3
↑   ↑   ↑   ↑   ↑                 ↑                      ↑
1st 2nd 3rd 4th 5th            3rd s.f.             4th s.f.
```

In rounding off significant figures with whole numbers we need to know the value of the significant figures:

```
1   4   5   7 . 3   2     The 1st significant figure is the thousands figure.
↑   ↑   ↑   ↑   ↑   ↑     The 2nd significant figure is the hundreds.
1st 2nd 3rd 4th 5th 6th   The 3rd significant figure is the tens, etc.
```

To round off to 1 significant figure, we would round off to the nearest thousand: 1000
To round off to 2 significant figures, we would round off to the nearest hundred: 1500
To round off to 3 significant figures, we would round off to the nearest ten: 1460

Example Round off 339.45 (a) to 1 s.f. (b) to 3 s.f. (c) to 4 s.f.

(a) The 1st significant figure is to the nearest hundred: 300
(b) The 3rd significant figure is to the nearest unit: 339
(c) The 4th significant figure is to the first decimal place: 339.5

Example Round off 0.00718 to (a) 1 s.f. (b) 2 s.f.

(a) 0.007 (b) 0.0072

Exercise 24

Round off these numbers to (a) 1 s.f. (b) 3 s.f.

1 29.05	**2** 5653	**3** 73 423	**4** 0.037 51	**5** 23.51
6 15.435	**7** 62.84	**8** 0.080 99	**9** 467.5	**10** 4090.09

Round off to the number of significant figures given in the brackets:

11 0.1255 (3)	**12** 14.7 (1)	**13** 0.6593 (2)
14 289.5 (2)	**15** 4227 (1)	

1.17 Standard form

The first person to use standard form to advance mathematics was John Napier, who published the first set of Logarithm Tables in 1614. These have now been replaced with the modern calculator.

Standard form is a way of representing large numbers on a calculator.

If you see $\boxed{3.8737\ \ 07}$ on a calculator this means:

$$3.8737 \times 10^7 \text{ or } 3.8737 \times 10 \times 10 \times 10 \times 10 \times 10 \times 10 \times 10$$

In standard form there are two parts to each number:

(i) the decimal part, with the decimal point after the first digit,

(ii) the power of ten by which we should multiply the decimal to change it back to an ordinary number.

Example   Write as ordinary numbers:
(a) 5.231×10^6 (b) $1.09\ \ 05$ (c) 1.423×10^{-4}

(a) $5.231 \times 10^6 = 5.231 \times 1\ 000\ 000 = 5\ 231\ 000$

(b) $1.09\ \ 05 = 1.09 \times 100\ 000 = 109\ 000$

(c) $1.423 \times 10^{-4} = 1.423 \times 0.0001 = 0.000\ 142\ 3$

Exercise 25

Write each of the following numbers as ordinary numbers.

1 7.5×10^{-4}	**2** 9.8×10^{-3}	**3** 3.75×10^{-5}
4 1.6×10^6	**5** 1.01×10^{-3}	**6** 7.63×10^5
7 6.2×10^3	**8** 7.0×10^4	**9** 9.21×10^{-3}
10 9.83×10^6		

Example   Write these numbers in standard form:
(a) 31420   (b) 0.0432   (c) 0.0052

(a) $31420 = 3.142 \times 10\ 000 = 3.142 \times 10^4$

(b) $0.0432 = 4.32 \div 100 = 4.32 \times 10^{-2}$

(c) $0.0052 = 5.2 \div 1000 = 5.2 \times 10^{-3}$

Exercise 26

Write each of the following numbers in standard form:

1 0.07	**2** 4500	**3** 0.35
4 800 000	**5** 0.008	**6** 0.027
7 24 000	**8** 0.0069	**9** 4000
10 14 000	**11** 0.000 008 5	**12** 0.0009

The mass of the sun is 1.9889×10^{27} tonnes, compared with the mass of the earth at 5.974×10^{18} tonnes.

You can also put standard form numbers into your calculator to answer problems.

Use the $\boxed{\text{EE}}$ or $\boxed{\text{EXP}}$ button on your calculator.

For example, you would put in 2.1×10^{-2} as $\boxed{2}\ \boxed{\cdot}\ \boxed{1}\ \boxed{\text{EXP}}\ \boxed{2}\ \boxed{+/-}$.

Exercise 27

Use your calculator to work out these problems. The answer to each question should be written (a) in standard form (b) as an ordinary number.

The weight of a graviton is 7.6×10^{-67} g, which is considerably lighter than the neutrino, which weighs 1.8×10^{-32} g.

1 $(1.3 \times 10^3) \times (6 \times 10^{-7})$	**2** $(6 \times 10^6) \times (2 \times 10^2)$
3 $(4 \times 10^8) \times (6 \times 10^{-3})$	**4** $(8 \times 10^{-3}) \times (4 \times 10^{-4})$
5 $(4.8 \times 10^3) \times (8 \times 10^{-4})$	**6** $(6 \times 10^5) \times (2 \times 10^2)$
7 $(6 \times 10^5) \times (2 \times 10^{-3})$	**8** $(7.2 \times 10^{-7}) \times (9 \times 10^3)$

1.18 Approximation and estimation

There are many times when we may want to approximate or estimate the answer to a calculation. For example, to see whether a calculator answer is reasonable whilst shopping, or to make a rough guess at a calculation at work. These require you to make an estimate. We can make such problems easier to do without a calculator by rounding, usually to the nearest 10 or 100.

Example Estimate the total of: £1.32 + £2.15 + 97p + 65p

£1.30 + £2.20 + £1.00 + 70p   ***Round the amounts to the nearest 10p.***

    +   +   ***Add in suitable pairs.***

= £3.20 + £2 = £5.20

Example $2.3475 \times 4.4273 = 10.393$. Use estimation to check whether the answer could be correct.

Round off to 2 significant figures: $2.3 \times 4.4 = \underline{10}.12$
We have rounded off to two significant figures, and used these rounded figures to do a calculation. This makes all the figures after the second significant figure in the answer inaccurate. Ignore them! Comparing the two 10s the answer appears to be accurate enough.

Exercise 28

Estimates of the circumference of the earth (in miles) are: Aristotle (fourth century BC) 40,000; Archimedes (third century BC) 30,000; Eratosthenes (second century BC) 25,000. True distance: 24850–24900.

Estimate the answers to these problems:

1 £1.38 + £2.49 + 78p + £1.03

2 344 g + 125 g + 270 g + 96 g

3 103 mm + 63 mm + 139 mm + 78 mm

4 £237 + £48 + £149 + £153

5 42 kg + 231 kg + 157 kg + 126 kg + 82 kg

6 152 cm + 302 cm − 48 cm + 98 cm − 121 cm

Use estimation to check the answers to these problems. Are they roughly correct or incorrect?

7 $48.25 \times 16.4 = 791.3$

8 $39.65 \times 0.953 = 37.786$

9 $36.803 \div 4.23 = 8.135$

10 $6.666 \div 0.384 = 17.36$

1.19 Appropriate accuracy

The examples in the previous section show us that there is sometimes a limit on the accuracy of an answer. This happens when the numbers we use have already been rounded.

Example 4.32 and 5.47 have both been rounded to 2 decimal places. Write down a reliable answer to 4.32×5.47.

$4.32 \times 5.47 = 23.6304$ *But this is inaccurate to two or more decimal places.*

Answer: 23.6   *Round off to one decimal place.*

Example 5420 and 5.47 have both been rounded to 3 significant figures. Write down an accurate answer to $5420 \div 5.47$.

$5420 \div 5.47 = 973.07$ *An accurate answer needs to be written to 2 significant figures.*

Answer: 970

A reasonable answer should have no more significant figures than that of any of the numbers in the calculation.

Exercise 29

Write down an answer, expressed to an appropriate accuracy. Each of the numbers below has been rounded.

1 12.97×0.35

2 0.612×20.471

3 $136.74 \div 8.60$

4 3.142×5.217

5 $2130 \div 3.57$ (3 s.f.)

6 6.213×15.24 (4 s.f.)

7 $54\,200 \div 43.2$ (3 s.f.)

8 $142.2 \div 7.2$

9 10.23×5.10

10 $12 \div 0.020$ (2 s.f.)

5.8 m

Bedroom   3.4 m

38 cm

11 Write down a reliable figure for the perimeter of the bedroom.

12 A field has dimensions of 48 m by 36 m, to the nearest metre. Write down a reliable figure for the area of the field.

13 The circumference of a lamp shade is 38 cm, to the nearest centimetre. What length of material would you buy to add a frill round 20 similar lampshades?

14 The diameter of a circular pond is 2.37 m. To find the circumference use $C = \pi D$, where π is 3.14, to 2 decimal places. Write a reliable answer for the circumference.

15 The classroom of a college measures 8.4 m by 5.3 m. What is the total floor area of 12 similar classrooms? Write your answer to an appropriate accuracy.

Note: Normally we write down the full and complete answer to a mathematical problem. We only write down an answer appropriately rounded when we have a practical situation where the figures have previously been rounded. In your working out always show your complete answer, followed by your appropriately rounded answer.

Review

Exercise 30   Do not use a calculator in this exercise.

Work out mentally:

1 How much longer is 627 mm than 439 mm?

2 Find the total of £327, £503, £239.

3 If 78 pens are to be placed into boxes of eight pens each, how many pens are left over?

4 A thimble weighs 8.5 g. What is the total weight of six of these thimbles?

5 A 200 ml bag of blood is emptied in drips of 0.2 ml. How many drips will a full bag hold?

You may use pen and paper methods to work out the answers to these remaining questions.

6 A graphical calculator costs £35. How much will 238 graphical calculators cost?

7 A local politician shares out 2103 local addresses equally amongst her 48 party volunteers. Any remaining she will visit herself. How many will the politician visit?

8 A sunflower is 933 mm tall. In a week it grows another 487 mm. How tall is it now?

9 A piece of wood, 600 mm in length, has 188 mm cut off. What length remains?

10 How many seconds are there in a day?

Without using a calculator, *estimate* the answers to these problems:

11 £4.21 + £1.53 + 80p + £3.48   **12** 58.4 × 849

13 98.99 ÷ 10.05   **14** £39.99 − (£1.52 × 5)

15 432 mg − 180 mg + 503 mg − 693 mg

Exercise 31

1 Add £$\frac{1}{2}$M to £35$\frac{1}{2}$K, where K = £1000, and M is a million.

2 Write in figures the number three million, four hundred and eight thousand, and five.

3 £5 407 890. (a) Write this number in words. (b) Round off this number (i) to the nearest £1000 (ii) to the nearest £100 (iii) to 4 significant figures.

4 Work out (a) 6^5 (b) 4^{-3} (c) 3^4 (d) 5^0 (e) $5^2 \times 4^3$ (f) $9^4 \div 3^3$.

5 Work out the following. Write your answers in their simplest form.

(a) $\frac{7}{12} = \frac{?}{36}$ (b) $\frac{1}{2} + \frac{1}{5}$ (c) $2\frac{3}{4} + 4\frac{2}{3}$ (d) $\frac{6}{7} - \frac{2}{3}$

(e) $2\frac{1}{2} - 1\frac{1}{3}$ (f) $\frac{3}{8} \times \frac{5}{6}$ (g) $3\frac{1}{2} \times 3\frac{1}{2}$ (h) $\frac{1}{3} \div \frac{3}{4}$

6 Six nails are each of length $1\frac{2}{3}$ inch. What is the total length when the nails are placed end to end?

7 How many pieces, each $\frac{2}{3}$ yd long, can be cut from a rope $2\frac{2}{3}$ yd long?

8 Five students out of a class of 30 were not wearing trainers. What fraction were wearing trainers?

9 Which is the heavier weight: $\frac{4}{5}$ of 35 kg, or $\frac{3}{4}$ of 36 kg?

10 Round off your answers to the following to 2 decimal places:

(a) 43.12 ÷ 1.4   (b) 1.42 × 3.9   (c) 7.401 × 0.8   (d) 43.21 ÷ 9

11 Round off your answers to the following to 3 significant figures:

(a) 210 × 34.7   (b) 434 ÷ 0.7   (c) 10.42 × 6.1   (d) 50.05 × 0.07

12 Write your answers to the following problems (i) in standard form (ii) an ordinary number:

(a) 3.2 × 0.008   (b) 3200 × 6700   (c) $3 \times 10^{-3} \times 5 \times 10^6$

Exercise 32

The following questions are all taken from GCSE papers.

1 The reference numbers of eight records are as follows:

21494731, 41239410, 41249372, 10504125, 10004527, 40425178, 11509273, 40901079.

Place these numbers in numerical order.   *(2 marks)*

[NEA]

2 A petrol tank is $\frac{3}{8}$ full. When a further 35 litres of petrol are put in, the tank will be completely full.

How many litres are there in a full tank?   *(3 marks)*

[NEA]

3 Louise and Matthew have their cars insured under a joint policy. They have received their renewal notice, and have to decide how they will pay the bill.

Motor Insurance Renewal	
First car: Net balance due:	£102.55
Second car: Net balance due:	£125.72
Alternative method of payment: deposit	£45.85
+ four consecutive monthly payments of	£48.34

How much more does it cost to pay by the alternative method? *(4 marks)*
[NEA]

4 Write in words the value of the digit 3 in the following numbers:
(a) 7342 *(1 mark)*
(b) 7.342 *(1 mark)*
[MEG]

5 Find the remainder when 12345 is divided by 37. *(2 marks)*
[MEG]

6 Light travels at 298 000 kilometres in 1 second. A light year is the distance travelled by light in 1 year. Calculate, in kilometres, giving your answer correct to 3 significant figures, how far light travels in a year of 365 days. *(4 marks)*
[LEAG]

7 (a) Calculate the value of
   (i) 5^3, *(1 mark)*
   (ii) 5^{-3}. *(1 mark)*

   (b) Find the smallest integer value of n for which 5^n is larger than five thousand. *(2 marks)*
[NEA]

8 I set off to town with a £5 note in my pocket.
I catch a bus which costs me 50p for a return fare.
I buy a candy bar for 21p, a can of cola for 30p, a pen for 95p and five 15p stamps.
I then met a friend who paid me the 50p he owed me, how much money do I return home with? *(4 marks)*
[LEAG]

9 (a) About two and half million people live in Birmingham.
   Write this number in figures. *(1 mark)*

   (b) Write £20 022 in words. *(1 mark)*
[MEG]

First Reading   Second Reading

10 Mr Baker reads his electricity meter every quarter to check on his electricity bill. These are the readings he made.

(a) How many units of electricity have been used by the Baker household between the two meter readings?   *(2 marks)*

Electricity costs 7.2p per unit.
(b) Work out the cost of the units used.   *(2 marks)*

There is a standing charge of £3.75 a quarter on the electricity bill.
(c) What is the total cost of Mr Baker's electricity bill for this quarter?   *(2 marks)*

Mr Baker saves £5 a week towards his electricity bill.
(d) How much does he save each quarter (13 weeks)?   *(2 marks)*

(e) What is the difference between the bill and the amount Mr Baker has saved?   *(2 marks)*
[LEAG]

11 On Bob's 45th birthday his children Leon, Kate, Luke and Lara are aged 15, 9, 5 and 3 respectively.

(a) On Bob's 49th birthday which of his children will have an age which is a factor of Bob's age?   *(1 mark)*

(b) On Bob's 43rd birthday what was the difference between his age and the combined ages of his children?   *(2 marks)*

(c) How old will Bob be when the combined ages of his children becomes more than his age?   *(2 marks)*
[SEG]

12 (a) Write down the value of 4^3.   *(1 mark)*

(b) Write down the value of 2^n, when
   (i) $n = 0$ *(1 mark)*
   (ii) $n = -1$.   *(1 mark)*
[SEG]

13 The mass of one electron is

0.000 000 000 000 000 000 000 000 92 grams

(a) Write this number in standard form.   *(2 marks)*

(b) Writing your answers in standard form, what would be the mass of
   (i) 3 electrons,
   (ii) three million electrons?   *(4 marks)*
[NEA]

14 (a) Express the number 302 176 637 in standard form.   *(2 marks)*

(b) Give an approximation for the number 302 176 637 correct to 3 significant figures.   *(1 mark)*

(c) At the Pompidou Centre in Paris a number is displayed which decreases by one every second. Thus, it decreases by 60 every minute. At present, Monday 4 June 1990, it reads 302 176 637.

What will the date be when the number displayed reaches zero? Show your calculations and estimates carefully. *(4 marks)*

[LEAG]

It's a fact!
– SOMEONE IN THE UK IS BURGLED EVERY 66 SECONDS –

15 Assuming that this statement is true, find correct to 2 significant figures, the number of burglaries in the UK in 1 year. *(3 marks)*

[MEG]

16 Imran wants to buy a radio cassette player but wants to get the best deal possible. He has found two ways to buy the item he wants.

(i) He can buy it from his mother's catalogue by paying £4 per week for 15 weeks.
Work out the cost by this method. *(2 marks)*

(ii) He can buy it from a shop by taking out a hire purchase (HP) agreement.
The cash price is £55 and the HP terms require a deposit of 10% and 12 monthly instalments of £4.75.
Work out the cost by this method. *(3 marks)*

(iii) Which is Imran's best deal? *(1 mark)*

[LEAG]

17 Express the following fractions as decimals.

(a) $\frac{5}{8}$ *(1 mark)*

(b) (i) $\frac{1}{13}$ to three significant figures *(1 mark)*

(ii) $\frac{7}{9}$ to four decimal places *(1 mark)*

(iii) $\frac{5}{11}$ to thirteen decimal places *(2 marks)*

[NEA]

18 The lengths of material required to make up a blouse and skirt in an old pattern were

Blouse

Bust in inches	32	34	36	38
Material in yards	$1\frac{5}{8}$	$1\frac{3}{4}$	$1\frac{7}{8}$	2

Skirt

Waist in inches	24	26	28	30
Material in yards	$2\frac{1}{2}$	$2\frac{5}{8}$	$2\frac{3}{4}$	$2\frac{7}{8}$

(a) How many yards of material would be needed to make a blouse for a woman with a 34 inch bust? *(1 mark)*

(b) How many yards of material would be needed to make a skirt for a woman with a 26 inch waist? *(1 mark)*

(c) Susan has a 34 inch bust and a 26 inch waist.
She decides to make herself a matching blouse and skirt.
Working in fractions calculate the total number of yards of material she should buy. *(2 marks)*
[LEAG]

19 The number of kilometres from Earth to Mars is approximately 230 000 000.

(a) Write this number in standard form. *(1 mark)*

(b) A space rocket takes 2 years to travel from Earth to Mars. Given that there are 365 days in a year, calculate

(i) the number of hours in 2 years, *(2 marks)*

(ii) the average speed of the space rocket in kilometres per hour, correct to 1 significant figure. *(2 marks)*
[MEG]

20 Jim had been taught about Standard Form.
"The Eiffel Tower is 2.95×10^5 millimetres high!" he said.
Write down the height of the Eiffel Tower in metres. *(2 marks)*
[MEG]

Ideas for investigations

1 The area of a rectangle = length × width.
The measurements for the length and width have both been rounded to one decimal place.

Choose your own figures to work with.

(a) What is the (i) maximum (ii) minimum length possible?

(b) What is the (i) maximum (ii) minimum width possible?

(c) What is the (i) maximum (ii) minimum area possible?

(d) What is the difference between the maximum and minimum areas?

Repeat the investigation for different figures. How does your choice of figures affect your results? What happens if your figures are rounded to two decimal places? Or to one, two significant figures?

2 Multiply several powers of 2 together (e.g. $2^2 \times 2^3 \times 2^2 = 2^?$) writing your answer in index form. Repeat, with a different combination of powers of 2. Repeat with several combinations of powers of 3 (e.g. $3^3 \times 3^2 \times 3^3 \times 3^4 = 3^?$). What do you find this time?

Can you find a rule which you can easily use to find the answer in cases like this? If so, describe your rule, and show that it works for other examples/numbers.

Can you find a rule that works when you divide two identical numbers with different powers (e.g. $3^7 \div 3^2$)?

3 Jillian collected a box of apples from her tree. She used half of them for a pudding. She then used half of the remainder for a pie. She gave three-quarters of those that were left to her children for lunch, and had two left over. How many apples did she get from the tree?

Describe any strategies that you use (even if they don't work). Show, in detail, how you obtain the answer.

4 Susan has £200 to spend on athletics badges. She tries a number of suppliers. Susan wants to buy exactly 100 badges. For each of the following suppliers show whether it is possible to buy exactly 100 badges.

(a) Badges Incorporated: Gold badges are £20 each, silver £1 each, and bronze 20p each.

(b) Signatories PLC: Gold badges are £20 each, silver £1 each, and bronze are two for 50p.

(c) Make up your own companies and prices.

PERCENTAGES 2

2.1 Percentages

'One hundred' is one of the most important numbers in mathematics. In so many ways the number 100 is used in problems:

$$100 \text{ cm} = 1 \text{ m} \qquad 100\text{p} = £1 \qquad 3.27 = 3\frac{27}{100} \qquad 100\text{c} = \$1$$

Percentages also use the number 100 – percentages are directly linked to the number 100, since each per cent is one hundredth.

Example Change the following percentages into (a) a decimal (b) a fraction:
17%, 20%, 12½%

$$17\% \rightarrow \frac{17}{100} \rightarrow \text{(a)} \ 0.17 \qquad \text{(b)} \ \frac{17}{100}$$

$$20\% \rightarrow \frac{20}{100} \rightarrow \text{(a)} \ 0.20 = 0.2 \qquad \text{(b)} \ \frac{1}{5}$$

$$12\tfrac{1}{2}\% \rightarrow \frac{12\frac{1}{2}}{100} \rightarrow \text{(a)} \ 0.125 \qquad \textit{On a calculator, 12.5 ÷ 100 is 0.125.}$$

$$\text{(b)} \quad \frac{12\frac{1}{2}}{100} = \frac{25}{200} = \frac{1}{8} \qquad (\times 2)$$

Exercise 1 Write each of the percentages as (a) a decimal (b) a fraction.

1 40%	**2** 35%	**3** 15%	**4** 44%
5 27%	**6** 82½%	**7** 32½%	**8** 17½%
9 4¾%	**10** 15¼%		

To change a decimal or a fraction into a percentage we multiply by 100.

Example Change the following decimals into a percentage: 0.7, 0.19, 0.345

$$0.7 \times 100 = 70\%$$
$$0.19 \times 100 = 19\%$$
$$0.345 \times 100 = 34.5 \text{ or } 34\tfrac{1}{2}\%$$

Example Change the following into a percentage: $\frac{3}{5}, \frac{5}{8}, \frac{1}{3}$

$$\tfrac{3}{5} \times 100 = \tfrac{300}{5} = 60\%$$
$$\tfrac{5}{8} \times 100 = \tfrac{500}{8} = 62.5\% \text{ or } 62\tfrac{1}{2}\%$$
$$\tfrac{1}{3} \times 100 = \tfrac{100}{3} = 33.33\% \text{ or } 33\tfrac{1}{3}\%$$

Exercise 2   Write each of the following as percentages:

1 0.3   **2** $\frac{1}{2}$ **3** 0.35   **4** $\frac{3}{8}$ **5** $\frac{4}{5}$

6 1.32   **7** 0.3125   **8** $\frac{5}{16}$ **9** $\frac{7}{12}$ **10** $\frac{15}{16}$

Example   What percentage of these diagrams are shaded?

$\frac{1}{3} = 33\frac{1}{3}\%$ $\frac{1}{8} = 12\frac{1}{2}\%$ $\frac{4}{9} = 44\frac{4}{9}\%$

Exercise 3   Write each shaded part as a percentage of the whole.

1   **2**   **3**   **4**

The Egyptians thought that the fraction $\frac{2}{3}$ had magical properties. Whenever they had to find $\frac{1}{3}$ of something, they always used to find $\frac{2}{3}$ and then divide by 2!

5   **6**   **7**   **8**

Exercise 4   Write in order of size, starting with the smallest.

1 $50\%, \frac{3}{5}, 0.4$ **2** $32\%, \frac{1}{5}, 0.35$ **3** $33\%, \frac{1}{3}, 0.3$ **4** $0.80, 70\%, \frac{3}{4}$

5 $28\%, \frac{7}{20}, 0.25$ **6** $63\%, \frac{3}{5}, 0.65$ **7** $59\%, \frac{9}{20}, 0.55$ **8** $75\%, \frac{5}{8}, 0.7$

2.2   **Finding percentages**

Percentages are always fractions of one hundred. Percentages are a convenient way of showing fractions of quantities. We frequently need to change these percentage fractions back into actual quantities.

When finding percentages of money, you may need to round off the answer to the nearest penny.

Example   Find (a) 16% of £14.00 (b) 10% of £2.25 (c) $12\frac{1}{2}$% of £59.40

(a) 16% of £14.00 $= \frac{16}{100} \times 14.00 = \frac{224}{100} = £2.24$

(b) 10% of £2.25 $= \frac{10}{100} \times 2.25 = \frac{22.5}{100} = £0.225 = £0.23$ to the nearest penny

(c) $12\frac{1}{2}$% of £59.40 $= \frac{12.5}{100} \times 59.40 = \frac{742.5}{100} = £7.425 = £7.43$
to the nearest penny

We can find percentages of any quantity, including measurements.

Note: Some calculators have percentage keys. How they work depends upon the calculator. If you have a % key, find out how it works. For example to find 16% of £14.00 press the following keys:

$\boxed{1}$ $\boxed{4}$ $\boxed{\times}$ $\boxed{1}$ $\boxed{6}$ $\boxed{\%}$ ***Do not press*** $\boxed{=}$.

You should get the answer 2.24.

Exercise 5   Find:

1 10% of £80	**2** 15% of £7.20	**3** 20% of 80 g
4 40% of 150 mm	**5** 25% of 36 kg	**6** 10% of 30 cm
7 5% of 300 t	**8** 35% of £23	**9** 15% of £4.80
10 8% of 500 m		

2.3 **Increase and decrease by a percentage**

Percentages are frequently used to represent an increase or a decrease of a quantity. There are two commonly used methods for working out increase or decrease. The choice of which to use is yours!

Example   'Local Government Officers receive a $5\frac{1}{2}$% wage increase.'
Shreena works for the local council. Her salary is £12 800.
What will be her new salary?

Method 1:

£12 800 $\times \frac{5.5}{100} = \frac{70400}{100} = £704$ increase

New salary is £12 800 + £704 = £13 504

34

Or by calculator keys: $\boxed{1}$ $\boxed{2}$ $\boxed{8}$ $\boxed{0}$ $\boxed{0}$ $\boxed{\times}$ $\boxed{5}$ $\boxed{\cdot}$ $\boxed{5}$ $\boxed{\%}$ $\boxed{+}$

Note: Your calculator might work it out a different way.

Method 2:

If her present salary is represented by 100%, then an increase of $5\frac{1}{2}\%$ on this will mean a salary represented by $105\frac{1}{2}\%$. New salary is:

$$£12\,800 \times \frac{105.5}{100} = \frac{1\,350\,400}{100} = £13\,504$$

Example SALE: 30% OFF ALL PRICES

What is the sale price of a coat normally priced at £48?

Method 1:

$$\frac{30}{100} \times £48 = \frac{£1440}{100} = £14.40 \text{ decrease}$$

Sale price is £48 − £14.40 = £33.60

Or by calculator keys: $\boxed{4}$ $\boxed{8}$ $\boxed{\times}$ $\boxed{3}$ $\boxed{0}$ $\boxed{\%}$ $\boxed{-}$ $\boxed{=}$

But again, check whether your calculator does it this way.

Method 2:

If the normal price is represented by 100%, then a decrease of 30% leaves: 100% − 30% = 70%

Sale price: $\frac{70}{100} \times £48 = \frac{£3360}{100} = £33.60$

In 1990 the inflation rate in Nicaragua was 13 500%. The highest inflation in the UK was 26.9%, during 1974/5.

Exercise 6

In this exercise answers should be rounded to the nearest penny, if necessary. *Increase* the following amounts by the percentage shown:

1 £420 by 85%   2 1250 g by 85%   3 400 g by 77%

4 £460 by 60%   5 £250 by 30%

Decrease the following by the percentage shown:

6 240 m by 53%   7 3000 ml by 86%   8 £4.50 by 35%

9 £32 by $10\frac{1}{2}\%$ 10 £9.50 by $6\frac{1}{2}\%$

Exercise 7

1 A £36 coat is reduced by $12\frac{1}{2}$%. How much will it now cost?

2 The 50 000 population of a town has increased this year by 6%. What is the population now?

3 A dining room suite costs £625. In a sale the price is reduced by 15%. What is the sale price?

4 Mortgage payments of £230 are to be increased by $5\frac{1}{2}$%. What will the new payments be?

5 Attendance at a play was recorded as 120 people. The following night the attendance increased by 8%. What was the attendance on the second night?

6 In one year 1500 t of potatoes were grown on a farm. The crop increased by 18% the following year by use of a fertiliser. How many tonnes were grown the following year?

7 A man pays 25% tax on earnings of £3500. How much has he left after paying tax?

8 A garage offers a 20% reduction on a £130 car service. How much will you pay?

2.4 VAT

Value Added Tax is added on to bills, prices or receipts for services. The VAT rate is set by the Chancellor of the Exchequer. In the past, 15% and $17\frac{1}{2}$% have been used as VAT rates. In theory the VAT rate could be set at any percentage.

Exercise 8

VAT was introduced as a result of the UK joining the EC. Before VAT the UK had Purchase Tax, which was a tax on purchases, but not services.

1 Find the $17\frac{1}{2}$% VAT on a £75.80 bill for a meal for four.

2 15% VAT is added to a telephone bill for £80.60. What is the total bill?

3 A lawn mower costs £125.80 + VAT at 15%. What is the total cost?

4 A table is advertised as £78 + VAT. What is the total purchase price if VAT is $17\frac{1}{2}$%?

5 Typewriters cost £129.99 plus 15% VAT. What is the total cost of buying a typewriter?

2.5 Hire purchase

Hire Purchase became popular in the 1920s, and at that time was used mainly as a way of buying cars.

A Hire Purchase (HP) agreement is signed when you buy an item, but it is **rented** to you, until all payments have been made. The item is then yours to keep. Most HP agreements require you to make an initial percentage deposit, and a number of monthly payments.

Example   The HP terms on the TV set are a 15% deposit, and 36 monthly payments of £12.70.

Find: (a) the total cost of the HP agreement
(b) the amount saved if the TV is bought for cash.

(a) 15% of £380   = £57.00   ***Deposit***
36 × £12.70   = £457.20   ***Monthly payments***
Total HP price = £514.20

(b)   HP   £514.20
− Cash   £380.00
—————
£134.20

Exercise 9

Find: (a) the total cost of the HP agreement
(b) the difference between the cost of the HP, and the cash price.

1   Photographic equipment costs £350. The HP agreement requires a 20% deposit, and 30 payments of £24.90.

2   A leather armchair normally costs £360. It can be bought on HP with 24 monthly payments of £15.50, and a deposit of 25%.

3   A kitchen table is offered with a £200 cash price, or 20% deposit with ten payments of £21 each.

4   A £225 electric typewriter can also be bought with an HP agreement, requiring a deposit of 20%, and 12 monthly payments of £20.99.

5   The HP agreement for a £4950 motorbike is an initial deposit of 20%, plus 36 payments of £136.55.

6   A hi-fi centre has a price tag of £575. It can be paid for with 12 monthly payments of £45, after a deposit of 15%.

Hire Purchase is called Instalment Credit in other parts of the world.

2.6 **Simple interest**

Simple interest calculations are used to find the *approximate* interest gained once money is invested. It is assumed in each case that the interest rate remains constant.

$$I = \frac{P \times R \times T}{100} = \frac{PRT}{100}$$ where I = Interest, P = Principal (amount), R = Rate of Interest (%), T = Time (years)

The world's biggest commercial bank (in 1992) is the Dai-Ichi Kango Bank Ltd. of Japan.

Example   Find the simple interest when £200 is invested for $1\frac{1}{2}$ years at an interest rate of 9.5% p.a. (p.a. means per annum, or per year).

$$I = \frac{PRT}{100} = \frac{£200 \times 9.5 \times 1.5}{100} = £28.50$$

Example   Approximately how long would it take for £300 to produce £40 simple interest at a rate of 8.25% p.a.?

In this problem we have P = £300, I = £40, R = 8.25%

$$I = \frac{PRT}{100}, \text{ so } £40 = \frac{£300 \times 8.25 \times T}{100}$$ ***Put in the values.***

$$= 24.75 \times T$$ ***As £300 × 8.25 ÷ 100 = £24.75***

so $T = \frac{£40}{£24.75} = 1.61$ years   ***Divide both sides of the equation by the same amount of 24.75.***

= 1 year 7 months, rounded to the nearest month   ***0.61 years is 0.61 × 12 months***

Exercise 10

The interest in this exercise is simple interest.

1 Find the interest when £650 is invested for 6 years at 12% p.a.

2 Find the interest when £200 is invested for $3\frac{1}{2}$ years at 9% p.a.

3 Find the interest when £265 is invested for 6 months at 9% p.a.

4 Find the interest when £600 is invested for $4\frac{1}{2}$ years at $8\frac{1}{4}$% p.a.

5 Find the time it takes for an amount of £198 to produce £84 interest at $7\frac{1}{2}$% p.a.

6 Find the time it takes for an amount of £500 to produce £110 interest at 10% p.a.

7 An amount of £500 is invested for $3\frac{1}{2}$ years, and gains £123 interest. What is the rate of interest?

8 Find the interest when £150 is invested for 4 years at $12\frac{1}{2}$% p.a.

9 What amount of money has been invested when it takes $4\frac{1}{2}$ years for an amount of £105 interest to be earned, at a rate of interest of 14% p.a.?

10 Find the time it takes for an amount of £850 to produce £200 interest at 11% p.a.

2.7 Compound interest

A more accurate, and fairer way of calculating interest is by **compound** methods. Interest in many accounts is **accredited** every year, or every six months, or even every day! This means that the interest is added to the amount invested. The total will then continue to earn interest.

Example   Find the interest when £200 is invested for 3 years at an interest rate of 9.5% p.a. The interest is accredited every year.

1st year: $\frac{£200 \times 9.5 \times 1}{100}$ = £19.00   ***Total amount now £200 + £19.00 = £219.00***

2nd year: $\dfrac{£219.00 \times 9.5 \times 1}{100} = £20.81$

Total amount now £219.00
+ £20.81 = £239.81

3rd year: $\dfrac{£239.81 \times 9.5 \times 1}{100} = £22.78$

Total amount now £239.81
+ £22.78 = £262.59

Total interest earned is £262.59 − £200 = £62.59

Example Find the interest when £200 is invested for $1\frac{1}{2}$ years at an interest rate of 9.5% p.a. The interest is accredited every 6 months.

The first evidence of the use of compound interest is found in tables used by Babylonian businessmen, dated approximately 700 BC.

1st 6 months: $\dfrac{£200 \times 9.5 \times 0.5}{100} = £9.50$

Total amount now
£200 + £9.50
= £209.50

2nd 6 months: $\dfrac{£209.50 \times 9.5 \times 0.5}{100} = £9.95$

Total amount now
£209.50 + £9.95
= £219.45

3rd 6 months: $\dfrac{£219.45 \times 9.5 \times 0.5}{100} = £10.42$

Total amount now
£219.45 + £10.42
= £229.87

Total interest earned is £229.87 − £200 = £29.87

How does this compare with the example in section 2.6, where the interest was worked out by simple interest methods?

Note: In the worked example above all answers have been rounded to the nearest penny.

Exercise II

1 £4000 is invested for $1\frac{1}{2}$ years at 10% p.a. compound interest which is accredited every 6 months. What is the total interest earned in this time?

2 £500 is invested for 3 years at 9% p.a. compound interest which is accredited annually. What is the total interest earned in this time?

3 £700 is invested for 2 years at $8\frac{1}{2}$% p.a. compound interest which is accredited every 6 months. What is the total interest earned in this time?

4 £650 is invested for 2 years at 7% p.a. compound interest which is accredited annually. What is the total interest earned in this time?

5 £180 is invested for 4 years at $10\frac{1}{2}$% p.a. compound interest which is accredited annually. What is the total interest earned in this time?

6 £80 is invested for $1\frac{1}{2}$ years at $8\frac{1}{4}$% p.a. compound interest which is accredited every 6 months. What is the total interest earned in this time?

2.8 **Wages and salaries**

A record salary was earned by Michael Milken, who was paid a salary of $550m by Drexel Buraham Inc. (USA).

If you work for someone else (rather than being self-employed) you are paid a wage, which is normally paid weekly or monthly. There are several ways in which wages are calculated:

Salary: an agreed wage for the whole year, divided equally per week or per month

Time Rate: by the number of hours worked

Piece Rate: by the number of items produced or processed, or jobs done

Commission: a percentage of the sales

The amount paid for an hour's work during the normal working week is called the **basic rate**. Any work done outside the normal working week is **overtime**, and its usually paid at time and a quarter, time and a half, or double time.

Example The basic rate is £2.80 Calculate the overtime rates.

Time and a quarter is £2.80 × 1.25 = £3.50

Time and a quarter = 1.25 × basic rate.

Time and a half is £2.80 × 1.5 = £4.20

Time and a half = 1.5 × basic rate.

Double time is £2.80 × 2 = £5.60

Double time = 2 × basic rate.

TIME SHEET		
DAY	BASIC	OVERTIME
Mon.	8	
Tue.	8	
Wed.	$6\frac{1}{2}$	
Thu.	$7\frac{1}{2}$	
Fri.	7	1
Sat.		3

Example The basic rate of pay at a factory is £2.65. Overtime is paid at time and a half from Monday to Friday, and double time at the weekend. Calculate the weekly wage.

Basic rate   = 37 hours × £2.65   = £98.05

Time and a half = 1 hour × £2.65 × 1.5 = £3.98

Double time   = 3 hours × £2.65 × 2 = £15.90

Total wage is £117.93.

Piece rate is paid by the amount of work done.

Example Martin is paid 2p for each circuit board he assembles per day, up to 500. After this he is paid 3p per board. How much does he earn if he makes 800 boards?

500 × 2p = £10.00
300 × 3p = £9.00
800 made = £19.00

Some people are paid a commission. This is usually a percentage of the actual sales figures for a product or service. Commission is usually paid to sales people, as an incentive for them to perform better. Profits arising out of sales may be passed back to other members of the firm in the form of bonuses, which is a form of commission.

Example   Selene sells perfume. She is paid a basic rate of £1.80 per hour, plus 5% commission on sales. During one week she works for 35 hours, and sells perfume to the value of £873. How much is she paid?

$35 \times £1.80 = £63$ *Basic salary*

$5\% \text{ of } £873 = \frac{5}{100} \times £873 = £43.65$ *Commission*

Total earnings = £63 + £43.65 = £106.65

Exercise 12

Calculate the weekly wage in questions 1–4.

1 A mechanic works a basic $37\frac{1}{2}$-hour week, and overtime is paid at time and a half. The basic hourly rate is £4.70 per hour. She works 5 hours overtime (a total of $42\frac{1}{2}$ hours).

2 A man on an assembly line works a basic 40-hour week. His basic rate of pay is £3.80 per hour. The 4 hours overtime worked is paid at time and a quarter.

3 Ms Fairclough is a supervisor. Her basic week is 38 hours at £4.10 per hour. She also works 5 hours overtime a week at time and a half.

4 A woman works a 38-hour basic week, at the basic rate of £4.15 per hour. Her overtime is made up of 4 hours at time and a half, and 2 hours at double time.

5 A man earns £154.44. He has worked 39 hours at basic rate. What is his basic hourly rate?

Income Tax was first introduced in 1799 for incomes above £60 p.a.!

6 Michelle earns £40.80 for 5 hours work at the weekend on double time. What basic hourly rate is she paid?

7 For each article up to a maximum of 200 a worker is paid 7p. Above this limit she is paid 8p. How much is she paid for making 360 articles?

8 Brian is paid 15p for each piece of artwork up to 100. After that he is paid a rate of 22p per piece. How much will he earn if he does 130 pieces of artwork?

9 A woman is paid 45p for each page of typing she does for a firm. What will she earn for a 250-page document?

10 A printer employs part-time staff to deliver leaflets at the rate of £4.80 for every complete 100 leaflets. How much is someone paid for delivering 1450?

11 Barry is paid £3.75 each for the express delivery of container boxes. If he delivers more than 20 in a day, he is paid an *extra* 50p per box. How much will he be paid for delivering 26 boxes?

12 A car salesman receives 4% commission on the sale of a £2000 car. How much is this?

13 A woman is paid £80 in a week, and commission of 4% on £600. How much is she paid?

14 Bill sells cosmetics at the door. He is paid £2.05 per hour, and 15% commission on sales. How much is he paid for 5 hours work and sales of £120?

15 Val sells newspapers in the precinct. She is paid a basic rate of £1.20 per hour, and also gets $3\frac{1}{2}$% commission on sales. How much is she paid for 25 hours work, and sales of £205 during the week?

16 A man in a shoe shop earns £1.23 per hour, and commission of 8% on sales. How much is he paid for 38 hours work, and sales of £480 during the week?

2.9 Expressing in percentages

There will be times when you might need to express one number as a percentage of another.

Example   Colin has gained 68 marks out of 85. Write this as a percentage.

$$\frac{68}{85} \times 100 = 68 \div 85 \times 100 = 80\%$$ ***Multiply by 100 to change a fraction to a percentage.***

Example   Sue's weekly salary has been increased from £172 to £195. Find the percentage increase, writing your answer to one decimal place.

Actual increase = £195 − £172 = £23

Percentage increase = $\dfrac{\text{actual increase}}{\text{original figure}} \times 100 = \dfrac{£23}{£172} \times 100 = 13.4\%$

Example   The cost of a holiday to the USA has fallen from £730 to £650. What is the percentage decrease?

Actual decrease = £730 − £650 = £80

Percentage decrease = $\dfrac{\text{actual decrease}}{\text{original figure}} \times 100$

$= \dfrac{£80}{£730} \times 100$

$= 10.96\%$ (to 2 d.p.)

Exercise 13

Main constituents of air:

Nitrogen 78%,
Oxygen 21%,
Argon 0.9%,
Carbon Dioxide 0.01–0.1%

1 There were 8410 people at a sports concert; 4030 were female. What percentage were male?

2 The amount of liquid in a container rises from 8 litres to 10.5 litres. What is the percentage increase?

3 It is found that 8 minutes out of every 60 minutes on television is spent on advertisements. What percentage is this?

4 Of 48 letters taken to the post, 18 are first class. What percentage are second class?

5 In a delivery of 80 apples, 12 were bad. What percentage were bad?

6 Sandra can earn £180 per week. Her net pay is £103. What percentage is this of her weekly earnings?

7 The number of students at a college rises from 1832 to 2009. What is this as a percentage increase?

8 The cost of a satellite system has fallen from £380 to £250. What is the percentage decrease in price?

9 In an evening class of 30 adults, 14 are women. What percentage are (a) women (b) men?

10 A car park has 120 cars. Of these 65 are of foreign make. What percentage are (a) foreign (b) British?

2.10 Inverse percentages

Inverse percentage is used when we are given an amount *after* a percentage change, and wish to find the original amount.

Example   A bathroom suit costs £305.50 after VAT at $17\frac{1}{2}\%$ has been added. Calculate the price without VAT.

The original price (without VAT) represents 100%.
The £305.50 (with VAT) represents $100\% + 17\frac{1}{2}\% = 117\frac{1}{2}\%$ of the original price.

So $117\frac{1}{2}\% \rightarrow £305.50$ *This is $117\frac{10}{2}\%$.*

$1\% \rightarrow \dfrac{£305.50}{117.5}$ *To find 1%.*

$100\% \rightarrow \dfrac{£305.50}{117.5} \times 100$ *To find 100%.*

$= £260$

Example   After a wage increase of $6\frac{1}{2}\%$ a worker's salary is £8679.75. What was his salary before the increase?

$$100\% + 6\tfrac{1}{2}\% = 106\tfrac{1}{2}\%$$ ***After the increase.***

$$106.5\% \rightarrow £8679.75$$ ***This is 106.5%.***

$$1\% \rightarrow \frac{£8679.75}{106.5}$$ ***To find 1%.***

$$100\% \rightarrow \frac{£8679.75}{106.5} \times 100 = £8150$$ ***To find 100%.***

Example   A car has had its price reduced by 15% to £6800. How much money has been taken off its price?

The original price is represented by 100%.

$$100\% - 15\% = 85\%$$ ***This represents a reduction of the original price.***

$$85\% \rightarrow £6800$$ ***This is 85%.***

$$1\% \rightarrow \frac{£6800}{85}$$ ***To find 1%.***

$$100\% \rightarrow \frac{£6800}{85} \times 100 = £8000$$ ***To find 100%.***

Its price has been reduced by £8000 − £6800 = £1200.

Exercise 14

1   An aeroplane ticket to Brussels has risen by 25% to £109. What was the original price of the ticket?

2   A car stereo has its price increased by $7\frac{1}{2}\%$ to £172. What was the original price?

3   A cooker costs £728.50 inclusive of VAT at $17\frac{1}{2}\%$. What is its price without the VAT?

4   A coat has been reduced by $12\frac{1}{2}\%$ to £56 in a sale. What was its original price?

5   A table costs £276 inclusive of VAT at 15%. What is its price without the VAT?

6   A portfolio of shares is sold for £2112, a loss of 12%. Find the price at which they were originally bought?

7   A man weighs 220 kg, having lost 12% of his original weight. What was his original weight?

8   A building job costs £15 040 inclusive of $17\frac{1}{2}\%$ VAT. How much does it cost without the VAT?

9   The value of a motorbike has decreased by 32% to £2584. What was its original value?

10   The quarterly rental charge for a telephone system has been increased by 14% to £20.52 What was the charge before the increase?

Review

1 Copy and complete the table.

Decimal	Fraction	Percentage
0.9	$\frac{9}{10}$	90
	$\frac{3}{8}$	
		45%
		$62\frac{1}{2}$%
	$\frac{2}{3}$	

2 Which is the greater: $\frac{2}{3}$ of £139.53, or 49% of £186?

3 Find 23% of £35.

4 Calculate $42\frac{1}{4}$% of £3500.

5 A salary of £8300 is increased by $4\frac{3}{4}$%. (a) What is the new salary?
   (b) By how much has it been increased?

6 If 1750 kg is decreased by 15%, what is the new weight?

7 A garage offers $12\frac{1}{2}$% off a service normally costing £160. How much will
   the service now cost?

8 The price of an adventure holiday is increased by $5\frac{1}{2}$% from £350. How
   much will it now cost?

9 Find the cost of an exhaust system priced at £56 + VAT at $17\frac{1}{2}$%.

10 A new central heating system is advertised at £946. HP terms are quoted
    as 17% deposit, plus monthly instalments of £39.90 over two years. How
    much *more* expensive is the HP price, compared with the cash price?

11 An amount of £2000 is invested for 2 years at an interest rate of 8% p.a.
    (a) Calculate the simple interest over 2 years. (b) Calculate the compound
    interest, if the interest is accredited every 6 months.

12 The cost of a gas fire is now £76.84, an increase of 13% on the original
    price. What was the original price of the gas fire?

13 A company makes food processors. The price of a processor is increased
    from £60 to £72. What is the percentage increase?

14 A train ticket was £25 a year ago, but is £29 now. What is the percentage
    increase?

15 A man's wages have increased by $6\frac{1}{4}$% to £127.50. What wage did he
    receive before the increase?

16 A woman receives a basic wage of £1.80 per hour; overtime is at time and
    a quarter. How much will she receive for 38 hours at basic rate and 4
    hours at overtime rate?

17 A salesman receives a wage of £1.50 per hour, plus $12\frac{1}{2}$% commission on
    sales. What will be his wage for 35 hours work, and sales of £1850?

18 In a morning Barry is paid 50p for each machined part up to 40 parts. He
    is paid 70p for each part over the 40 that he machines. How much will he
    receive in a morning in which he makes (a) 30 parts (b) 55 parts?

Exercise 16   The following are all questions taken from GCSE papers.

1 The road sign on the left shows a 1 in 5 steep hill. It is being replaced by a sign which gives the slope as a percentage. What is the percentage figure?
[NEA]

2 A trade union negotiates the following rise in wages on behalf of its members: 5% of weekly wage or £6 per week, whichever is greater.
  One employee finds that, for him, there is no difference between a rise of 5% and a rise of £6 per week. Calculate this employee's weekly wage before the rise.
[NEA]

3 Kurt's father has decided to buy him a drum kit. The recommended price is £1000 (plus VAT at 15%). By paying cash Kurt's father gets a discount of 10%.

(a) Work out the discount on the £1000 recommended price.

(b) What is the cash price?

VAT at 15% is added.
(c) What is the VAT on the cash price?

(d) What price does Kurt's father actually pay for the drum kit?
[LEAG]

4 A teacher ordered some new textbooks. She worked out the total cost from the prices in the bookseller's catalogue and this came to £590.

(a) The catalogue was an old one and prices had increased by 8%. Calculate the new total cost. (2 marks)

(b) The bookseller will allow a discount of $12\frac{1}{2}$% of the new total cost. How much will the books now cost? (2 marks)
[MEG]

5 Complete the telephone bill shown below.

DATE	METER READING	UNITS USED	PRICE PER UNIT	AMOUNT (£)
28/4/90	32 225			
29/1/90	31 198		4.40p	
		Rental Charges		18.15
		Total Charges (excluding VAT)		
		Value Added Tax at 15%		
		Total Charges (including VAT)		

[MEG]

6 All the students in a College were asked questions about "Smoking". Some of the results are given in the table.

	Have smoked	Have never smoked	Total
Males		132	237
Females	187	169	
Total		301	593

(a) Fill in the missing entries in the table.

(b) What percentage of females have never smoked? [NEA]

7 Young conifer trees increase their height by 15% each year. In the Spring of 1989 Alice planted a young conifer tree that was 120 cm tall. Calculate the height of the tree in

(a) Spring 1990, (b) Spring 1992. [NEA]

8 Scientists estimate that, unless steps are taken to reduce the pollution in the North Sea, the seal population there will decrease by 15% each year.

In October 1990 the seal population of the North Sea was estimated at 5000.

If no action were taken to reduce pollution in the North Sea, what would be the estimated seal population of the North Sea in

(a) October 1991? *(2 marks)*

(b) October 1993? *(4 marks)*
  [NEA]

9 There were two bottles of copper sulphate solution on a shelf in a laboratory.

The 3 litre bottle, A, was 55% full.
The 2.5 litre bottle, B, was three-quarters full.
The laboratory assistant was asked to fetch the bottle which contained the most copper sulphate solution. Which bottle should have been taken?
  [NEA]

10 An engineer needs to cut a piece of metal $\frac{1}{9}$ of an inch by $\frac{2}{9}$ of an inch. He works in decimals.

(a) (i) Change $\frac{1}{9}$ to a decimal. *(1 mark)*

(ii) Change $\frac{2}{9}$ to a decimal. *(1 mark)*

(b) Write down a fraction which is equal to 0.888888888. . . *(1 mark)*
  [SEG]

11 The cost of a single ticket for a bus journey is 36p. A book of twelve single tickets for the same journey costs £3.72.

   (a) How much is saved on each journey by buying a book of tickets?

   (2 marks)

   (b) Express, correct to one decimal place, this saving as a percentage of the cost of buying a single ticket.

   (3 marks)

   [SEG]

12 A political party made an election promise to the effect that "we will increase government spending on the NHS by 8% every year that we are in power".
   When this party came to power in 1990, the government spending on the NHS was £175 billion.

   (a) If they kept their promise, how much would they spend on the NHS in 1990, their first year in power?

   (2 marks)

   (b) The party kept their promise, and increased NHS spending by 8% each year.
      What would be the spending on the NHS after the third increase?

   (3 marks)

   [NEA]

13 A newsagent pays boys and girls to deliver the morning papers.
   Daniel works 6 mornings per week and is paid £4.56 at the end of each week.

   (a) How much does Daniel earn each day?

   (1 mark)

   (b) The starting time for the boys and girls is 7.15 am.
      Daniel is paid a bonus of 15p per day for each day he arrives for work before 7.15 am.
      One week Daniel arrived for work at the following times:

6.55 am	7.00 am	7.10 am
7.20 am	7.05 am	7.20 am

   (i) How many days was Daniel late for work?

   (ii) Calculate Daniel's wages for this week including any bonuses earned.

   (3 marks)

   (c) The last three houses on Daniel's round are numbers 34, 36 and 38 London Road.
      Number 34 London Road has The Guardian, number 36 The Sun and number 38 The Daily Mirror.
      One morning Daniel mixed these newspapers up. No one had the right newspaper.
      The Daily Mirror was *not* delivered to number 34.
      Which house received which paper?

   (2 marks)

   [NEA]

14 Mr Singh decides to buy a new television set. He decides on the following set that is advertised in the local electrical shop.

Cash Price only £275
H P terms – 10% deposit
24 monthly payments of £12.50

(a) Work out the deposit needed if Mr Singh buys the TV on HP.

(3 marks)

(b) Work out the total cost of the 24 monthly payments. *(2 marks)*

(c) What is the total HP price of the TV? *(2 marks)*

(d) How much extra would Mr Singh have to pay for the TV if he bought it on HP instead of paying the cash price? *(2 marks)*

[LEAG]

Ideas for investigations

1 A couple make and sell document cases. The weekly sales figures over a period of six weeks are:

283, 297, 255, 218, 298, 323

What is the average number sold in a week?

The couple employ three workers who each expect a wage of about £120 per week for making the document cases, which are sold for £25 each. The normal working week is 36 hours, and the normal work rate is about 90 document cases per worker in a week ($2\frac{1}{2}$ per hour). To produce more will require overtime at time and a quarter, or a faster rate of working.

The manager has three options when it comes to paying the wages of the workers: (a) time-rate working (b) piece-rate working (c) a commission on the number of cases sold.

Work out the basic rate of pay under each of the three options. Use your figures to calculate the extra weekly wage bill in producing the extra document cases needed per week. Comment on the consequences of the three options: from the point of view of the workers, and the manager. Can you propose any recommendations? Can you describe any other options?

2 A man has £500, which is invested in an account. The interest rate is 10%. Calculate how long it would take to double the investment if the account is accredited at the end of (a) every year (b) every six months (c) every three months. Repeat the investigation for different interest rates (e.g. 8%, 7%, 11%, 12%).

3 Find out from your local Estate Agent or Building Society the cost of buying a house. Find the details of a house you might want to buy from the Estate Agent, along with details of other charges you may face when buying a house. (a) How much will it cost you to buy the house? (b) What will be the monthly outgoings once you have bought the house?

NUMBER RELATIONS

3.1 Ratio

A ratio is a way of representing the relationship between two or more quantities.

Example   There are nine boxes which are divided between a van and a lorry. The van can carry three boxes, the lorry can carry six boxes. Represent this as a ratio in its simplest form.

The boxes are shared between the van and the lorry in the ratio 3 : 6.

3 : 6 can be simplified to become   3 :   6 = 1 : 2
÷3   ÷3

This relationship tells us that the lorry is carrying twice as much as the van.

Exercise 1   Write these ratios in their simplest form:

1 2 : 8   **2** 3 : 6   **3** 18 : 12   **4** 7 : 21   **5** 5 : 20

6 4 : 6   **7** 4 : 10   **8** 42 : 49   **9** 8 : 4   **10** 15 : 30

Example   Simplify the ratios
(a) 16 kg : 800 g   (b) £2 : 40p   (c) 10 mm : 1 m

A ratio compares two quantities which are *alike*: we first need to change the units.

(a)   16 kg : 800 g = 16000 g : 800 g = 20 : 1   ***Change all the units to grams.***

(b)   £2 : 40p = 200p : 40p = 5 :1   ***Change all the units to pence.***

(c)   10 mm : 1 m = 10 mm : 1000 mm = 1 : 100   ***Change all the units to millimetres.***

Exercise 2   Write these ratios in their simplest form.

1 £3 : 25p	**2** 55 g : 2 kg	**3** 30 cm : 1 m
4 2 km : 250 m	**5** £1.50 : 50p	**6** 10 g : 0.5 kg
7 £1.25 : 10p	**8** 4 kg : 40 g	**9** 800 cm : 4 km
10 50 g : 1 kg	**11** 10 cm : 2 mm	**12** £2.80 : £3.50

Example   Express these ratios in the form 1 : n (a) 2 : 3 (b) 10 : 35

To change a ratio into the form 1 : n, divide both numbers by the number on the left-hand side.

(a) $2 : 3 = \frac{2}{2} : \frac{3}{2} = 1 : 1.5$ *Divide both sides by 2.*

(b) $10 : 35 = \frac{10}{10} : \frac{35}{10} = 1 : 3.5$ *Divide both sides by 10.*

Exercise 3   Express these ratios in the form 1 : n

1 12 : 3	**2** 7 : 21	**3** 2 : 15	**4** 5 : 9	**5** 4 : 10
6 5 : 12	**7** 2 : 10	**8** 12 : 48	**9** 2 : 5	**10** 3 : 27

One common use of ratios in the form 1 : n is in map scales.

A ratio is a comparison between two quantities. Ratios, using fractions, can be related to decimals and percentages.

'4% of nothing is nothing. We want 12%.' Quoted during a pay dispute, The Daily Telegraph, 15th June 1982.

Example   Change the following into a decimal and a percentage:

(a) 4 : 5 (b) 3 : 20

Fraction   Decimal   Percentage

(a) $4 : 5 \rightarrow \frac{4}{5} = 4 \div 5 = 0.8 \rightarrow \times 100 = 80\%$ *The first number is 80% of the second number.*

(b) $3 : 20 \rightarrow \frac{3}{20} = 3 \div 20 = 0.15 \rightarrow \times 100 = 15\%$ *The first number is 15% of the second number.*

Exercise 4   Change the following as indicated.

ALL CHANGE

1 10 : 35 into a fraction	**2** 1 : 5 into a decimal
3 16 : 64 into a percentage	**4** 18 : 12 into a decimal
5 5 : 15 into a fraction	**6** 4 : 10 into a percentage
7 8 : 16 into a decimal	**8** 2 : 5 into a percentage
9 7 : 10 into a fraction	**10** 5 : 2 into a fraction

Example $2 : 5 = 4 : ?$ Find the missing number.

We use the relationship between the numbers to work out what the missing number is.

$2 : 5 = 4 : ?$ So we have $2 : 5 = 4 : 10$

Both sides of the ratio are multiplied by 2.

Example $4 : ? = 20 : 35$ Find the missing number.

We use the relationship between the numbers to work out what the missing number is.

$4 : ? = 20 : 35$ So we have $4 : 7 = 20 : 35$

Both sides of the ratio are multiplied by 5.

Exercise 5

'All animals are equal, but some are more equal than others.' George Orwell, Animal Farm.

Find the missing number in each question.

1 $1 : 6 = 5 : ?$ **2** $? : 20 = 3 : 4$

3 $2 : 5 = ? : 10$ **4** $1 : 9 = ? : 27$

5 $6 : 5 = ? : 10$ **6** $1 : 6 = ? : 42$

7 $? : 6 = 12 : 18$ **8** $3 : ? = 4 : 12$

9 $24 : 14 = 12 : ?$ **10** $5 : 2 = ? : 8$

Example In a class the ratio of males : females is $1 : 2$. If there are nine males, how many females are there?

M   F   M   F
$1 : 2 = 9 : ?$
So $2 \times 9 = 18$ females

Note that the number of males has been multiplied by 9.

Exercise 6

1 Two lengths of wood are in the ratio $4 : 7$. The longer length is 35 cm. What is the shorter length?

2 Two soap packets contain powder in the ratio $3 : 10$. The smaller contains 1 kg of powder. What weight of powder does the larger packet contain?

3 An alloy contains iron and copper in the ratio $5 : 1$. A block of this alloy contains 30 kg of iron. What weight of copper does it contain?

4 In a rectangle the ratio of the width to the length is $5 : 12$. The length is 30 cm. Find the width.

5 In making concrete you need sand and cement in the ratio $4 : 1$; 30 kg of cement has been delivered. What weight of sand is needed?

6 The speed of two boats is in the ratio $9 : 4$. The speed of the second boat is 10 km/h. What is the speed of the first boat?

7 The teacher to student ratio is $1 : 18$. If a college has 180 staff, how many students are there?

8 A machine makes electrical components, of which 2 in 35 are faulty. If it has made 16 faulty components how many good ones has it made?

3.2 Proportional parts

Example Norman and his daughter have won £10 000 in a competition, which cost 80p to enter. Norman paid 50p, and his daughter paid 30p. How should they share the winnings?

$50 : 30 = 5 : 3$ *Add the parts to make 8 altogether.*

£10 000 ÷ 8 = £1250   *Divide the total by 8 to find each part.*

Norman has 5 parts, and his daughter has 3 parts:

So $5 \times £1250 : 3 \times £1250$ *Calculate their actual amounts.*

$= £6250 : £3750$

Norman's share is £6250, and his daughter's is £3750.
(Check: £6250 + £3750 = £10 000)

Exercise 7

1 Divide £35 in the ratio 4 : 3

2 Divide 600 g in the ratio 3 : 2

3 Divide £14.91 in the ratio 2 : 5

4 Divide 48.24 m in the ratio 2 : 7

5 Divide 32 cm in the ratio 3 : 5

6 Divide 48 kg in the ratio 3 : 5

7 If 75 cm is divided in the ratio 3 : 2, how long is each section?

8 The ratio of boys to girls in a youth club is 4 : 5. There are 72 members. How many boys and how many girls are there?

9 Chris needs to make 600 g of short-crust pastry. Flour and fat are needed in the ratio 2 : 1. How much flour is needed?

10 A company posts 387 letters in a week. The ratio of 1st to 2nd class letters is normally 2 : 7. How many 2nd class stamps are needed in a week?

Example Brian and Jane have divided an amount of money in the ratio 3 : 5. Brian's share is £36. How much was the original amount of money?

The ratio is 3 : 5   *Brian's share is 3 parts out of 8.*

£36 ÷ 3 = £12   *Find 1 part.*

So 8 parts (the whole) is 8 × £12 = £96.

Exercise 8

1 A lorry is loaded with fruit and vegetable boxes in the ratio 5 : 7. The fruit has a weight of 8.5 tonnes. What is the total weight of both fruit and vegetables?

2 A quantity of alloy is made from copper and zinc in the ratio 5 : 6. The weight of copper used is 25 kg. What will be the final weight of the alloy?

3 A rope is cut into two lengths in the ratio 3 : 4. The longer of the lengths is 113.2 metres. What was the length of the original single rope?

4 The weight of two boxes is in the ratio 4 : 5. The heavier box has a weight of 97.5 kg. What is the total weight of the two boxes?

5 A cable is cut into two sections with lengths in the ratio 3 : 5. The shorter of the two lengths is 49.5 metres. What was the length of the original cable?

6 The directors of a company share an amount of money in the ratio 1 : 2 : 3. The Managing Director, who has the greatest share, receives £4572. What is the total amount of money they have to share between them?

One and one make two,
But if one and one
* should marry,*
Isn't it queer,
Within a year,
There's two and one to
* carry.*

3.3 Direct proportion

Direct proportion is when two quantities are directly related; an increase in one will result in a proportionately similar increase in the other.

Example Five similar books cost £29.95. How much will seven cost?

5 books cost £29.95.

1 book costs £29.95 ÷ 5 = £5.95. ◄——— *Always work back to one. This is called a unitary method.*

7 books cost £5.95 × 7 = £41.65.

Exercise 9

In the questions below, assure that all rates remain the same.

1 If 4 kg of sugar cost £2.12, how much will 7 kg cost?

2 Seven pencils cost 56p. How much will five pencils cost?

3 Betty takes 50 minutes to walk 4 km. How long will it take her to walk 3 km?

4 A woman is paid £18.20 for seven hours work at a Nursing Home. How much will she receive for five hours work?

5 Six razor blades cost 42p. How much will ten cost?

6 Four boxes weigh 30 kg. What weight will nine boxes be?

7 Fencing costs £10.80 for nine metres. How much will it cost for seven metres?

8 A machine makes 245 parts in 35 minutes. How many will it make in one hour?

3.4 Inverse proportion

With inverse proportion, two quantities are inversely related, and a *decrease* in one will result in a proportionately similar *increase* in the other.

The use of proportional methods for solving problems is one of the earliest techniques; both Egyptians and Greeks used it extensively.

Example   Five identical machines take 20 hours to complete production of an order for machine parts. One machine breaks down. How long will it now take to produce a similar order?

5 machines take 20 hours.

1 machine would take $20 \times 5 = 100$ hours.   ***Always work back to one.***

4 machines would take $100 \div 4 = 25$ hours.

Exercise 10

In the questions below, assume that all rates remain the same.

1   A local farmer employs 18 students in his orchard. It takes them three days to pick the apples. How long would it take 12 students?

2   Three men can paint a concert hall in 20 days. How long will it take five men?

3   Seven machines are used to complete an order in 21 hours. How long would it take three machines to complete a similar order?

4   To complete a harvest, a farmer needs two combine harvesters for six days. How long would it take if he had three combine harvesters?

5   Travelling at 30 m.p.h. it takes a car four hours for a journey. How long would the journey take at a speed of 40 m.p.h.?

6   Two secretaries can type a document between them in nine hours. How long would it take three secretaries working together?

7   Eggs are packed into boxes of six each. One hundred boxes are needed for a large order. If the eggs were to be packed into new boxes containing eight eggs each, how many of these new boxes would be needed?

8   It takes nine men 30 days to complete a contract. How long would it take 15 men?

3.5 House insurance

Once we have bought a house we need to protect it. If there is a fire, flood or storm damage an insurance policy pays for the repairs. We pay for the policy on a monthly or annual basis, whether we have damage or not. When the time comes to make a **claim** from the company for damage, they will pay the bills as long as the policy is up to date.

The cost of paying for the insurance policy is called the **premium.** House insurance can be divided into two separate policies: Buildings insurance and Contents insurance. By buildings we mean the actual structure of the house: walls, windows, roof, garage, floors and so on. The premium paid on the buildings is determined by the value of the house. The Contents insurance is for everything inside the house such as carpets and curtains, furniture, clothes, hi-fi, washing machine, and so on. This type of insurance is linked to the estimated value of the items inside the house.

Example   Richard has a house valued at £36 000, and contents estimated at a value of £25 000. His insurance company has annual charges of £1.85 per £1000 value for Buildings insurance, and £4.60 per £1000 estimated value for Contents insurance. What will be his total annual insurance bill?

House insurance normally covers a property from theft, fire, lightning, explosion, earthquake, storm and flood, riots, falling trees, subsidence, aircraft and vehicles.

Buildings: £36 000 ÷ 1000 × £1.85 = £66.60

Contents: £25 000 ÷ 1000 × £4.60   = £115.00

Total cost of insurance   = £181.60

Exercise II

1   Marie has a house which is worth £32 500. What would the house insurance cost per year at a rate of £1.92 per £1000 value?

2   Don obtains an insurance quotation of £5.25 per £1000 for the contents of his flat. What would be the annual change for insurance if he thinks the contents are worth about £14 900?

3   Vera has been asked to renew her Contents insurance. She estimates the value of all the contents to be £18 700, and is to be charged £0.45 per £100 insured. What will the new insurance premium be?

4   Martin has just bought a house for £36 450. How much will it cost him for House insurance at the rate of £1.82 per £1000?

House insurance does not normally cover damage from coastal erosion, faulty workmanship or accidental demolition, mining, or war.

5   Paul and Clare buy a house for £140 000. They have accumulated possessions for the house with an estimated value of £42 500. They receive quotations from an insurance company as follows: Buildings: £1.72 per £1000, Contents: £0.43 per £100. Find the total cost of insurance for the house and possessions.

3.6 Speed

This is a useful way for remembering rates in speed. From this sign you can write down these formulas:

Distance = Time × Speed

$$\text{Time} = \frac{\text{Distance}}{\text{Speed}}$$

$$\text{Speed} = \frac{\text{Distance}}{\text{Time}}$$

Example How long will it take a greyhound to race 238 m at 17 m/s?

$$\text{Time} = \frac{\text{Distance}}{\text{Speed}} = \frac{238}{17} = 14 \text{ seconds}$$

Example A horse takes 6 minutes to gallop 5 km.
What is the speed of the horse, in km/h?

$$\text{Speed} = \frac{\text{distance}}{\text{time}}$$

$$= \frac{5 \text{ km}}{0.1 \text{ h}}$$

Remember to change units:
6 min = $\frac{6}{60}$ h = 0.1 h

$$= 50 \text{ km/h}$$

Exercise 12

The fastest speed recorded by a jet-engined car is 1019 km/h, or 644.5 m.p.h.: Thrust 2, Richard Noble (GB), 4th October 1983.

1 An aeroplane flew at 400 m.p.h. How far did it travel in (a) 2 h (b) $3\frac{1}{2}$ h?

2 A car goes at a speed of 48 m.p.h. on the motorway. How long will it take to travel (a) 60 miles (b) 72 miles?

3 A motorbike travels for four hours and goes 160 miles. What is the average speed over this distance?

4 How long does it take a go-kart to go 60 miles around a circuit at 40 m.p.h.?

5 A bird flies 259 m in seven seconds. What is its speed in metres per second?

6 Brian cycles at an average speed of 24 km/h. How far will he go in $3\frac{1}{2}$ hours?

7 A boat goes a distance of 72 nautical miles in four hours. What is its average speed, in knots (nautical miles per hour)?

8 Majid can walk at a speed of 6 km/h. How far can he walk in 30 minutes?

3.7 Average speed

When calculating **average** speed we use: Speed = $\dfrac{\text{Distance}}{\text{Time}}$, as in the previous section. When calculating average speed over *more* than one distance we need to use:

$$\text{Average speed} = \frac{\text{Total distance}}{\text{Total time}}$$

Example   A car travels 2 hours at 30 m.p.h., and 100 miles at 25 m.p.h. What is the average speed for the journey?

1st part of journey: distance travelled = 2 × 30 = 60 miles

2nd part of journey: time taken = 100 ÷ 25 = 4 hours

$$\text{Average speed} = \frac{\text{total distance}}{\text{total time}}$$

Add the distances for the 2 parts of the journey.

$$= \frac{60 + 100 \text{ miles}}{2 + 4 \text{ hours}}$$

Add the times for the 2 parts of the journey.

$$= \frac{160}{6} \text{ m.p.h.} = 26\tfrac{2}{3} \text{ m.p.h.}$$

Exercise 13

Find the average speed for the whole journey in the following:

1 A coach travels at 42 km/h for 4 hours, and then a distance of 105 km over 3 hours.

2 A cyclist travels at 12 km/h for 2 hours, and then at 15 km/h for 4 hours.

3 A car travels at 65 km/h for 6 hours, and then at 85 km/h for 4 hours.

4 A lorry travels at 264 km/h over 8 hours, and then at 45 km/h for 4 hours.

5 A train travels 280 km at a speed of 70 km/h, and then a distance of 480 km over 6 hours.

6 A car travels 67 km in the first hour of its journey. It then drives 392 km at an average speed of 56 km/h.

7 A cyclist travels at 12 km/h for 6 hours, and then at 9 km/h for 3 hours.

8 A coach travels at 45 km/h for 5 hours, and then 252 km at an average speed of 63 km/h.

3.8 Foreign currencies

As people travel outside the country more frequently, and as we do more trade with other countries, particularly within Europe, we need to be able to change from pounds sterling to other currencies.

The rates shown are the amounts of foreign currency you will receive for your pound on a particular day.
These could change from hour to hour. The bank will also add a service charge whenever you change your money.

To change *out of* £sterling you *multiply* by the rate.

To change *back to* £sterling you *divide* by the rate.

TOURIST RATES

Australia 2.19 dollars
Austria 19.55 schillings
Belgium 57.26 francs
Canada 1.9945 dollars
Denmark 10.82 kroner
France 9.49 francs
Germany 2.79 marks
Greece 318 drachmae
Holland 3.14 guilders
Hong Kong 13.47 dollars
Ireland 1.04 punts
Italy 2100 lire
Malta 0.55 lire
New Zealand 3.01 dollars
Norway 10.93 kroner
Portugal 244 escudos
Spain 176 pesetas
Sweden 10.16 kronor
Switzerland 2.46 francs
Turkey 8134 lire
US 1.760 dollars

Example　(a)　Change £50 to dollars
　　　　　　(b)　Change £50IR into pounds sterling.

(a)　£50 × 1.7560 = $87.80　　*Multiply to change out of pounds.*

Paper money was an invention of the Chinese, first tried in AD 812.

(b)　£50IR ÷ 1.04 = £48.08 to the nearest penny.　*Divide to change back into pounds.*

Exercise 14

Change the following amounts, in pounds sterling, to the currency given. Round off, if necessary, to 2 decimal places.

1　£40 to schillings　　2　£65 to Italian lire　　3　£480 to marks

4　£15.20 to Swedish kronor　　　　　5　£800 to French francs

6　£727 to $US　　7　£222 to pesetas　　8　£135.50 to punts.

Change the following into pounds sterling. Round your answers, if necessary, to the nearest penny.

9　US $270　　10　156 guilders　　11　522 pesetas

12　415 Swiss francs　　13　75 Belgian francs　　14　6000 drachmas

15　85 Norweigian kroner　16　3500 escudos

Use the exchange rate given in the question:

17　A watch costs 475f in a Paris shop. If 12f = £1, what would the watch cost in pounds sterling?

18　A radio is bought in Rome for 48 000 lire. If 2000 lire is about one pound, what is the approximate cost of the radio in pounds sterling?

19　If 2.71 marks = £1, what would be the equivalent cost, in Germany, of a crate of manufactured parts, valued in this country at £9750?

20　A large cuckoo clock costs 96.25 Swiss francs. If you can get 2.75 Swiss francs for every £1, what is the cost in pounds sterling?

3.9 Directed numbers

The temperature shown is 3°C. What temperature will be 5° below this?
The temperature will fall to −2°C. This is a directed number.
Note: 5 is the same as +5.

Example (a) The temperature falls by 10°C from 6°C. What is the
temperature now?
(b) What is the difference in temperature from 3°C to −6°C?

(a) The temperature falls to −4°C.   10°C

(b) The difference in temperature is 9°C.   9°C

The highest temperature achieved is 300 000 000°C in the centre of a thermonuclear bomb. The lowest temperature is −273.15°C.

Exercise 15

Find the temperature when:

1 5°C falls by 6°C   **2** −1°C falls by 2°C   **3** 2°C falls by 9°C

4 3°C falls by 7°C   **5** −4°C rises by 6°C   **6** −2°C rises by 7°C

7 7°C falls by 13°C   **8** 5°C falls by 8°C   **9** −4°C rises by 3°C

Find the difference when the temperature changes from:

10 3°C to 6°C   **11** 3°C to −5°C

12 5°C to −6°C   **13** −1°C to 4°C

14 −1° to −4°C   **15** −2°C to 5°C

Example The temperature is 4°C. It falls by 7°C.
What is the new temperature?

This problem can be shown in writing:

$$(+4°C) + (−7°C) = −3°C \quad \text{or} \quad (+4) + (−7) = −3$$

Exercise 16

Work out the answers to these problems.

1 $(−2) + (+5)$ **2** $(−11) + (+7)$ **3** $(+9) + (−17)$

4 $(−3) + (−1)$ **5** $(+4) + (−4)$ **6** $(−12) + (+3)$

7 $(−3) + (0)$ **8** $(−11) + (+6)$ **9** $(−6) + (−6)$

Example   The temperature was 5°C; it is now −2°C.
What is the difference in temperature?

This problem can be solved by writing
(−2°C) − (+5°C) = −7°C, which is a fall of 7°C.

Exercise 17

Work out these differences:

1 (+3) − (+2)   **2** (+4) − (0)

3 (+5) − (−1)   **4** (−2) − (+7)

5 (−4) − (−5)   **6** (−9) − (+4)

7 (+11) − (+4)   **8** (+11) − (−4)

9 (+14) − (+21)

Example

$(+4) \times (−2) = −8$

$(+12) \div (+2) = +6$

$(−2) \times (+3) = −6$

$(−12) \div (−3) = +4$

$+ \times + = +$
$+ \times − = −$
$− \times + = −$
$− \times − = +$

Also works for ÷

Exercise 18

Use the rules given to find the answers to:

1 +5 × +4   **2** +8 ÷ +2   **3** −3 × +4

4 +10 ÷ −5   **5** −3 × +10   **6** −21 ÷ −3

7 +4 × −8   **8** −8 × −8   **9** −27 ÷ −3

10 −7 × −6   **11** −24 ÷ −6   **12** +6 × −9

Exercise 19

Work out:

1 (3) + (−1)   **2** (7) − (−2)   **3** (3) − (+2)

4 (−30) ÷ (+2)   **5** (−3) × (7)   **6** (−4) × (+3)

7 (−3) + (−1)   **8** (7) + (−2)   **9** (+4) + (+4)

10 (+9) × (−4)   **11** (+8) × (−5)   **12** (+18) ÷ (−3)

3.10 Some special numbers

Square numbers:

$1 \times 1 = \underline{1}$ $2 \times 2 = \underline{4}$ $3 \times 3 = \underline{9}$ $4 \times 4 = \underline{16}$

The Greeks were the first to investigate prime numbers, about the time of Pythagoras.

Cube numbers: $1 \times 1 \times 1 = 1$
$2 \times 2 \times 2 = 8$ } These are the cube numbers.
$3 \times 3 \times 3 = 27$

Prime numbers: These are numbers which do not have any other factors other than 1 and themselves: 2, 3, 5, 7, 11, 13, ...
Note: The number 1 is *not* a prime number.

Exercise 20

1 Write out the first twenty square numbers.

2 Write out the first twenty cube numbers.

3 Write out the first twenty prime numbers.

4 The number 20 can be made from 'square sums': $20 = 16 + 4 = 4^2 + 2^2$.

Which other numbers between 1 and 25 can be found by adding two square numbers?

5 Continue the pattern downwards:

$$1^2 = \quad 1 \times 1 \quad = ?$$
$$11^2 = \quad 11 \times 11 \quad = ?$$
$$111^2 = \quad 111 \times 111 \quad = ?$$
$$? = \quad ? \times ? \quad = ?$$

6 Continue the pattern downwards:

$$3^2 = \quad 3 \times 3 \quad = ?$$
$$33^2 = \quad 33 \times 33 \quad = ?$$
$$333^2 = \quad 333 \times 333 \quad = ?$$
$$? = \quad ? \times ? \quad = ?$$

3.11 Products of primes

All numbers can be made up from products of prime numbers, that is, a number of prime numbers multiplied together.

The highest known prime number is $391\,581 \times 2^{216\,193} - 1$, discovered on 6th August 1989 by a team in the USA.

Example   Find the prime products of (a) 540 (b) 210.

Take each prime in turn, starting with the smallest (2), and divide it into the number as many times as possible. Then divide by the next prime, and the next, until the number is reduced to 1.

(a) $2 \overline{) 540}$ (b) $2 \overline{) 210}$ *Always start with 2.*

     $2 \overline{) 270}$ $3 \overline{) 105}$

     $3 \overline{) 135}$ $5 \overline{) \;\; 35}$ *Divide by prime*

     $3 \overline{) \;\; 45}$ $7 \overline{) \;\;\; 7}$ *numbers only.*

     $3 \overline{) \;\; 15}$ 1

     $5 \overline{) \;\;\; 5}$

         1 So $210 = 2 \times 3 \times 5 \times 7$

So $540 = 2 \times 2 \times 3 \times 3 \times 3 \times 5$

Exercise 21

Express each of these numbers as a product of its prime factors:

1 36	**2** 96	**3** 1080	**4** 27	**5** 72
6 360	**7** 120	**8** 980	**9** 2940	**10** 4000
11 2600	**12** 1002	**13** 729	**14** 624	**15** 725

Review

Exercise 22

Write these ratios in their simplest form:

1 25 : 10	**2** 8 : 64	**3** 18 : 63
4 13 : 169	**5** 15p : £1.00	**6** 60 cm : 1 m
7 3 hours : 75 minutes	**8** 2 kg : 600 g	**9** £2.50 : 50p

Express in the form $1 : n$

10 12 : 3   **11** 20 : 4   **12** 8 : 5   **13** 45 : 4

14 Change 6 : 10 into a percentage.   **15** Change 3 : 10 into a fraction.

16 Change 4 : 16 into a fraction.   **17** Change 15 : 20 into a percentage.

18 Change 6 : 15 into a decimal.   **19** Change 70 : 150 into a fraction.

20 Change 9 : 10 into a decimal.

21 An alloy contains iron and copper in the ratio 5 : 2. A quantity of alloy contains 20 kg of iron. What weight of copper does it contain?

22 In making mortar you mix sand and concrete in the ratio 6 : 1. You need 140 kg of mortar. How much sand will you need?

23 In a rectangle the ratio of the width to the length is 5 : 7. The length is 42 cm. Find the width.

24 Divide 48 cm in the ratio 1 : 2

25 Divide £27 in the ratio 3 : 7

26 Divide 61.93 kg in the ratio 2 : 9

27 In a triangle the lengths of the sides are in the ratio 3 : 4 : 5. The perimeter is 96 cm. What is the length of each of the sides?

28 Ali, Betty and Clare share £240 in the ratio 10 : 8 : 7. How much do they each receive?

29 Seven rules cost £1.61. How much will three rulers cost?

30 Three identical textbooks cost £17.88. How much will ten of these textbooks cost?

31 It takes seven ladies 6 hours to complete a job of work. How long would it take eight ladies?

32 Six machines will produce 840 toys in a day. How many would seven machines produce in a day?

33 Mortgage repayments are £9.10 per £1000. What are the repayments on a house costing £65 500?

34 Remi has a house valued at £38 000, and contents at an estimated value of £31 000. His insurance company has an annual charge of £1.88 per £1000 value for Buildings insurance, and £4.80 per £1000 estimated value for Contents insurance. What would be the total annual insurance bill?

35 A car travels 100 miles in 2 hours. At what average speed was the car travelling?

36 Sally can walk at a speed of 4 m.p.h. How far will she walk in $1\frac{1}{4}$ hours?

37 A car drives for 2 hours at a speed of 50 m.p.h. It then covers the remaining 95 miles of its journey in $1\frac{1}{4}$ hours. What is the average speed for the whole journey?

38 In Berlin a leather coat costs 180 marks. How much is this in pounds sterling if the exchange rate is 2.8 marks = £1?

39 A couple wish to take £350 on holiday with them to Tenerife. How many pesetas will they get if the exchange rate is £1 = 3240 pta?

40 From the numbers below list all the (a) square numbers (b) cube numbers (c) prime numbers: 2, 4, 5, 7, 8, 9, 10, 11, 13, 18, 20, 21, 25, 27, 29

Exercise 23   The following are all questions taken from GCSE papers.

1 Paul goes on holiday to the U.S.A.

   (a) He changes £150 into American dollars at an exchange rate of
          £1 = $1.78.
   How many dollars should he receive?   (2 marks)

   (b) On his return, Paul has $40 left and changes this money into pounds. The exchange rate is now £1 = $1.69.
   How much should he receive, correct to the nearest penny?

                                                      (3 marks)
                                                      [MEG]

Sunday	−5°C
Monday	−4°C
Tuesday	−7°C
Wednesday	1°C
Thursday	5°C
Friday	0°C
Saturday	−4°C

2 The temperatures at noon in Montreal on the seven days of one week were as given:

(a) Calculate the mean (average) of these temperatures. *(3 marks)*

(b) On which of these seven days was the noon temperature below the average for the week? *(1 mark)*

[MEG]

3 A builder has a team of bricklayers to build houses for him.
A team of 12 bricklayers would usually build 8 houses each month.
The builder gets a contract to build houses in Swinton at the rate of 20 houses each month.
How many bricklayers will be in the team he needs to build houses at this rate? *(3 marks)*

[NEA]

4 Bronze is made only of copper and tin in the ratio 9 : 2.
How much copper would be needed to make 16.5 kilograms of bronze?
(2 marks)

[MEG]

5 The diagram represents the positions *J, K, L, M* of the homes of four friends Jatinder, Krishna, Lynda and Marla, respectively, and the roads between them.

(a) What is the shortest distance by road from *J* to *L*? *(2 marks)*

(b) Jatinda has some disco tickets which she wants to deliver to her three friends as quickly as possible. She cycles from her home to the homes of her three friends by the shortest possible route.

   (i) Which route does she take?

   (ii) How many kilometres will she have cycled when she reaches the home of the third friend?

   (iii) If she cycles at an average speed of 20 km/h, for how many minutes will she have cycled when she reaches the home of the third friend? *(5 marks)*

[MEG]

6 A 375 gram packet of Nicicles costs £1.08.

(a) Calculate the cost per gram of Nicicles in this packet. *(2 marks)*

(b) At the same rate, what would a 500 gram packet of Nicicles cost?
(3 marks)

[NEA]

7 James is mixing some wallpaper paste. The instructions on the packet say

   Enough for 12 rolls of wallpaper.
   Mix all the contents with 8 pints of water.

James does not want to make too much paste as he only has 3 rolls of wallpaper.
How much water does he need to use to make enough paste for his needs?

(3 marks)

[LEAG]

8 When Mackinder was in Spain, the exchange rate was 197.60 pesetas for £1. She bought a newspaper which would cost 25p at home.

(a) How many pesetas were equivalent to 25p? *(2 marks)*

Mackinder had to pay 160 pesetas for the newspaper.

(b) How many pence were equivalent to 160 pesetas? Give your answer to the nearest whole number. *(2 marks)*

(c) Mackinder said that the newspaper cost her more than three times as much in Spain as it would have done at home. Was she correct? Give a reason for your answer. *(2 marks)*

[MEG]

9 The prices of two identical jars of coffee, one in an English supermarket and one in a French supermarket, are shown in the diagram.

(a) The exchange rate is 11.2 francs to £1.

   (i) In which supermarket is the coffee cheaper?

   (ii) What is the difference between the prices, in pence? *(3 marks)*

(b) What would the exchange rate be if the two prices were the same?

(2 marks)

[MEG]

10 At the beginning of 1988 Mrs. McAllister started to pay into a special fund.

She pays £25 on the fifteenth of each month. At the end of each year 13.25% interest is added to the total amount in the fund.

This will happen every year until she retires.

(a) Calculate how much Mrs. McAllister pays into the fund each year.

(1 mark)

(b) Calculate how much she has in the fund on 1 January 1989.

(2 marks)

(c) Mrs. McAllister hopes to retire on 1 January 1992. How much will she have in the fund by then? *(3 marks)*

[NEA]

11 Anna is calorie counting. She buys a slab of Mountain Mint Cake.
Calculate the number of kcals per piece. *(3 marks)*
[SEG]

12 (a) On the 5th November 1988 an evening newspaper gave the following information:

'Lighting up time today begins at 4.43 p.m. this evening and ends at 7.24 a.m. tomorrow morning'.

State, in hours and minutes, the length of the period of lighting up time. *(2 marks)*

(b) On the same day the coldest recorded temperature was −3°C and the warmest recorded temperature was 5°C. By how many degrees did the temperature change that day? *(1 mark)*
[SEG]

13 $\frac{5}{3}, \frac{11}{8}, \frac{27}{19}, \frac{65}{46}, ..., ..., \quad .$

Each member of the sequence of fractions above is obtained from the previous member in the following way.

$$\frac{11}{8} = \frac{(2 \times 3) + 5}{3 + 5}$$

$$\frac{27}{19} = \frac{(2 \times 8) + 11}{8 + 11}$$

$$\frac{65}{46} = \frac{(2 \times 19) + 27}{19 + 27}$$

(a) Find the next two fractions in the sequence.

(b) Show that the next fraction after those is $\frac{915}{647}$. *(4 marks)*
[NEA]

14 Three teams took part in the final of a General Knowledge Quiz.
Team A finished 5 points behind Team B.
Team C scored 9 more points than Team A.

(a) Which team won the competition? *(1 mark)*

(b) Team B scored 26 points.
How many points did Team C score? *(1 mark)*

(c) The information given above could have been displayed as shown.

Fill in the remaining spaces in the table. *(3 marks)*
[NEA]

15 This diagram is of a North Sea oil-rig.

A is the top of the rig.
B is sea level.
C is the seabed.

(a) From the diagram estimate

    (i) the depth of the sea,

    (ii) the distance from the top of the oil-rig to the seabed.   *(2 marks)*

(b) In 1970 the price of a barrel of oil was 1.6 US dollars ($). By 1975 the price had increased by 500%. Calculate the cost of a barrel of oil in 1975.   *(3 marks)*

                                                                        [NEA]

16 In a GCSE mathematics course 180 marks are for examination papers and 120 marks are for coursework.

(a) Write the ratio of examination marks to coursework in its simplest form.   *(2 marks)*

(b) Robert obtains 108 marks for his examination papers and 72 for his coursework. What is his final percentage mark?   *(2 marks)*

(c) Kate obtains a final mark of 70%. She gains twice as many marks for her examination papers as she does for her coursework.
How many marks does Kate obtain for her coursework?   *(2 marks)*

                                                                        [SEG]

Ideas for investigations

1 A series of ratios are given as follows:

$$\frac{b}{a} = \frac{2}{1} = 2 \qquad \frac{c}{b} = \frac{3}{2} = 1.5 \qquad \frac{d}{c} = \frac{5}{3} = 1.6666$$

$$\frac{e}{d} = \frac{8}{5} = 1.6 \qquad \frac{f}{e} = \frac{13}{8} = 1.625$$

Continue the series of ratios until your answer remains almost unchanged (remains the same to 4 decimal places). You have then found the Golden Ratio.

Hint: The series of numbers this is based on is the Fibonacci series:

    1, 1, 2, 3, 5, 8, 13, 21, 34, 55, ...

2 Investigate these two patterns of numbers, and extend the series if possible. In each case explain how the series 'works'.

$$1^3 = \quad 1 = 1^2 - 0^2 \qquad\qquad 1^2 = 1$$
$$2^3 = \quad 8 = 3^2 - 1^2 \qquad\qquad 2^2 = 4 = 1 + 3$$
$$3^3 = 27 = 6^2 - ?^2 \qquad\qquad 3^2 = 9 = 1 + 3 + ?$$
$$4^3 = ? \,... \qquad\qquad\qquad\quad 4^2 = ...$$

3 Foreign currencies: How does the pound fare?
Monitor the rise and fall of the pound against a number of other currencies, recording the data on a graph. Which currencies appear to be stable when compared to the pound? You can obtain this information from newspapers.

Also find the commission charged for (a) buying (b) selling a foreign currency at various banks. Show how much money you are left with if you were to start with £100, change it into a foreign currency, and then back to pounds again.

PATTERNS AND 4 RELATIONSHIPS

4.1 Use of simple formulas

Example   If one button costs 7p, then the cost of buying n of these buttons is given by the formula:

$$c = 7 \times n \qquad \text{(or } c = 7n\text{)}$$

cost   number of buttons

So the cost of six buttons is given by $c = 7 \times 6 = 42$p.
What is the cost of 20 buttons?

The formula gives $c = 7 \times 20 = 140$. We must remember that this answer is in pence. Hence the cost is 140p or £1.40.

Exercise 1

Find the cost of buying:

1 3 buttons	**2** 8 buttons	**3** 14 buttons
4 38 buttons	**5** 200 buttons	**6** 1000 buttons

Example   The number of matchsticks (n) needed to make s squares is given by the formula:

$$n = 3s + 1.$$

How many matchsticks are needed to make six squares?

If $s = 6$, then
$$n = (3 \times 6) + 1$$

The brackets indicate that this calculation is done first.

$$= 18 + 1$$

Then the 1 is added.

$$= 19 \text{ matchsticks}$$

Exercise 2

Use the formula to find the number of matchsticks needed to make:

1 3 squares	**2** 8 squares	**3** 15 squares
4 12 squares	**5** 20 squares	**6** 52 squares

Exercise 3

1 The area of a rectangle is given by the formula $A = l \times h$, where l is the length and h is the height.
Use the formula to find the areas of these rectangles:

(a) $l = 8$ cm, $h = 5$ cm   (b) $l = 12$ m, $h = 4.5$ m

(c) $l = 2.3$ cm, $h = 3.7$ cm   (d) $l = 200$ km, $h = 150$ km

2 The perimeter of a rectangle is given by the formula $P = 2l + 2h$, where l is the length and h is the height.
Use the formula to find the perimeters of the rectangles in question 1.

3 A ball is dropped from a window in a tall building. Its speed is given by the formula $v = 10 \times t$, where t is the time (in seconds) that it has been falling. Use the formula to find the speed of the ball after:

(a) 2 s   (b) 7 s   (c) 15 s   (d) 22 s

4 The size of the exterior angle of a regular polygon is given by the formula

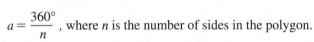

$$a = \frac{360°}{n}\text{, where } n \text{ is the number of sides in the polygon.}$$

Use the formula to calculate the exterior angle of a regular polygon with:

(a) 6 sides (hexagon)   (b) 8 sides (octagon)

(c) 15 sides   (d) 4 sides (square)

5 A taxi company charges C *pence* for a journey of n kilometres.
The formula is $C = 80 + 15n$. Find the fare for a journey of

(a) 2 km   (b) 5 km   (c) 10 km   (d) 30 km.

6 The time (t minutes) taken to travel to College depends on how far the student walks and how far the student travels on the bus. The formula for the time taken is $t = 11w + 4b$, where w is the walking distance and b is the distance travelled on the bus.

Find the time taken for these students to travel to College:

(a) Wendy, who walks 2 km and goes 7 km on the bus.

(b) Rashid, who walks 4 km and goes 3 km on the bus.

(c) Annette, who walks 3 km and goes 16 km on the bus.

(d) Michael, who walks 1 km and goes 5 km on the bus.

7 The amount of sleep (H hours approximately) that a child needs depends on its age (A years). A formula for the number of hours is given by $H = 17 - \frac{A}{2}$. Work out how many hours of sleep are needed by:

(a) Henrietta, aged 4   (b) Miranda, who is 6 years old

(c) Julian, who is 12   (d) Craig, a 15-year-old

4.2 Substituting into a formula

In exercise 3, you were **substituting** numbers into a formula, to work out a value of, or **evaluate**, the formula.

Example If $v = u + 10t$, work out v when (a) $u = 5$ and $t = 4$
(b) $u = 17.4$ and $t = 3.6$.

(a) $v = 5 + (10 \times 4)$ ◄──── *Do the substitution first,*
$\quad = 5 + 40$ ◄──── *without any working out.*
$\quad = 45$

Then work out the formula.

(b) $v = 17.4 + (10 \times 3.6)$
$\quad = 17.4 + 36$
$\quad = 53.4$

The first true electronic calculator was produced in Britain by the Bell Punch Company in 1963. It had a display 20 centimetres wide, and could perform only the four basic functions of adding, subtracting, multiplying and dividing.

Note: Do not try to substitute numbers into the formula *and* do a calculation at the same time. You are likely to make errors. Invariably you will gain method marks for substituting the correct figures into the formula, so set your work out in two stages:
1 Replace letters in the formula by the correct numbers.
2 Complete the calculations.
Although it may seem unnecessary to follow these steps in the simple examples given, more complicated formulas, or numbers, can give rise to errors if such a procedure is not followed.

Exercise 4

Evaluate these formulas:

1 $P = 5 \times k$.   Find P when   (a) $k = 3$ (b) $k = 10$ (c) $k = 16$

2 $t = 30s$.   Find t when   (a) $s = 2$ (b) $s = 6$ (c) $s = 0.5$

3 $m = 2n + 10$.   Find m when   (a) $n = 4$ (b) $n = 8$ (c) $n = 1$

4 $R = \dfrac{60}{I}$.   Find R when   (a) $I = 12$ (b) $I = 30$ (c) $I = 4$

5 $v = 40 + 10t$.   Find v when   (a) $t = 5$ (b) $t = 3.5$ (c) $t = 35$

6 $q = 4r + s$.   Find q when   (a) $r = 8$ and $s = 7$ (b) $r = 20$ and $s = 20$

7 $x = 25 - \dfrac{100}{g}$.   Find x when   (a) $g = 10$ (b) $g = 50$ (c) $g = 4$

Example Find the area of this rectangle, using the formula $A = l \times h$

Without noticing, you may write $A = 2 \times 50 = 100$

This is wrong, because the formula requires both measurements to be in the *same* units.

2 m
50 cm

In using formulas, you will need to take care to:

(i) use the correct units in the formula,

(ii) adjust your answer, if necessary, to a more sensible unit.

You can say either:

200 cm

50 cm

$A = 200 \text{ cm} \times 50 \text{ cm}$
  $= 10\,000$ square centimetres
    $(10\,000 \text{ cm}^2)$

or:

2 m

0.5 m

$A = 2 \text{ m} \times 0.5 \text{ m}$
  $= 1$ square metre
    (1 m^2)

Both answers are correct: $1 \text{ m}^2 = 10\,000 \text{ cm}^2$

Exercise 5

1 Find the area of a skirting board 2.6 m long and 15 cm wide. Give your answer in (a) m^2 (b) cm^2.

2 On a horse-racing track there is a straight stretch which is used for races of seven furlongs. It measures 1.5 km long by 18 m wide. How many square metres does this straight cover?

3 A roll of wallpaper is 51 cm wide and 10.05 m long.
   (a) What is its area, in square metres, to one decimal place?
   (b) A wall is 3.8 m long and 2.5 m high. Will two rolls of wallpaper be enough to cover the wall?

4 Each quarter, Mrs Graham's gas bill is worked out from the formula $C = S + (n \times 1.6)$p, where S is the standing charge in £, and n is the number of kilowatt-hours of gas used during the quarter. How much is her gas bill, if the standing charge is £10.48, and she uses 1335 kilowatt-hours of gas?

5 The volume of a plank of wood is given by the formula $V = l \times w \times h$. Find the volume, in cubic centimetres, of a plank 1.2 m long, 18 cm wide and 10 mm thick.

6 The formula for the volume of an unsharpened pencil is $V = A \times l$, where A is the area of the end of the pencil and l is its length. If $A = 22 \text{ mm}^2$, and $l = 17$ cm, what is the volume of the pencil? Give your answer in cubic centimetres.

7 The Smiths are having a new concrete floor put in their garage. The garage is 7.8 m long and 5.2 m wide. The new floor is to be 15 cm thick. What volume of concrete, in cubic metres, will the Smiths need to order? (Use the same formula as in question 5.)

Product Information
4 rolls
280 sheets per roll
Sheet size 139 mm × 112 mm
Total area .... sq. m.

8 The information given on the wrapping of a pack of toilet rolls is shown. The total area, however, is blurred. What is the total area, in square metres?

4.3 Relationships: number patterns

What does this machine do?

It is easy to see that it *multiplies* each number by 10. If 5 is the input, then $5 \times 10 = 50$ will be the output.

The **rule** which changes each input into the corresponding output is:

(input) $\times$ 10 = (output)

Example What machine changes 10 into 28, 20 into 58, and 30 into 88?

If we add 2 to each of the second set of numbers, it will become {30, 60, 90}, which is 3 times the first set of numbers. The rule is that each number is *multiplied* by 3, then 2 is *subtracted*.

Note: The rule must work for *each* number in turn.

Exercise 6

In each question write, in words, the relationship between the two sets of numbers.

1 {3, 4, 10}, {6, 8, 20}   2 {8, 10, 12}, {7, 9, 11}

3 {2, 9, 14}, {6, 27, 42}   4 {1, 6, 8}, {6, 11, 13}

5 {30, 40, 50}, {3, 4, 5}   6 {4, 12, 18}, {1, 9, 15}

7 {4, 5, 8}, {41, 51, 81}   8 {6, 7, 8}, {13, 15, 17}

9 {5, 8, 9}, {19, 31, 35}   10 {3, 5, 7}, {9, 25, 49}

4.4 Writing formulas for relationships

Looking at the example above, where {4, 7, 9} became {40, 70, 90), we can write a **formula**, using letters and numbers, to simplify the relationship, or rule.

Take a number from the first set and call it x.

Take the *matching* number from the second set, and call it y.

Then the formula connecting x and y is:

$$y = 10x$$

Similarly, for {10, 20, 30} becoming {28, 58, 88}, the formula for this relationship is:

$$y = 3x - 2$$ ***Check that the rule works for each number.***

Exercise 7

Work out the formula for each question in exercise 6.

Newtown
Cricket Club

Annual fee: £20
Match fee: £2

The eleventh-century Persian poet, Omar Khayyám, spent most of his time in the study of algebra. His work on algebra was known throughout Europe, but at that time his now famous poem, 'The Rubaiyat', was not admired.

Example

John wishes to join a cricket club. The annual membership fee is £20, and in addition a fee of £2 is payable for each game John plays. We can write this as a formula for working out how much John will have to pay for the year, depending on the number of games he plays.

If £A is the total amount, then

$$£A = £20 + £(2 \times g)$$

where g is the number of games John plays.
If John plays in four games, the total to pay will be

$$£A = £20 + £(2 \times 4) = £20 + £8 = £28$$

If he plays in 15 games, the total fees will be

$$£A = £20 + £(2 \times 15) = £20 + £30 = £50$$

Exercise 8

Middleton
SPORTS CENTRE

Membership fee: £12.00
Rates per hour:
Squash: £2.20
Snooker: £2.50
Tennis: £1.70
Badminton: £1.50

1 Alison's local sports centre charges a membership fee of £12. In addition it costs £1.70 per person for an hour of tennis.
   (a) Work out a formula for the cost (£C) of joining the sports centre and playing h hours of tennis.
   (b) How much will it cost Alison for joining and playing ten hours of tennis?

2 For using her car to travel to an examination board meeting, Sylvia can claim 40p per mile for the first 30 miles, and then 20p per mile for the rest of the journey.
   (a) If the total journey is m miles, write an expression for the distance travelled in which she can claim 20 per mile.
   (b) Work out a formula for the total travel claim (£C) for a journey of m miles.
   (c) How much can she claim for a journey of 100 miles?

3 Darren wishes to paint his house, and needs to hire some scaffolding from a hire company. The company charges a standard fee of £8.50, and then £1.50 per day.
   (a) Write down a formula for the hire charge (£H) if Darren wishes to hire the scaffolding for d days.
   (b) If he uses the scaffolding for nine days, what will be the hire charge?

4 Marina knits woolly hats and scarves. She sells the hats for £2.50 each and the scarves for £3.50 each.
   (a) Write down a formula for the amount of money (£M) she will take if she sells h hats and s scarves.
   (b) How much will she take if she sells six hats and five scarves?

5 A car salesman is paid £240 per week, plus a commission of £45 for every car that he sells.
   (a) Write down a formula for his weekly pay (£P) if he sells c cars in a week.
   (b) How much will he be paid for a week in which he sells eight cars?

4.5 Use of calculators

Although calculators do 'number-crunching' very well, not all operate in exactly the same way. You will need to be aware of which buttons to press, in which order, on *your* calculator, so that you become proficient at knowing how to use it most effectively.

First of all, we shall look at the four main functions: $+$, $-$, $\times$ and $\div$.

Example A grocer sells Cheshire cheese for £1.10 per kilogram. How much will it cost for a piece weighing 1.8 kg?

Cost $= 1.10 \times 1.8 = £1.98$ *Check, by working out $\dfrac{1.98}{1.8}$, which is 1.10.*

Example A train travels from Edinburgh to London, a distance of 660 km, in a time of $5\frac{1}{2}$ hours.
What is its average speed for the journey?

$$\text{average speed} = \frac{\text{total distance travelled}}{\text{total time taken}}$$

$$= \frac{660}{5.5}$$ *Check, by working out 120×5.5, which is 660.*

$$= 120 \text{ km/h}$$

Example A publishing company sells a text book for £9.95.

(a) Write down a formula for working out the cost (£C) of n of these books.

(b) What is the cost of (i) 3 (ii) 28 (iii) 60 of these text books?

(a) $£C = £9.95 \times n$

$= £(9.95)n$

When the number has a decimal point, it is usual either to leave in the '×' sign or to put in a bracket: £(9.95)n.

(b) (i) $£C = £9.95 \times 3 = £29.85$

(ii) $£C = £9.95 \times 28 = £278.60$

(iii) $£C = £9.95 \times 60 = £597$

Remember that, when you are working in £'s, 278.6 means £278.60.

Example I receive a telephone bill every three months. The last four bills were £93.65, £105.04, £87.63 and £94.20. Next year, instead of paying each bill when it arrives, I would prefer to pay 12 equal amounts, one each month. What would this monthly payment have been last year, in order to pay the total of the four bills?

Total amount = £93.65 + £105.04 + £87.63 + £94.20 = £380.52
Monthly payment = £380.52 ÷ 12 = £31.71

Note: It is always worth checking your answer by doing the 'opposite' or 'inverse' process. In this case, check that your answer of £31.71, when multiplied by 12, does give £380.52.
It is also worth adding the four amounts in a different order, just in case you entered a mistake, e.g. £78.63 instead of £87.63. Although it takes an extra few seconds, it is always worth doing.

Exercise 9

In this exercise, do not worry about units. Work out the numerical value of these formulas, and check your answer by performing the 'inverse' process.

1 $G = 3h$, when $h = 15.8$

2 $m = 14.8 \times L$, when $L = 3.87$

3 $r = \dfrac{c}{6.28}$, when $c = 28.26$

4 $Y = 29.6 - 2d$, when $d = 12.4$

5 $h = 5p + 0.585$, when $p = 0.379$

6 $J = \dfrac{K}{16}$, when $K = 1024$

7 $A = l \times b$, when $l = 19.3$ and $b = 14.4$

8 $t = \dfrac{6.28}{w}$, when $w = 15.7$

9 $d = 2M + 3N$, when $M = 85.6$ and $N = 50.5$

10 $x = \dfrac{10}{y}$, when $y = 2.63$

4.6 Use of memory

The earliest known example of automation is a water clock thought to have operated in Egypt about 200BC. Water flowed out through a small hole near the bottom of a large tank and into a jar marked with a scale to show hours.

Most calculators have a **memory**, in which you can store a particular number until you need to use it.

The memory is most helpful in two main situations:
 (i) when a number is used repeatedly,
 (ii) when a long number in the display has to be divided into some other number.

Example In an examination, the mark scored on Paper 1 is multiplied by 0.65. This reduced mark is then used in working out the final grade. Work out the reduced marks for these actual Paper 1 marks: 83, 50, 69, 27, 47, 39, and 66.

First of all, enter 0.65 into your calculator, and transfer it to the memory (follow the instructions for *your* calculator).
Then follow these steps:

 (i) Enter 83 into your calculator.

 (ii) Press $\times$ followed by the read memory button followed by $=$. The answer of 53.95 should appear.

Now repeat steps (i) and (ii), for each of the scores 50, 69, . . . 66.

Example Work out the value of P, if $P = \dfrac{20}{k}$ and $k = 3.14 \times 4.62$

 (i) Using a calculator, $k = 14.5068$.

 (ii) I need the display clear, so that I can enter the number 20. Hence transfer the display of 14.5068 into the memory.

 (iii) Now enter 20, and then press $\div$ followed by the read memory button, followed by $=$.

The answer, 1.3786638, is now in the display. It is sensible to round off such an answer, to either 2 or 3 significant figures, since the original numbers are given to three figures. Hence $P = 1.38$ or 1.4.

Exercise 10

Use your calculator, and the memory where necessary, to work out the values of these formulas. In each question, state (i) the full calculator display (ii) the answer rounded to three significant figures.

1 $T = 5.474 \times k$, when $k = 3.186$ 2 $R = \dfrac{V}{0.831}$, when $V = 240$

3 $w = 38.46 \times a$, when (a) $a = 7$ (b) $a = 6.892$ (c) $a = 17.4$

4 $b = \dfrac{500}{l \times h}$, when $l = 10.5$ and $h = 6.93$

5 $d = 44.3 - (2.7 \times e)$, when (a) $e = 11$ (b) $e = 16.2$ (c) $e = 17$

4.7 **Rules of indices**

How many grains of rice will there be on the 11th square of a chessboard, if there is 1 grain on square one, 2 grains on square two, 4 grains on square three, 8 grains on square four, etc? (The answer is on page 82)

1 Multiplication

Look at these four equations, all of which mean the same:

(i) $8 \quad \times \quad 4 \quad = 32$

(ii) $2 \times 2 \times 2 \times 2 \times 2 = 32$ *Writing 8 as 2 × 2 × 2, and 4 as 2 × 2.*

(iii) $2^3 \quad \times \quad 2^2 = 32$ *Writing 2 × 2 × 2 as 2^3, and 2 × 2 as 2^2.*

(iv) $2^5 \quad = 32$

In (iii) the small '3' in 2^3 is called a **power** or **index** (more than one index are called indices).

It refers to the number of 2's that are multiplied together (3 of them). Again, in (iv), the small '5' in 2^5 means $2 \times 2 \times 2 \times 2 \times 2$ (5 of them).

Comparing (iii) and (iv) we can see that $2^3 \times 2^2 = 2^5$.
When two numbers (in this case 8 and 4) are written as powers of the same number (in this case the number 2), then we can:

  multiply them by **adding** the powers

For example $3^2 \times 3^3 = 3^5$ *Check: 9 × 27 = 243*
       and $5^3 \times 5 = 5^4$ *$5^1 = 5$*

Using algebra, we can write:

$x^3 \times x^4 = x^7$

$a^5 \times a = a^6$ *a = a^1*

$r^4 \times r^2 \times r^3 = r^9$

Exercise II

Simplify these expressions:

1 $2^4 \times 2^2$ **2** $x^2 \times x^6$ **3** $y^3 \times y^3$ **4** $a \times a^4$

5 $4^2 \times 4^3$ **6** $2^5 \times 2^5$ **7** $t^2 \times t^2 \times t^2$ **8** $10^6 \times 10^3$

9 $m^2 \times m \times m^2$ **10** $10^2 \times 10^2 \times 10$

Example   Simplify
(a) $5p^3 \times 4p^2 \times p$ (b) $(3t^2)^2$ (c) $7a^2 \times 2ab$ (d) $10m^3n \times 6mn^3$

(a) This is the same as
$5 \times p^3 \times 4 \times p^2 \times p$
$= 5 \times 4 \times p^3 \times p^2 \times p^1$
$= 20 \times p^6$
$= 20p^6$

(b) $(3t^2)^2 = (3 \times t^2) \times (3 \times t^2)$
$= 3 \times 3 \times t^2 \times t^2$
$= 9 \times t^4$
$= 9t^4$

(c) $7a^2 \times 2ab$
$= 7 \times a^2 \times 2 \times a \times b$
$= 7 \times 2 \times a^2 \times a \times b$
$= 14 \times a^3 \times b$
$= 14a^3b$

(d) $10m^3n \times 6mn^3$
$= 10 \times m^3 \times n \times 6 \times m \times n^3$
$= 10 \times 6 \times m^3 \times m \times n \times n^3$
$= 60 \times m^4 \times n^4$
$= 60m^4n^4$

Exercise 12   Simplify these expressions:

1 $3a \times 2a$

2 $5t \times 6t$

3 $(4b^3)^2$

4 $2p^2q \times 4pq$

5 $7s \times 4s^2t$

6 $(2ab)^2 \times 2ab$

7 $(m^2n^2)^3$

8 $4 \times 10^3 \times 2.5 \times 10^2$

9 $(2 \times 10^3) \times (3 \times 10^4)$

2 Division

Look again at the four equations under 'multiplication'.

From (i) we could write: $32 \div 4 = 8$

Using the index notation: $2^5 \div 2^2 = 2^3$

When two numbers (in this case 32 and 4) are written as powers of the same number (in this case the number 2), then we can:

   divide them by **subtracting** the powers

So $3^4 \div 3^1 = 3^3$
$7^5 \div 7^3 = 7^2$
$x^8 \div x^3 = x^5$

Example   Simplify
(a) $m^3 \div m^2$ (b) $18c^5 \div 6c^2$ (c) $q \times 6q^3 \div 3q^2$ (d) $mn^7 \div mn^4$

(a) $m^3 \div m^2 = m$
(b) $18c^5 \div 6c^2 = \frac{18}{6} \times (c^5 \div c^2) = 3c^3$
(c) $q \times 6q^3 \div 3q^2 = 6q^4 \div 3q^2 = \frac{6}{3} \times (q^4 \div q^2) = 2q^2$
(d) $mn^7 \div mn^4 = (m \div m) \times (n^7 \div n^4) = 1 \times n^3 = n^3$

PATTERNS AND RELATIONSHIPS

Exercise 13

Simplify these expressions:

1 $4^3 \div 4^2$ **2** $5^3 \div 5$ **3** $r^6 \div r^3$

4 $S^5 \div S$ **5** $12x^8 \div x^3$ **6** $a^3 \times a^2 \div a^1$

7 $20b^4 \div 10b^3$ **8** $p^2q^3 \div p^2q$ **9** $10^2 \times 10^5 \div 10^3$

The answer to the problem on page 80 is 1024. By the 21st square there will be over a million grains of rice.

Example Simplify $a^3 \div a^5$.

This is the same as $\dfrac{a \times a \times a}{a \times a \times a \times a \times a}$

Since $\frac{a}{a} = 1$, the fraction can be written as:

$$\frac{1}{a \times a} = \frac{1}{a^2}$$

In general, if the higher power of a is in the denominator, then the fraction can be simplified to

$$\frac{1}{\text{difference between the powers}}.$$

Example Simplify (a) $a^3b^2 \div a^5 b$ (b) $6m^2 n^2 \div 3m^4 n^4$
(c) $5yz^3 \div 20y^3 z^3$ (d) $4ab^2 c^3 \div 6a^3 b^2 c$

(a) $a^3 b^2 \div a^5 b = \dfrac{a \times a \times a \times b \times b}{a \times a \times a \times a \times a \times b}$

$$= \frac{b}{a^2}$$

When terms are multiplied or divided, we consider each letter in turn, after any numbers.

(b) $6m^2 n^2 \div 3m^4 n^4 = \dfrac{6 \times m^2 \times n^2}{3 \times m^4 \times n^4} = \dfrac{2}{m^2 n^2}$

(c) $5yz^3 \div 20y^3 z^3 = \dfrac{5 \times y \times z^3}{20 \times y^3 \times z^3} = \dfrac{1}{4y^2}$ $z^3 \div z^3 = 1$

(d) $4ab^2 c^3 \div 6a^3 b^2 c = \dfrac{4 \times a \times b^2 \times c^3}{6 \times a^3 \times b^2 \times c} = \dfrac{2c^2}{3a^2}$

Exercise 14

Simplify these expressions:

1 $\dfrac{y^2}{y^5}$ **2** $\dfrac{5a^3}{a^5}$ **3** $\dfrac{a^3 b^2}{a^2 b^3}$ **4** $\dfrac{10x^3 y}{2x^2 y^4}$

5 $\dfrac{3pq}{9 p^2 q^2}$ **6** $\dfrac{2m^3 n^3}{m^2 n^2}$ **7** $\dfrac{12xy}{4xy^2}$ **8** $\dfrac{c^2 d}{c^3}$

82

4.8 Simplifying algebraic expressions

There are many opportunities for errors when simplifying algebraic expressions. Care must be taken to follow the various rules for combining terms. There are two main approaches that can help:

(i)   plenty of practice!

(ii) substituting simple numbers in place of the letters in the original expression and in your simplified expression to see if they give the same answers.

Example   Simplify these expressions:

(a) $3p - p + 4p$ (b) $2j - k + 5j - 3k$ (c) $12m - 5 - 4m$

(a) $3p - p + 4p$

$\quad = 3p + 4p - p$ ***Taking the '+' terms first.***

$\quad = 7p - p$

$\quad = 6p$

Check: take $p = 2$, $3p - p + 4p = 6 - 2 + 8 = 12$.

Our answer is $6p$, which *is* 12 when $p = 2$.

Group terms with the same letters.

(b) $2j - k + 5j - 3k$ $\qquad\qquad$ (c) $12m - 5 - 4m$

$\quad = 2j + 5j - k - 3k$ $\qquad\qquad\quad = 12m - 4m - 5$

$\quad = 7j - 4k$ $\qquad\qquad\qquad\quad = 8m - 5$

Exercise 15

You can check your answers by substituting a number for each letter, and seeing if your solution gives the same answer as the original question.

Simplify these expressions:

1 $4x - 3x + 7x$ $\qquad\qquad$ **2** $5 - 3y + 4y$

3 $a + 6b - 3a$ $\qquad\qquad$ **4** $4w + 2w - 3w$

5 $6g - 7h - 5g + 3g + 3h$ $\qquad$ **6** $3c + 5 - 2c - 4$

7 $8a - 5b - 2a + 3b$ $\qquad\quad$ **8** $5p + 3p - q - 4p$

9 $x + x + x + 3 - 2x$ $\qquad\quad$ **10** $3y - 5z + y + 2z - 4y + 3z$

Example   Simplify $4c^2 \times 5c$

You may make a slip and write down $20c^2$ as your answer.

Trying $c = 3$, say, the original expression will be
$(4 \times 3 \times 3) \times (5 \times 3) = (36 \times 15) = 540$

Putting $c = 3$ into your simplified answer will give $20 \times 3 \times 3 = 180$.

Clearly there is a mistake: you have forgotton that $c^2 \times c = c^3$ and your answer should therefore be $20c^3$ ($20 \times 27 = 540$).

Example Simplify
(a) $3a^3 + 5a^3$ (b) $7a^2 - 2a^2$ (c) $3a^3 + 7a^2$

(a) There are 3 'lots' of a^3 and 5 'lots' of a^3: altogether there are 8 'lots' of a^3.
Hence $3a^3 + 5a^3 = 8a^3$

(b) Here there are 7 'lots' of a^2, from which are taken 2 'lots' of a^2 leaving 5 'lots' of a^2.
Hence $7a^2 - 2a^2 = 5a^2$

(c) We cannot simplify this expression any further – you *cannot add* (or subtract) different powers of a number – you can only multiply (or divide) them.

An expression such as $x^3 + 5x^2 - 3x - 4$ cannot be simplified further, as the terms cannot be combined.
If, however, we have $x^3 + 5x^2 - 3x^2 - 4$, then we *can* simplify this a little, to $x^3 + 2x^2 - 4$, because $5x^2 - 3x^2 = 2x^2$.

Exercise 16   Simplify these expressions, if possible.

1 $c + 2c + 3c + c$ 2 $4m + 5 - m + 3$ 3 $6x + 2x + 2x - 5x$

4 $3v - 5 - v - 1$ 5 $11a + 2a - 3 + 5a$ 6 $11 + 2a^2 - 3 - 5a^2$

7 $6k^3 - 4 - 5k^3 + 4$ 8 $p + 2q^2 + 3p + 4q^2$ 9 $3x - 7y + 7x - 3y$

10 $3x + 7y - 7x - 3y$ 11 $d^4 + 3d^4$ 12 $4r^3 - 3r + r^3 + r$

13 $3ab^2 + 2a^2b$ 14 $2t^2 \times 3t + 5t^3$ 15 $p^2 + 5pq - 3pq - 15$

16 $6w^2 - \dfrac{10w^5}{5w^3}$ 17 $\dfrac{(3a)^2}{a}$ 18 $x^4 - \dfrac{x^7}{x^3}$

4.9 Brackets

The perimeter of this rectangle is $l + l + h + h$ or $l + h + l + h$

We can write these as $2l + 2h$ or $2 \times (l + h) = 2(l + h)$

We use the **bracket** to show that $(l + h)$ is worked out first, and the answer then doubled.

As both ways of writing the perimeter are the same,

$2(l + h) = 2l + 2h$

Example Write these expressions without brackets:
(a) $2 \times (h + 3)$ (b) $3(a - 8)$ (c) $4(2v^3 + w)$ (d) $20(3 - 2y)$

(a) $2 \times (h + 3) = (2 \times h) + (2 \times 3) = 2h + 6$
(b) $3(a - 8) = 3a - (3 \times 8) = 3a - 24$
(c) $4(2v^3 + w) = (4 \times 2v^3) + (4 \times w) = 8v^3 + 4w$
(d) $20(3 - 2y) = (20 \times 3) - (20 \times 2y) = 60 - 40y$

Exercise 17 Write these expressions without brackets:

1 $4(c + 5)$ 2 $5(a - 2)$ 3 $3(4x + 1)$

4 $2(r^2 + r - 6)$ 5 $8(7 - 3h)$ 6 $3(x^3 + 2x)$

7 $10(3t + 10)$ 8 $3(a + 2) + 2(2a - 1)$ 9 $4(y + 3) - 2(2y)$

The same rule holds if there is a letter in front of the bracket.

Example Write these expressions without brackets:

(a) $a(a + 2)$ (b) $p(3p - 2q)$ (c) $5c^3(c + 3d)$

(a) $a(a + 2) = a^2 + 2a$

(b) $p(3p - 2q) = 3p^2 - 2pq$

(c) $5c^3(c + 3d) = 5c^4 + 15c^3 d$

In an expression it is usual to write the numbers first, then the letters. For example, in (b) we could have written p3p – p2q. This is not wrong, but not as useful for further work.

Exercise 18 Write these expressions without brackets:

1 $b(b - 5)$ 2 $t(t + 3)$ 3 $m(m^2 + 4m)$

4 $h(8h - 9)$ 5 $3d(d + 7)$ 6 $(5x^2)^2 + 5x^2$

7 $4v^2(v^2 - 3v + 1)$ 8 $2pr(r + h)$ 9 $3xy(5x - 2y)$

When brackets appear, they are dealt with first, before simplifying.

Example Simplify:

(a) $5x + 2(x - 3y)$ (b) $p(r + s) - r(p + q)$ (c) $20 - 3(4x - 3)$

(a) $2(x - 3y) = 2x - 6y$
    Hence $5x + 2(x - 3y) = 5x + 2x - 6y$
                        $= 7x - 6y$

First expand the brackets.
Then add like terms.

(b) $p(r + s) = pr + ps$
            $- r(p + q) = -rp - rq$
    $p(r + s) - r(p + q) = pr + ps - rp - rq$
    $pr - rp = pr - pr = 0$
    Hence $p(r + s) - r(p + q) = ps - rq$

Expanding the first bracket.
Expanding the second bracket.
Taking both brackets together.
As rp = pr.

(c) $-3(4x - 3) = -12x + 9$
    Hence $20 - 3(4x - 3) = 20 - 12x + 9 = 29 - 12x$

Removing the bracket.

Remember:
'–' × '–' = '+'.

Exercise 19 Simplify these expressions:

1 $3(x + 2y) + 4x$ 2 $5(c - d) - 2c + 3d$

3 $3a + 4(5a - 6)$ 4 $4(2p - 6q) - 3p + q$

5 $5(a^3 + b) + 2(a^3 - b)$ 6 $a(b - 2c) + 2b(a + c)$

7 $16 - 3(x^2 + 4)$ 8 $a(bc - 2) - b(ac - 3)$

4.10 Multiplying brackets

What is the area of this rectangle?

The area is $(k + 2)$ multiplied by $(k + 5)$.

Also, from the four rectangular shapes, the area is $k^2 + 5k + 2k + 10$.

Hence $(k + 2) \times (k + 5) = k^2 + 5k + 2k + 10$
$$= k^2 + 7k + 10$$

We can obtain the right-hand side by:

(i)   multiplying *each* term in the second bracket by k,

(ii) multiplying *each* term in the second bracket by 2,

(iii) adding the answers.

Example   Write these expressions without brackets:
(a) $(x + 6)(x - 2)$ (b) $(2n + 3)(3n + 4)$ (c) $(f - 8)(3f - 5)$.

(a) $(x + 6)(x - 2)$ $= x^2 - 2x + 6x - 12$ *This is x(x − 2)*
and 6(x − 2).

$= x^2 + 4x - 12$ *Adding.*

(b) $(2n + 3)(3n + 4)$ $= 6n^2 + 8n + 9n + 12$ *This is 2n(3n + 4)*
and 3(3n + 4).

$= 6n^2 + 17n + 12$ *Adding.*

(c) $(f - 8)(3f - 5)$ $= 3f^2 - 5f - 24f + 40$ *'−' × '−' = '+'.*

$= 3f^2 - 29f + 40$

Exercise 20

Multiply these brackets, and simplify the answers.

1 $(x + 1)(x + 2)$ **2** $(x + 6)(x + 5)$

3 $(2x - 1)(x + 4)$ **4** $(a + 3)(a + 3)$

5 $(y - 10)(2y + 3)$ **6** $(x - 1)(x + 1)$

7 $(3t - 5)(2t - 3)$ **8** $(m + 5)(5m + 1)$

9 $(5c + 6)(5c + 6)$ **10** $(10x + 1)(10x - 1)$

4.11 Factorising algebraic expressions

From the section on brackets, we know that

$$x(y - 3z) = xy - 3xz$$

The terms x and $y - 3z$ are the two **factors** of the expression $xy - 3xz$, because when they are multiplied together they are equal to the expression.

How can we find factors of an algebraic expression?

Example   Factorise these expressions:

(a) $4x + 6y$ (b) $4pq - 3pr$ (c) $r^2 + 2rh$ (d) $3t - 6at^2$

We have to look for factors which are **common** to each term.

(a) Each term has a factor of 2.

$$\begin{aligned} 4x + 6y &= 2 \times 2x + 2 \times 3y \\ &= 2(2x + 3y) \end{aligned}$$ *Putting in a bracket.*

(b) $4pq - 3pr$
$$\begin{aligned} &= p \times 4q - p \times 3r \\ &= p(4q - 3r) \end{aligned}$$ *There is a common factor of p.*

(c) $r^2 + 2rh = r(r + 2h)$ *The common factor is r.*

(d) There are *two* factors common to both terms: 3 and t.
We can 'take out' each factor separately:
$$\begin{aligned} 3t - 6at^2 &= 3(t - 2at^2) \\ &= 3t(1 - 2at) \end{aligned}$$ *Taking out the 3 first.*
   Then taking out the t.

Or:

$$\begin{aligned} 3t - 6at^2 &= t(3 - 6at) \\ &= 3t(1 - 2at) \end{aligned}$$ *Taking out the t first.*
   Then taking out the 3.

In either case, the answer is the same as when both factors are taken out together: $3t - 6at^2 = 3t(1 - 2at)$.
Note: It is as well to check, by multiplying out the brackets, that the original expression is obtained.

Exercise 21

Factorise each of these expressions completely (i.e. take out *all* the common factors).

1 $2a + 4b$	**2** $6p - 2q$	**3** $100x - 10y$
4 $3a + 4ab$	**5** $pqr + rst$	**6** $mn - 4n$
7 $8gt + 12ht$	**8** $3ab - 4ac + 5ad$	**9** $2xy - 3xz$
10 $ut + 5t^2$	**11** $c^2d - cd^2$	**12** $2ab^2 - 6ab + a$
13 $5s^3 + 20$	**14** $x^2yz + xy^2z + xyz^2$	**15** $36d^3 - 12d^2$
16 $2ap + ap^3$	**17** $a^2x + ax^2$	**18** $3y - 2y^3$
19 $a^4bc - a^3b^2c$	**20** $2\pi r^2 + 2\pi rh$	

4.12 Sequences

Example Work out the next two numbers in each of these sequences:

(a) 3, 6, 9, 12, 15, ..., ...

(b) 11, 15, 19, 23, 27, ..., ...

(c) 90, 83, 76, 69, 62, ..., ...

(d) 5, 10, 20, 40, ..., ...

(a) This is simply the 3-times table; the next two numbers are 18 and 21.

(b) Each number is 4 greater than the previous number; so the next two numbers are 31 and 35.

(c) Here the numbers are getting smaller, by 7 each time. The next two are, therefore, 55 and 48.

(d) This sequence is different from the other three. Instead of *adding* or *subtracting* a fixed number each time, we *multiply* by 2 to get the next number. the next two will be 80 and 160.

Exercise 22

The Babylonians were the first to use arithmetic about 4000 years ago. They counted in sixties. The Hindus invented the system we now use, called Arabic numerals because the Arabs brought them to Europe.

For each sequence (a) work out the next two numbers (b) write down in words how you worked out your answers.

1 13, 18, 23, 28, 33, 38, ..., ...

2 67, 64, 61, 58, 55, ..., ...

3 2, 6, 18, 54, ..., ...

4 96, 48, 24, 12, ..., ...

5 4, 5, 7, 10, 14, 19, ..., ...

6 2, 6, 12, 20, 30, 42, ..., ...

7 100, 91, 82, 73, 64, ..., ...

8 1, 1, 2, 3, 5, 8, 13, 21, ..., ...

9 8, 20, 9, 18, 10, 16, 11, 14, ..., ...

10 8, 13, 20, 29, 40, ..., ...

4.13 Methods of generating sequences

There are two main ways of generating a sequence:

1 Working out how to obtain the next term from the previous term(s).

2 Finding a rule for writing down any term.

In the previous examples we used method 1. We looked at how each term compared with the previous term.
For example, in the sequence 14, 20, 26, 32, ..., we can see that 6 is added to each term to give the next one.

Method 1

This method can be described as the **difference method**, because we write down the difference between each term and the previous term. The difference is 6 each time, so the next term will be $32 + 6 = 38$, and the following will be $38 + 6 = 44$.

Sequence: 14   20   26   32   **38**   44 ◄——— *New terms.*
Difference: +6   +6   +6   **+6**   **+6**

If we try this method with example (d) on page 88, then we obtain:

Sequence: 5   10   20   40   **80**   *Next term.*
Difference: +5   +10   +20   **+40**   *Next difference.*

In fact the set of differences is the same as the sequence. So 40 will be the next difference making the next number in the sequence 80.
The next difference will be 80, which will make the next number in the sequence 160, and so on.

Exercise 23   Use the difference method to work out the next two numbers in each sequence.

1   7, 10, 13, 16, 19, ..., ...   2   7, 10, 14, 19, 25, ..., ...
3   3, 10, 17, 24, 31, ..., ...   4   9, 10, 12, 15, 19, ..., ...
5   50, 46, 42, 38, 34, ..., ...   6   2, 2, 4, 6, 10, 16, 26, ..., ...
7   8, 12, 18, 26, 36, 48, ..., ...   8   9, 12, 13, 16, 17, 20, 21, ..., ...
9   10, 20, 35, 55, 80, 110, ..., ...   10   16, 26, 38, 52, 68, 86, ..., ...

Method 2

This method needs to have each term connected to its position along the sequence. The process is helped by writing down each term underneath its **position** in the sequence.

Example   Work out a rule for calculating *any* term (say the nth) in the sequence 4, 8, 12, 16, 20, ...

We write down each term underneath its position in the sequence.

Position (n)	1	2	3	4	5	6	7
Term	4	8	12	16	20	*	*

Here, each term is equal to 4 times its position.
So the 8th term will be $4 \times 8 = 32$, the 9th term will be $4 \times 9 = 36$, and so on.

What will be the 20th term, the 25th term and 200th term?

The 20th term will be $4 \times 20 = 80$, the 25th term will be $4 \times 25 = 100$, and the 200th term will be $4 \times 200 = 800$.

PATTERNS AND RELATIONSHIPS

In this method, we can easily work out any term, however far along the
sequence it is. The difference method would take a while to reach the 20th
term, never mind the 200th!
We say that the rule for calculating the nth term is $4 \times n$ or $4n$.

Example Work out the rule for the nth term of the sequence
8, 11, 14, 17, 20, ...

Writing down each term
underneath its position
in the sequence.

Position (n)	1	2	3	4	5
Term	8	11	14	17	20

Using the difference method, each term is 3 greater than the previous term: so
we write down the sequence $3n$:

Position (n)	1	2	3	4	5
$3n$	3	6	9	12	15
Term	8	11	14	17	20

Now we can see that each term in the given sequence is 5 greater than the $3n$
sequence: the rule for calculating the nth term is therefore $3n + 5$.
For example, the next (6th) term is $(3 \times 6) + 5 = 23$.

Exercise 24

For each sequence (a) work out the rule for calculating the nth term (b) work
out the 7th and the 50th term.

1 3, 5, 7, 9, 11, ...   2 4, 9, 14, 19, 24, ...   3 12, 15, 18, 21, 24, ...
4 5, 6, 7, 8, 9, 10, ... 5 7, 17, 27, 37, 47, ...   6 6, 10, 14, 18, 22, ...
7 10, 12, 14, 16, 18, ... 8 0.5, 1, 1.5, 2, 2.5, ... 9 −2, −1, 0, 1, 2, 3, ...

4.14 Further sequences

Example For the sequence 1, 4, 9, 16, 25, 36, ...:
(a) What are the next two terms?
(b) What is the rule for calculating the nth term?

(a) The difference method will give:

Sequence:	1		4		9		16		25		36		**49**		**64**
Difference:		+3		+5		+7		+9		+11		**+13**		**+15**	

The next two differences are 13 and 15 (the next two odd numbers); this
means that we can work out the next two numbers in the sequence.

(b) To work out the rule, we begin by writing down each term underneath its
position in the sequence:

Position (n)	1	2	3	4	5	6
Term	1	4	9	16	25	36

Each term is the square of n, its position: the rule for calculating the nth term
is therefore n^2.

90

Exercise 25

For each sequence, work out (a) the next two terms (b) the rule for the nth term.

1   2, 5, 10, 17, 26, 37, ...

2   2, 8, 18, 32, 50, ...

3   0, 3, 8, 15, 24, ...

4   4, 16, 36, 64, 100, ...

5   5, 11, 21, 35, 53, ...

Hint: In each case, the rule contains the term n^2. Write down the sequence n^2, underneath the position sequence n.

Example   For the sequence $\frac{2}{3}, \frac{3}{4}, \frac{4}{5}, \frac{5}{6}, \frac{6}{7}, ...$ work out (a) the next two terms (b) the rule for the nth term.

(a) The next two terms are clearly $\frac{7}{8}$ and $\frac{8}{9}$.

(b) It is usual to consider the numerators as one sequence, and the denominators as another sequence.

Position (n)	1	2	3	4	5
Numerators	2	3	4	5	6
Denominators	3	4	5	6	7

The nth term of the numerators is $n + 1$.
The nth term of the denominators is $n + 2$.

The nth term is therefore $\dfrac{n+1}{n+2}$.

Exercise 26

Blaise Pascal, a seventeenth-century French mathematician, made the first mechanical calculator when he was only 20 years old.

Work out (a) the next two terms (b) the rule for the nth term.

1 $\frac{1}{2}, \frac{1}{3}, \frac{1}{4}, \frac{1}{5}, \frac{1}{6}, \cdots$

2 $\frac{1}{2}, \frac{1}{4}, \frac{1}{6}, \frac{1}{8}, \frac{1}{10}, \cdots$

3 $\frac{2}{5}, \frac{3}{6}, \frac{4}{7}, \frac{5}{8}, \frac{6}{9}, \cdots$

4 $\frac{1}{3}, \frac{3}{5}, \frac{5}{7}, \frac{7}{9}, \frac{9}{11}, \cdots$

5 $\frac{3}{8}, \frac{4}{10}, \frac{5}{12}, \frac{6}{14}, \frac{7}{16}, \cdots$

6 $\frac{1}{2}, \frac{3}{4}, \frac{5}{6}, \frac{7}{8}, \frac{9}{10}, \cdots$

7 $\frac{1}{4}, \frac{2}{6}, \frac{3}{8}, \frac{4}{10}, \frac{5}{12}, \cdots$

8 $\frac{1}{2}, \frac{2}{5}, \frac{3}{8}, \frac{4}{11}, \frac{5}{14}, \cdots$

9 $\frac{4}{7}, \frac{5}{8}, \frac{6}{9}, \frac{7}{10}, \frac{8}{11}, \cdots$

10 $\frac{2}{3}, \frac{5}{6}, \frac{8}{9}, \frac{11}{12}, \frac{14}{15}, \cdots$

Example   Find the next two terms in the sequence:

1, 1, 2, 3, 5, 8, 13, 21, ..., ...,

(a) Using the difference method:

1		1		2		3		5		8		13		21	
	0		1		1		2		3		5		8		**13**	**21**

The two sequences are identical (except for the '0' at the start). The next difference will therefore be 13, and the next 21, which makes the next two numbers $21 + 13 = 34$ and $34 + 21 = 55$. The sequence will continue:

1	1	2	3	5	8	13	21	34	55	89	144	233	...
[0	1	1	2	3	5	8	13	21	34	55	89	...]	

91

(b) Another way to look at this sequence is to take any *two* consecutive numbers, and add them: e.g. $2 + 3 = 5$, $13 + 21 = 34$. Any term is therefore equal to the sum of the two previous terms.

This is a Fibonacci series, named after an Italian mathematician.

Other sequences can be formed by adding the previous three terms, or by adding the first term to twice the second term to obtain the next term, or by adding the two previous terms and then adding 1. There are other ways in which previous terms can be combined to give the next term.

Exercise 27

Work out the next three terms in each of these sequences. Write down the rule in each case.

1 3, 3, 6, 9, 15, 24, 39, ..., ..., ...

2 1, 3, 4, 7, 11, 18, 29, ..., ..., ...

3 1, 1, 2, 4, 7, 13, 24, 44, ..., ..., ...

4 1, 3, 5, 9, 17, 31, 57, ..., ..., ...

5 1, 2, 6, 16, 44, 120, 328, ..., ..., ...

6 3, 5, 9, 15, 25, 41, 67, ..., ..., ...

4.15 Flowcharts

Example   What is the output (i.e. the **Print** box) of this flow chart?

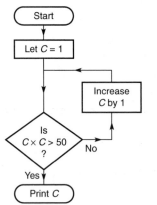

Oval boxes contain orders to start and stop.

Rectangular boxes contain instructions to be followed.

Diamond-shaped boxes contain a question with a 'yes' or 'no' answer.

When $C = 1$, $C \times C = 1$. This is less than 50, so we exit along the 'No' path, which takes us round the loop. C is then increased to 2; $C \times C = 4$, which is less than 50, so we continue round the loop. When $C = 8$, $C \times C = 64$, which is greater than 50. We exit by the 'Yes' path; the output is 8.

Exercise 28   Write down the output from these flow diagrams. In some cases there is a set of numbers as the output. Follow the instructions exactly.

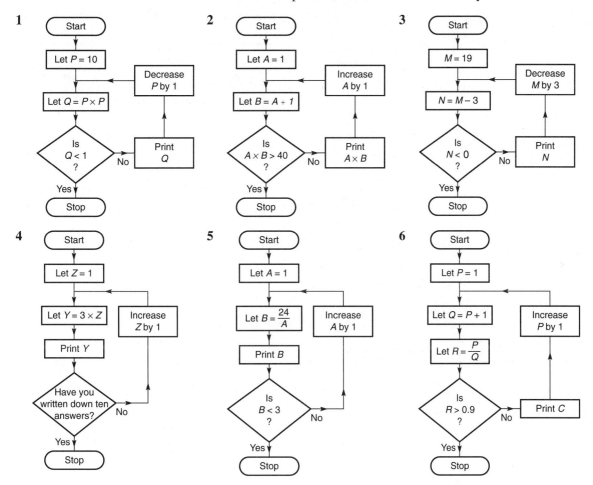

Exercise 29   Make up a flow chart, with a loop, which will produce these outputs. Ensure that instructions are in rectangular boxes, and decisions are in diamond-shaped boxes.

1 3, 6, 9, 12, 15   2 1, 2, 4, 8, 16, 32

3 1, 4, 9, 16, 25, 36, 49, 64, 81, 100   4 11, 13, 15, 17, 19

Review

Exercise 30   1 The charge, £C, for hiring a cement-mixer from an industrial hire firm is given by the formula $C = 12 + 4.5d$, where d is the number of days that the cement-mixer is hired.

How much will it cost to hire the cement-mixer for (a) 2 days (b) 5 days (c) a fortnight?

2 The sum of the first n counting numbers is given by the formula:

$$S = \frac{n(n+1)}{2}.$$

Use the formula to work out (a) $1 + 2 + 3 + 4 + 5$ (b) $1 + 2 + ... + 20$ (c) $1 + 2 + ... + 99 + 100$

3 The cost of entry (£M) to a theme park is given by $M = 9X + 6Y$, where X is the number of adults and Y is the number of children in the party. What is the entrance fee to the theme park for (a) 2 adults and 3 children (b) 4 adults and 7 children (c) a party of 8 adults and 30 children?

Work out the value of each of these formulas:

4 $K = 3H - 16.8$, when (a) $H = 7$ (b) $H = 27.4$ (c) $H = 5.6$

5 $B = 100 - 13.4z$, when (a) $z = 5$ (b) $z = 6.76$

6 $m = 3n + 7p$, when (a) $n = 8$ and $p = 6$ (b) $n = 7.83$ and $p = 6.08$

Simplify these expressions by collecting like terms together:

7 $3x + y + x + 4y$ **8** $p + 7 + 5p - 3$

9 $x - 2x - 3y + 4x + 5y$ **10** $12 - 3x + 5 - 2x$

Write these expressions without brackets:

11 $5(x + 3)$ **12** $4(x - 8) + 3(x + 4)$

13 $5x + 3(x - 4)$ **14** $5(x - 3) + 2(x + 1)$

15 $3(4x + 5y) - 2(5x - 2y)$ **16** $2(3x^2 + 4x - 5) + x^2 + 3(x - 7)$

17 $(x + 3)(x + 2)$ **18** $(2x - 3)(x + 5)$

19 $(x - 10)(x - 10)$ **20** $(x - 10)(x + 10)$

Work out the next two terms in each sequence:

21 $3, 6, 11, 18, 27, 38, ..., ...$ **22** $400, 200, 100, 50, ..., ...$

23 $x^2, 2x^3, 3x^4, 4x^5, ..., ...$ **24** $5, 7, 11, 19, 35, ..., ...$

25 $100, 88, 77, 67, 58, ..., ...$

Exercise 31   The following questions are all taken from GCSE papers.

1 The area of shapes of this type is given by the formula

$$A = \tfrac{1}{2}(a + b) \times h.$$

Work out the area of these two shapes of the same type. (All measurements in cm)

(i) $a = 10$ $b = 12$ $h = 5$ *(3 marks)*

(ii) $a = 2.5$ $b = 3.5$ $h = 1.5$ *(3 marks)*

[LEAG]

2 Gregory's wages are worked out using the formula

Wages = Number of hours worked × Rate of pay + bonus − deductions.

What are Gregory's wages if the number of hours worked is 40, the rate of pay is £1.20, the bonus is £12 and the deductions are £8.60?

(4 marks)
[LEAG]

3

tower 1   tower 2   tower 3

One centimetre cubes are used to build towers, as shown.
Tower 1 is made up of one cube.
Tower 2 is made up of three cubes, and so on.

(a) **Copy and complete** the following table.

Tower number (t)	1	2	3	4	5	6
Number of cubes (c)	1	3	6	10		

(2 marks)

block 1
(tower 1 + tower 2)

block 2
(tower 3 + tower 4)

(b) The formula connecting the number of cubes c in tower t is $c = \frac{1}{2}t(t+1)$. Use the formula to find the number of cubes in tower 20. *(2 marks)*

(c) The towers are placed together to form blocks, as shown.

   (i)   How many cubes are there in block 3? *(1 mark)*
   (ii)   How many cubes are there in block 4? *(2 marks)*
   (iii) How many cubes are there in block 10? *(2 marks)*

(d) The number of cubes in tower t is equal to the number of cubes in block b. State one set of values of t and b when this is true. *(2 marks)*
[SEG]

4 Consider this list of fractions. They form a pattern.

$$\frac{1}{2}, \frac{2}{3}, \frac{3}{4} \cdots$$

(a) Write down the next fraction in the list. *(1 mark)*
(b) Write down the 10th fraction in the list. *(1 mark)*
(c) Write down the 100th fraction in the list. *(1 mark)*
(d) As you go further along the list, the values of the fractions get closer to a certain number. What is this number? *(1 mark)*
[SEG]

Diagram 1

Diagram 2

Diagram 3

5 Sam draws a series of diagrams using squares. She counts the number of small squares in each diagram. The table shows her results.

Diagram number	Number of small squares
1	$2 = 1 \times 2$
2	$6 = 2 \times 3$
3	$12 = 3 \times 4$
4	
5	

(a) (i) Complete **your** table for the next two diagrams in the series.

(2 marks)

(ii) Calculate the number of small squares in Diagram 20.

(1 mark)

(iii) Find an expression in terms of n for the number of small squares in the nth diagram. *(2 marks)*

(b) Find an expression in terms of n for the number of small squares in the nth diagram of the following series:

Diagram 1   Diagram 2   Diagram 3

(3 marks)

[SEG]

6 The overall stopping distance D feet of a car moving at speed V miles per hour is worked out as follows.

At 30 miles per hour $D = 2.5\ V$
At 50 miles per hour $D = 3.5\ V$
At 70 miles per hour $D = 4.5\ V$

(a) Show that the overall stopping distance at 30 miles per hour is 75 feet. *(1 mark)*

(b) Find the overall stopping distance at 50 miles per hour. *(2 marks)*

(c) Find the overall stopping distance at 70 miles per hour. *(2 marks)*

[NEA]

Ideas for investigations

1 In the sequence of square numbers 1, 4, 9, 16, 25, ..., we can write down the **differences** between each term and the previous one:

Terms in the sequence: 1   4   9   16   25   36   ...
Differences: 3   5   7   9   11   ...

Repeating the process to find **second** differences will give:

Terms in the sequence:	1		4		9		16		25		36		...
1st difference:		3		5		7		9		11		...	
2nd difference:			2		2		2		2		...		

What will be the **third** differences?
What will be the **fourth** differences? Continue finding the differences in this way.

Investigate the first, second, third, etc. differences in these sequences.

(a) 6, 7, 9, 12, 16, 21, 27, ...

(b) 2, 8, 18, 32, 50, 72, 98, ...

(c) 1, 8, 27, 64, 125, 216, 343, 512, 729, 1000, ...

(d) 2, 2, 4, 6, 10, 16, 26, 42, 68, 110, 178, ...

(e) 2, 3, 5, 9, 17, 33, 65, 129, 257, 513, ...

Can you suggest any general rules that apply to this method of differences?

Further work
Can you use the 'difference' method to work out the next two terms in each of the sequences above?

2 *Fibonacci sequence*
Each term in a 'Fibonacci sequence' is worked out by adding together the two previous terms. Starting with 1 and 1, the sequence will be:

1, 1, 2, 3, 5, 8, 13, 21, 34, 55, 89, 144, 233, ...

A 1 Take any *three* consecutive numbers in the sequence (e.g. 8, 13, 21).
2 Multiply the first and third together. $(8 \times 21 = 168)$
3 Find the square of the middle number. $(13 \times 13 = 169)$

Repeat steps 1, 2 and 3 for *any* set of three consecutive numbers.
What do you notice? Write down your conclusions.

B Make a new sequence, by *dividing* each term by the previous one

Sequence:	1	1	2	3	5	8	13	21	34	55	89	...
Divisions:		1	2	1.5	1.67	1.6	1.625	...				

Continue for another few terms. What do you notice?
Write down your conclusions.

Now repeat, but this time divide each term by the *next* one.
What do you notice?
Compare both 'division' sequences.

FORMULAS, EQUATIONS AND INEQUALITIES

'I'm very well acquainted, too, with matters mathematical
I understand equations, both the simple and quadratical!'

W.S. Gilbert, The Pirates of Penzance

5.1 Simple equations

Example   Joe receives 8p change when he hands over 80p for two 'Choco' bars. How much does one 'Choco' bar cost?

The process of working out the answer – quite simple in this case – can be made into a problem where we have to **solve an equation**.

We can write this as:

Cost of two bars = 80p − 8p   *An equation has an 'equals'*
                   = 72p   *sign between the two sides,*
Cost of one bar   = 72p ÷ 2   *which must balance.*
                   = 36p

Exercise 1   Answer these questions. Most of them can be done in your head, but write down all the steps in your thinking, as in the examples above, to show the processes you have gone through (e.g. subtracting, dividing by 2, etc.).

1 Mike has read 53 pages of a book. There are 174 pages altogether in the book. How many more pages has he to read?

2 How much will be made from ticket sales for a college Gala night, if 138 tickets are sold at £3.00 each?

3 Barbara buys three oranges. She receives 16p change from a £1 coin. How much does one orange cost?

4 There are 60 houses in a street. Elsie delivers milk to 24 houses on one side of the street, and to 19 houses on the other side.
   How many houses does Elsie *not* deliver to?

5 Brian has a £15 book token. He would like to buy three books, which cost £4.99, £6.50 and £5.25. How much extra money will Brian need in order to buy the books?

6 Shafiul buys two sandwiches and a can of lemonade at lunchtime. He receives 28p change from £2. If each sandwich costs 73p, how much is the can of lemonade?

7 Joan is using the photocopier to make five copies of an examination paper. There are nine pages on the paper. If the counter on the photocopier reads 487 when Joan starts, what will be the reading after she has made the five copies?

5.2 Using letters

By using single letters instead of words, we can reduce the amount of writing that is necessary in order to solve equations.

Looking at the example, if the cost of a bar of 'Choco' is b pence then we can write: $2 \times b = 80 - 8$

or $\qquad 2b \quad = 72$

Hence $b \quad = \frac{72}{2}$

$\qquad b \quad = 36$

Less writing is needed but the same mathematical steps are shown. We have solved an algebraic equation: we have worked out the value of a letter representing a quantity, which in this example is money.

An effective way of solving equations is to imagine a balance with two scale pans. To maintain the balance, whatever we do to one side we must do to the other.

For example if we add 3 to one side we must add 3 to the other.

If we divide one side by 4 we must divide the other side by 4.

Example Solve these equations: (a) $x + 8 = 12$ (b) $t - 3 = 11$ (c) $3m = 15$.

(a) If we *subtract* 8 from each pan, we will be left with x on one pan, and $12 - 8 = 4$ on the other. So $x = 4$.

We can write this algebraically as:

$$x + 8 = 12$$
$$x + 8 - 8 = 12 - 8$$
$$x = 4$$

(b)
$$t - 3 = 11$$
$$t - 3 + 3 = 11 + 3$$
$$t = 14$$

Adding 3 to each pan to get t by itself.

(c) $3m = 15$
$$\frac{3m}{3} = \frac{15}{3}$$
$$m = 5$$

Dividing each side by 3 to get just one m.

Exercise 2

Solve these equations. Draw a balance if you wish.

1 $x + 5 = 8$ **2** $k + 14 = 20$ **3** $5 + t = 27$

4 $12 + y = 22$ **5** $x - 5 = 11$ **6** $r - 16 = 4$

7 $y - 1 = 7$ **8** $p + 25 = 80$ **9** $z + 8 = 8$

Example   Solve the equation $\frac{c}{4} = 6$.

On one pan we have $\frac{c}{4}$, or a quarter of c.

We need to *multiply* each side by 4,
in order to get c by itself.

$$\frac{c}{4} \times 4 = 6 \times 4$$
$$c = 24$$

Exercise 3

Solve these equations:

1 $\frac{x}{2} = 8$ **2** $\frac{y}{3} = 10$ **3** $\frac{t}{6} = 3$ **4** $\frac{p}{4} = 4$ **5** $\frac{m}{2} = 100$

6 $\frac{s}{7} = 2$ **7** $\frac{x}{10} = 9$ **8** $\frac{t}{8} = 8$ **9** $\frac{d}{4} = 0$ **10** $\frac{x}{5} = 6$

In exercises 2 and 3 there has been only *one* operation to perform, addition, subtraction, multiplication or division.
When there is more than one operation, the 'scale pan' approach can often help to decide the strategy for solving the equation.

Example   Solve the equation $3x + 5 = 17$

The aim is to arrive at an equation with just x on one side.
If we firstly remove the 5, then we will have $3x$, which we know how to deal with (divide both sides by 3).

Writing this algebraically:

$$3x + 5 = 17$$

$$3x + 5 - 5 = 17 - 5 \qquad \textit{Subtracting 5 from both sides.}$$

$$3x = 12$$

$$x = \frac{12}{3} \qquad \textit{Dividing both sides by 3.}$$

$$x = 4 \qquad \textit{Check in the original equation:}$$
$$\textit{(3 × 4) + 5 = 12 + 5 = 17}$$

Example   Solve the equation $\frac{t}{5} - 6 = 2$.

$$\frac{t}{5} - 6 = 2$$

$$\frac{t}{5} - 6 + 6 = 2 + 6 \qquad \textit{Adding 6 to each side.}$$

$$\frac{t}{5} = 8$$

$$\frac{t}{5} \times 5 = 8 \times 5 \qquad \textit{Multiplying both sides by 5.}$$

$$t = 40$$

Example   Find k, if $\frac{5k}{8} = 10$.

There is nothing to add or subtract.

$$\frac{5k}{8} = 10$$

$$\frac{5k}{8} \times 8 = 10 \times 8 \qquad \textit{Multiplying both sides by 8.}$$

$$5k = 80$$

$$\frac{5k}{5} = \frac{80}{5} \qquad \textit{Dividing both sides by 5.}$$

$$k = 16$$

Exercise 4   Solve these equations. Draw scale pans if you wish.

1 $2x + 1 = 5$ **2** $3k + 4 = 19$ **3** $5 + 4t = 21$

4 $9 + 2y = 33$ **5** $10y - 1 = 89$ **6** $6p + 2 = 50$

7 $\frac{2x}{3} = 4$ **8** $\frac{3y}{5} = 6$ **9** $\frac{4t}{7} = 8$

$\frac{7d}{2}$ *is the same as* $\frac{7}{2}d$.   **10** $\frac{7}{2}d = 21$ **11** $\frac{3d}{4} = 45$ **12** $\frac{4s}{5} = 0$

5.3   Further equations

An equal mixture of water (freezing point 0°C) and ethanediol (freezing point −13°C) produces an antifreeze with a freezing point of about −37°C.

Example   Solve the equation $x + 2 = 8 - x$

As we said in an earlier example. 'The aim is to arrive at an equation with just x on one side.'

When there is a letter on each side, we can add or subtract the letter. We will not upset the balance, as long as we do the *same* to each side. Here we can *add* an x to each side:

$$x + 2 = 8 - x$$
$$x + x + 2 = 8 - x + x$$
$$2x + 2 = 8$$

We now have an equation with the letter on *one* side as before.

$$2x + 2 - 2 = 8 - 2$$
$$2x = 6$$
$$x = 3$$

Check in original: $x + 2 = 3 + 2 = 5$, and $8 - x = 8 - 3 = 5$

Example   Find z, if $5z - 11 = 3z + 5$.

$$5z - 11 = 3z + 5$$
$$5z - 11 - 3z = 3z + 5 - 3z$$ **Subtracting $3z$ from both sides.**
$$2z - 11 = 5$$ **The z terms are now on one side.**
$$2z - 11 + 11 = 5 + 11$$ **Proceeding as in the previous example.**
$$2z = 16$$
$$z = \frac{16}{2}$$
$$= 8$$ **Check in original:**
$(5 \times 8) - 11 = 40 - 11 = 29$,
and $(3 \times 8) + 5 = 24 + 5 = 29$

Exercise 5

Solve these equations:

1 $2x + 3 = 5 + x$ 2 $3k + 1 = 2k + 4$ 3 $5 + t = 7 - t$

4 $6 + 4y = 2y + 16$ 5 $3x - 6 = 14 + x$ 6 $2r - 7 = 5 - r$

7 $10y - 1 = 89$ 8 $8p + 2 = 50$ 9 $5x - 20 = 80$

5.4 Useful tips in solving equations

A An equation can be written with the sides exchanged.

For example $3d - 6 = 1 - 4d$ is the same as $1 - 4d = 3d - 6$, and $12 = 5z + 2$ is the same as $5z + 2 = 12$.

B When there are terms containing the same letter on *both* sides, ensure that when you remove one of these terms from one side, then the remaining term is *positive*. If it is not, then you should have removed the term from the other side.

For example, in solving the equation $11 - 3x = 5 - x$ we could *add x* to each side.

$$11 - 3x = 5 - x$$

$$11 - 3x + x = 5 - x + x$$

$$11 - 2x = 5$$

This has given us a '$-2x$' term.

Although we can still work with negative terms, it is better (especially when we come to inequalities later in the chapter) to have **positive** algebraic terms. To achieve this, we should have *added 3x* to each side.

$$11 - 3x = 5 - x$$

$$11 - 3x + 3x = 5 - x + 3x$$

$$11 = 5 + 2x$$

$$5 + 2x = 11 \qquad \text{\textit{Using tip A.}}$$

$$2x = 11 - 5 \qquad \text{\textit{Subtracting 5 from each side.}}$$

$$2x = 6$$

$$x = 3$$

C If the equation has a *negative* algebraic term, then *add* this term to each side.

For example, if we are given

$$30 - 4x = 2;$$

then we can add $4x$ to each side:

$$30 - 4x + 4x = 2 + 4x$$

$$30 = 2 + 4x$$

Whatever x is, then −4x will be cancelled out by +4x.

$$2 + 4x = 30$$

Using tip A.

$$4x = 30 - 2$$

$$4x = 28$$

$$x = \frac{28}{4}$$

$$x = 7$$

Check that your answer satisfies the *original* equation. For example, in C above, put $x = 7$, and work out

$$30 - (4 \times 7) = 30 - 28, \text{ which } does \text{ equal } 2$$

So far, all answers have been positive whole numbers.

5.5 Negative and fractional solutions

Example   Solve the equations (a) $3v + 7 = 1$ (b) $4s = 11$.

(a) $3v + 7 = 1$

$$3v + 7 - 7 = 1 - 7$$

$$3v = -6$$

Subtracting 7 from both sides.

$$v = \frac{-6}{3}$$

Dividing by 3.

$$v = -2$$

(b) $4s = 11$

$$\frac{4s}{4} = \frac{11}{4} = 2\frac{3}{4}$$

Dividing by 4.

$$s = 2\frac{3}{4}$$

Exercise 6   Solve these equations; answers may be negative or fractional (or both!).

1 $x + 7 = 4$ 2 $k + 14 = 10$ 3 $5 + 2t = 3$

4 $12 - y = 5$ 5 $6 - 5x = 21$ 6 $3r - 16 = 4$

7 $2y - 1 = 7$ 8 $8p + 25 = -7$ 9 $6x + 30 = 0$

10 $4z + 13 = 3$ 11 $b + 5 = 8 - b$ 12 $5 - 2c = 11 + c$

13 $60 - 3h = 2h + 10$ 14 $2y + 3 = 4y + 5$ 15 $23 = 3 - 3m$

16 $6 + r = 4 - 4r$ 17 $0 = 2 - 3t$ 18 $41 = 21 - 2g$

5.6 Brackets

A room is w metres long and 3 metres wide. We can write its perimeter in two ways:

Either $2(w + 3)$ *or* $w + 3 + w + 3$, which is $2w + 6$.

As these are the same,

$2(w + 3) = 2w + 6$.

W m

3 m

If the perimeter is 18 m, then:

$2(w + 3) = 18$, or
$2w + 6 = 18$

We have removed the bracket, multiplying each term by 2: we now have an equation which we know how to solve.

$$2w + 6 = 18$$
$$2w + 6 - 6 = 18 - 6$$
$$2w = 12$$
$$w = 6$$

The length of the room is 6 metres.

Example   Solve the equation $2(4x + 1) = 3x + 12$.

$$2(4x + 1) = 3x + 12$$

Multiplying each term inside the bracket by 2.

$$8x + 2 = 3x + 12$$
$$5x + 2 = 12$$

Subtracting 3x from each side.

$$5x = 12 - 2$$
$$5x = 10$$

$$x = \frac{10}{5}$$
$$x = 2$$

Exercise 7   Solve these equations. Remove any brackets by multiplication. Check your answers in the original equations. Some answers are negative and/or fractions.

1 $2(t-3)=8$ 2 $5(H+3)=20$

3 $3(n+5)-14=25$ 4 $2(2c-1)-7=11$

5 $16+3(x-4)=28$ 6 $10(2x+3)=10$

7 $5(2s+7)=15$ 8 $9x+2(x+7)=36$

9 $5(3b-4)=8b+1$ 10 $4(w+3)-2=2$

11 $6(2r-7)=0$ 12 $1-z=z-1$

13 $3-5x=2(2x-3)$ 14 $4(4y+1)=3(5y+4)$

15 $6x+5=2(2x+1)$ 16 $2(3k-5)+3(3k+4)=17$

17 $5(3p-1)-9=16$ 18 $9(v+1)=4(2v+3)$

19 $3(6g-3)=4(5g-4)$ 20 $t-1=3(5-t)$

5.7   Fractions

We have dealt with equations such as: $\frac{z}{4}=5$.

We multiply by 4, to give $z=5\times4=20$.

What can we do, however, when the z is in the denominator?

When a letter occurs in the denominator, then *multiply* each side by the denominator.

Example   Solve the equation $\frac{6}{z}=3$.

In this example we multiply each side by z.

$$\frac{6}{z}=3$$

$$\frac{6}{z}\times z=3\times z$$ ***Whatever the value of z, $\frac{6}{z}\times z=6$.***

$$6=3z$$

$$3z=6$$ ***Using tip A.***

$$z=2$$

Example   Solve the equation $\frac{42}{3p-1}=3$.

To bring the p term on to the numerator, we *multiply* each side by $(3p-1)$.

$$42 = 3 \times (3p - 1)$$

$$42 = 3(3p - 1)$$

$$42 = 9p - 3$$

$$9p - 3 = 42 \qquad \textit{Using tip A.}$$

$$9p = 42 + 3$$

$$9p = 45$$

$$p = \frac{45}{9}$$

$$= 5$$

Check: $\frac{42}{3p-1} = \frac{42}{15-1} = \frac{42}{14}$, *which is 3.*

Exercise 8 Solve these equations:

1 $\frac{12}{x} = 3$ **2** $\frac{8}{t} = 4$

3 $\frac{10}{n} = 2$ **4** $\frac{100}{p} = 20$

5 $\frac{5}{x-1} = 5$ **6** $\frac{15}{t} + 4 = 7$

7 $\frac{16}{s} - 7 = 1$ **8** $5 + \frac{12}{x} = 11$

5.8 Problems

Example Mike has £6.30 more than Jim. Together the boys have £21.10.
How much does each boy have?

In this case we might go on guessing for a while before we hit on the answer.
By writing an **equation** we can solve the problem.
We need to use a letter: let us say that Mike has £A.
Then Jim will have £A − £6.30.
Together this comes to £A + £A − £6.30, or £$2A$ − £6.30.
As we are told this is £21.10, we can write an equation:

$$£2A - £6.30 = £21.10$$

$$£2A = £21.10 + £6.30 \qquad \textit{Adding £6.30 to each side.}$$

$$£2A = £27.40$$

$$£A = £13.70$$

Hence Mike has £13.70 and Jim has £7.40, which together make £21.10.

Exercise 9   Form an equation, and solve the problem.

1 Jack and Jill have £50 together. Jill has £12 more than Jack.

   (a) Let Jack have £X. How much has Jill?

   (b) Write an expression, containing X, for the amount they have together.

   (c) Write an equation, and solve it. Write down how much each has.

2 A bill of £177.50 can be paid by a deposit of £20, plus nine equal payments. How much is each of these payments?

3 Charles is one year younger than Betty. Their ages add up to 37. How old is Charles? (Let Charles be c years old.)

4 The perimeter of this rectangle is 46 cm.

   (a) Write an expression, containing t, for the perimeter of the rectangle.

   (b) Write an equation, and solve it, to find the length of the rectangle.

5 An apple weighs twice as much as a banana, and an orange weighs 23 g more than a banana. If all three weigh 143 g, how much does each weigh? (Let the banana weigh b grams.)

6 Mr and Mrs Hardy and their daughter Judith have picked raspberries at a 'pick-your-own' raspberry farm. At the weighing counter, Judith's basket weighs only one third of Mr Hardy's basket. Mrs Hardy's basket weighs the same as Mr Hardy's. Altogether they have picked 14 kg of raspberries. How much has each picked? (Let Judith's basket weigh j kilograms.)

7 Edwina wants to make a triangular flower bed in her garden. She wants the two long sides to be equal in length, and twice as long as the short side. If she has 30 m of plastic edging, what will be the lengths of the three sides? (Let the short side be s metres.)

8 For her new triangular flower bed, Edwina went to the local garden centre and bought some tulip bulbs at 60p each, and twice as many daffodil bulbs at 40p each. If she received 20p change from a £10 note, how many of each bulb did she buy? (Let the number of tulip bulbs she bought be t.)

5.9 Solving equations by 'trial and improvement'

This square has an area of 9 cm^2.
What is the length of a side?

We are in fact solving the equation $x^2 = 9$.
The solution we require is $x = 3$. ($x = -3$ is also a solution, since $-3 \times -3 = +9$, but, as we are finding a length, we can ignore any negative solutions.)

9 cm^2

10 cm²

What is the length of the side of this square, which has an area of 10 cm²?

Let us guess at 3.1 cm.
    Now $3.1 \times 3.1 = (3.1)^2 = 9.61$.
So 3.1 cm is a little short for the length of the side of this square.
    Trying 3.2 cm: $(3.2)^2 = 10.24$; so 3.2 cm is rather too long. It would seem reasonable to try 3.15 cm, as a better guess.
    Trying 3.15: $(3.15)^2 = 9.9225$, which is near to 10, but *just* too short.
    Trying 3.16: $(3.16)^2 = 9.9856$ – the nearest so far.
    Trying 3.17: $(3.17)^2 = 10.0489$ – just too long.
A better answer will be between 3.16 and 3.17; try 3.165.
    Trying 3.165: $(3.165)^2 = 10.017225$, just too long.
    Trying 3.163: $(3.163)^2 = 10.004569$ – very near.
    Trying 3.162: $(3.162)^2 = 9.998244$ – just too short.

We could go on trying numbers between 3.162 and 3.163 until we arrived at the accuracy we needed. However, if we need an answer to 2 decimal places, then 3.16 will be the nearest that we can get.
Hence the side of the square will be 3.16 cm, to 2 decimal places.

In an adult the skin covers an area of about 1.7 square metres, and weighs about 3 kilograms.

Many equations which are non-linear (i.e. other than those which can be arranged into the form $ax + b = c$) can be solved as accurately as is needed, by starting with a reasonable 'guess', and then improving on that guess, as we have done to solve $x^2 = 10$ above.

Example   Solve the equation $x^2 + 2x = 7$.

    Trying $x = 1$: $1^2 + (2 \times 1) = 3$
    Trying $x = 2$: $2^2 + (2 \times 2) = 8$
A solution seems to be between $x = 1$ and $x = 2$, probably nearer 2.
    Trying $x = 1.8$: $(1.8)^2 + (2 \times 1.8) = 6.84$ – too small.
    Trying $x = 1.9$: $(1.9)^2 + (2 \times 1.9) = 7.41$ – too big.

As 6.84 is 0.16 below 7, and 7.41 is 0.41 above 7, it would seem reasonable to try a number nearer to 1.8 than 1.9, say 1.83.
    Trying $x = 1.83$: $(1.83)^2 + (2 \times 1.83) = 7.0089$ – very close.
    Trying $x = 1.82$: $(1.82)^2 + (2 \times 1.82) = 6.9524$ – too small.
Hence a solution of the equation $x^2 + 2x = 7$ is:

   $x = 1.83$ to 2 decimal places

Exercise 10

Solve these equations, to 2 decimal places, using the 'trial and improvement' process. Check your answer by trying the numbers 0.01 above and 0.01 below your answer.

1 $x^2 = 30$ **2** $2x^2 = 100$ **3** $x^3 + 1 = 14$ **4** $x^3 = 60$

5 $2x^2 + x = 25$ **6** $\frac{50}{x} = x$ **7** $\frac{x}{x+1} = 0.7$ **8** $x(x-2) = 300$

5.10   Simultaneous equations

If $2x + y = 12$, then there are many possible values for x and y that would satisfy the equation. For example $x = 3$ and $y = 6$ would satisfy the equation.

Also, $x = 4$ and $y = 4$ would work,

as would $x = 0$ and $y = 12$.

$$(2 \times 3) + 6 = 6 + 6 = 12$$
$$(2 \times 4) + 4 = 8 + 4 = 12$$
$$(2 \times 0) + 12 = 0 + 12 = 12$$

If, however, as well as satisfying $2x + y = 12$, we *also* had to have $x + y = 7$, then the only values that satisfy *both* equations simultaneously are $x = 5$ and $y = 2$.

(Check: $(2 \times 5) + 2 = 10 + 2 = 12$ and $5 + 2 = 7$.)

The process of finding the values of x and y when they have to satisfy *two* equations simultaneously, is called **solving simultaneous equations**.

Example   Solve the equations $4v + 5w = 33$ and $2v + 5w = 19$.

$$4v + 5w = 33$$
$$2v + 5w = 19$$

Writing one equation under the other.

$$2v = 14$$

Subtracting the second equation from the first one; the '5w' terms cancel each other.

Hence $v = \frac{14}{2} = 7$

To find w, substitute the value of $v (= 7)$ into the first equation.

$$(4 \times 7) + 5w = 33$$

$$28 + 5w = 33$$

We know how to solve this linear equation.

$$5w = 33 - 28$$

$$5w = 5$$

$$w = 1$$

Check in the second equation:
$(2 \times 7) + (5 \times 1) = 14 + 5 = 19$, which is correct.

Exercise II   Solve these equations simultaneously.

1   $x + 2y = 5, x + y = 3$
2   $3a + 2b = 22, 2a + 2b = 16$
3   $3p + 4q = 19, 3p + 2q = 17$
4   $3x + y = 13, 6x + y = 19$
5   $m + n = 14, 5m + n = 38$
6   $4s + 4t = 24, 4s + t = 15$
7   $8a + 3b = 47, 3a + 3b = 27$
8   $2x + 3y = 23, 5x + 3y = 53$
9   $m + 3n = 13, 3m + 3n = 21$
10   $6y + z = 6, 2y + z = 2$

Example   Solve equations $4x + y = 17$ and $2x + 3y = 21$ simultaneously.

There is a different number of x's and y's in each equation. If we multiply the first equation by 3, then we will have a '$3y$' term in each. We could then take one away from the other.

$$12x + 3y = 51 \qquad \textit{Equation 1 multiplied by 3.}$$
$$2x + 3y = 21 \qquad \textit{Equation 2.}$$
$$12x - 2x = 51 - 21 \qquad \textit{Subtract equation 2.}$$
$$10x = 30$$
$$x = 3$$

To find y, substitute this value of x into one of the *original* equations:

$$(4 \times 3) + y = 17$$
$$12 + y = 17$$
$$y = 17 - 12 \qquad \textit{Check in the other equation:}$$
$$y = 5 \qquad \textit{(2 × 3) + (3 × 5) = 6 + 15 = 21.}$$

Exercise 12

We can multiply an equation by any number we like: e.g.
$3x + 2y = 8$
is the same as
$6x + 4y = 16$,
or $30x + 20y = 80$.

Solve these equations simultaneously: multiply one equation by a number, so that the *same* term appears in each equation, and then subtract.

1 $2x + y = 14$
      $x + 3y = 22$

2 $3a + 2b = 7$
      $a + 4b = 9$

3 $p + 5q = 20$
      $2p + 3q = 19$

4 $u + 2v = 16$
      $2u + 3v = 29$

5 $4x + 3y = 31$
      $2x + 7y = 21$

6 $c + d = 7$
      $3c + 5d = 27$

7 $3x + y = 14$
      $2x + 3y = 28$

8 $5p + 3q = 14$
      $4p + q = 7$

9 $2s + 3t = 25$
      $s + 4t = 25$

The process is similar if there are negative signs in one or other of the equations.

Example   Solve simultaneously $2x + y = 13$, $3x - y = 7$.

$$2x + y = 13 \qquad \textit{Writing the equations one under the other.}$$
$$3x - y = 7$$

If we now *add* these equations, then the '$+y$' term and the '$-y$' term will cancel each other out. This will leave:

$$2x + 3x = 13 + 7$$
$$5x = 20$$

Hence, $x = 4.$

$$(2 \times 4) + y = 13 \qquad \textit{Substituting in the first equation.}$$
$$8 + y = 13$$
$$y = 5 \qquad \textit{Check in the other equation:}$$
$$\textit{(3 × 4) − 5 = 12 − 5 = 7.}$$

111

Example Solve simultaneously $2x - 3y = 7$, $3x + y = 27$.

$$2x - 3y = 7$$ ***Writing the equations one under the other.***
$$3x + y = 27$$

Multiplying the second equation by 3 will mean that we have a '$-3y$' in the first equation, and a '$+3y$' in the second; adding will cancel these out.

$$2x - 3y = 7$$
$$9x + 3y = 81$$
$$11x = 88$$ ***Adding the equations.***
$$x = \frac{88}{11} = 8$$

$$(2 \times 8) - 3y = 7$$ ***Substituting in the first equation.***
$$16 - 3y = 7$$
$$16 = 7 + 3y$$ ***Using tip C.***
$$7 + 3y = 16$$ ***Using tip A.***
$$3y = 16 - 7$$
$$3y = 9$$ ***Check in the other equation:***
$$y = 3$$ ***(3 × 8) + 3 = 24 + 3 = 27.***

Exercise 13

Solve these equations simultaneously.

1 $4d + e = 13$ **2** $x - 2y = 2$ **3** $3p + 2q = 33$
$3d - e = 1$ $3x + 2y = 38$ $p - q = 1$

4 $2x - 3y = 0$ **5** $a + b = 20$ **6** $2u - v = 3$
$2x + 3y = 48$ $a - b = 6$ $2u + v = 13$

7 $5a - 3b = 3$ **8** $4s - t = 5$ **9** $2x + y = 99$
$2a + b = 10$ $2s + 3t = 13$ $x - y = 48$

Example Solve the equations $5x + 2y = 26$, $4x - 3y = 7$ simultaneously.

$$5x + 2y = 26$$ ***Writing the equations one under the other.***
$$4x - 3y = 7$$

Whatever we multiply one equation by, we cannot make the same number of either x's or y's. In these cases we have to multiply *each* equation by a *different* number.

$$15x + 6y = 78$$ ***Multiplying the first equation by 3.***
$$8x - 6y = 14$$ ***Multiplying the second equation by 2.***
$$23x = 92$$ ***Adding the equations.***
$$x = \frac{92}{23}$$
$$x = 4$$

$$(5 \times 4) + 2y = 26 \qquad \textit{Substituting in the first equation.}$$
$$20 + 2y = 26$$
$$2y = 26 - 20$$
$$2y = 6 \qquad \textit{Check in the other equation:}$$
$$y = 3 \qquad (4 \times 4) - (3 \times 3) = 16 - 9 = 7.$$

Exercise 14 Solve these equations simultaneously.

1 $2x + 3y = 7$ 　　　 **2** $5a - 2b = 1$ 　　　 **3** $4p - q = 29$
$3x + 4y = 11$ 　　　　　 $2a + 3b = 27$ 　　　　　 $p - q = 2$

4 $a + 6b = 15$ 　　　 **5** $4u - 3v = 1$ 　　　 **6** $2y + 5z = 23$
$4a - 5b = 2$ 　　　　　 $5u - 2v = 10$ 　　　　　 $3y + 2z = 29$

7 $6d + e = 50$ 　　　 **8** $4x - 3y = 2$ 　　　 **9** $2x - 3y = 10$
$2d + 5e = 26$ 　　　　　 $3x + 4y = 14$ 　　　　　 $2x + y = 10$

Exercise 15 In these equations, the values of x and y can be positive, negative, whole numbers or fractions. Make sure that your answers satisfy both equations.

1 $2x + 3y = 14$ 　 **2** $3x - 4y = 7$ 　 **3** $x - 3y = 6$
$2x + y = 10$ 　　　　 $x + 2y = 9$ 　　　　 $x + 2y = 1$

4 $x - 3y = 1$ 　　 **5** $4x - y = 18$ 　 **6** $5x + 3y = 5$
$2x + y = 16$ 　　　　 $2x + y = 6$ 　　　　 $2x + y = 1$

7 $x + 2y = 13$ 　 **8** $2x - 3y = 13$ 　 **9** $2x - 3y = 5$
$7x - y = 1$ 　　　　 $x - 4y = 14$ 　　　　 $3x + 2y = 40$

10 $x + y = 1$ 　 **11** $2x + y = 5$ 　 **12** $2x - 5y = 25$
$x - y = 9$ 　　　　 $4x + 3y = 14$ 　　　　 $x + y = 23$

13 $x - 2y = 0$ 　 **14** $5x + 2y = 0$ 　 **15** $4x + 2y = 8$
$3x + 4y = 15$ 　　 $3x + y = 1$ 　　　　 $2x - 5y = 10$

5.11　Use in problems

Example　Two T-shirts and a pair of jeans cost Carl £28. Five T-shirts and a pair of the same jeans cost Carla £43. How much is a T-shirt? How much is a pair of jeans?

We can simplify the writing by letting £t = cost of a T-shirt, and £j = cost of a pair of jeans. We can then write:

$$2t + j = 28 \text{ for Carl}$$
$$\text{and } 5t + j = 43 \text{ for Carla}$$

$$5t + j = 43$$
$$2t + j = 28$$

Writing the first equation under the second.

$$3t = 15$$

Subtracting.

$$t = \frac{15}{3}$$
$$= 5$$

So a T-shirt costs £5.

Going back to Carl's clothes, we can now work out the cost of a pair of jeans:

$$2t + j = 28$$
$$(2 \times 5) + j = 28$$

Substituting.

$$10 + j = 28$$
$$j = 18$$

So the jeans must cost £18.

Checking with Carla's clothes: $5t + j = (5 \times £5) + £18 = £25 + £18 = £43$, which is correct.

Exercise 16

1 Fred buys three buns and a scone for 27p, and Freda buys a bun and two scones for 24p. How much does a bun cost? How much does a scone cost? (Let a bun cost b pence and a scone cost s pence.)

2 Four nails and a screw weigh 28 g, and two nails and three screws weigh 34 g. What does one nail weigh? What does one screw weigh? (Let a nail weigh n g and a screw weigh s g.)

3 Joanne needs 30 cm of wooden beading for a model she is making. The shop sells either type A or type B beading. Four pieces of type A and three of type B come to 30 cm. Also, three of type A and six of type B come to 30 cm. How long is a type A piece, and how long is a type B piece?

4 Five copies of book X and four of book Y cost £46 altogether. If two copies of book X cost the same as three copies of book Y, how much does each book cost?

5 Three apples and two oranges cost 88p, and an apple and three oranges cost 76p. How much does one apple cost?

5.12 Manipulating formulas

In the formula $P = Q + 12$, we can work out the value of P, if we are given a value of Q. For example, if $Q = 3$, then $P = 3 + 12 = 15$.

How can we find Q, however, if we are told that $P = 20$?

One way is to rearrange the formula to give $Q = \dots$.

Using the 'balance' idea that we used when solving equations, we can see that, in order to get Q by itself on one side, we need to subtract 12 from each side.

$$P = Q + 12$$

$$P - 12 = Q$$

$$Q = P - 12 \qquad \textbf{\textit{Using tip A.}}$$

$$\text{When } P = 20, \text{ then } \quad Q = 20 - 12$$

$$Q = 8$$

Example Rearrange the formula $s = ut$, into the form $t = \dots$.

On the balance, we need to divide each side by u:

$$s = ut$$

$$\tfrac{s}{u} = t$$

$$t = \tfrac{s}{u} \qquad \textbf{\textit{Using tip A.}}$$

Exercise 17   Rearrange these formulas, to make the letter in brackets the subject of the formula. If 't' is the letter in brackets the answer should be '$t = \dots$'.

1 $c = d + 5$ (d) 2 $3m = 12 + n$ (n)

3 $y = x - 2$ (x) 4 $4r = 10 - s$ (s)

5 $t = 2p$ (p) 6 $5g = 3h$ (h)

7 $m = 2p - 5$ (p) 8 $a = 4 + 3k$ (k)

9 $P = \tfrac{k}{V}$ (V) 10 $x = mz$ (z)

11 $f = \tfrac{330}{v}$ (v) 12 $\tfrac{w}{3} = 2d$ (d)

Example   Write a formula for working
out R, if $e = v + 2R$

$$e = v + 2R$$

$$e - v = 2R \qquad \textit{Subtracting v from each side.}$$

$$2R = e - v \qquad \textit{Using tip A.}$$

$$R = \tfrac{1}{2}(e - v) \text{ or } \tfrac{e-v}{2}$$

Exercise 18   Rearrange these formulas to give an expression for the letter stated.

Temperature falls by about 6°C for every 1000 metres of altitude. Hence the top of Mt. Kilimanjaro in Tanzania in the tropics is covered in snow all the year round.

1 $V = IR : R = \dots$ 2 $d = 3a + b : b = \dots$

3 $p = \tfrac{3q}{2} : q = \dots$ 4 $C = 2\pi r : r = \dots$

5 $y = mx + c : m = \dots$ 6 $z = 2x + 3 : x = \dots$

7 $a = \tfrac{v-u}{t} : v = \dots$ 8 $x = 3(d - 4) : d = \dots$

9 $F = \tfrac{9C}{5} + 32 : C = \dots$ 10 $k = \tfrac{PV}{T} : V = \dots$

5.13   Evaluating formulas

Example   In the formula $A = 3x + y$, find x when $A = 40$ and $y = 4$.

There are two main ways of tackling this type of problem:

1 Substitute the numbers into the formula, and then solve the resulting equation.
2 Rearrange the formula, as in exercise 18, then substitute the numbers.

Method 1 $40 = 3x + 4$ Method 2 $A = 3x + y$

$36 = 3x$ $A - y = 3x$

$12 = x$ $x = \tfrac{A-y}{3}$

$$x = \tfrac{40-4}{3}$$

$$x = \tfrac{36}{3}$$

$$= 12$$

Exercise 19   Find the value of the letter stated in these formulas. Use whichever method you prefer.

1   $B = 2(t - 12)$; find t when $B = 56$

2   $3y = x + 2.4$; find x when $y = 0.6$

3   $v = u + 10t$; find u when $t = 5$ and $v = 70$

4   $2a = 3b + 4c$; find b when $a = 20$ and $c = 5.5$

5   $l = 3p + 17$; find p when $l = 50$

6   $y = mx + c$; find m when $y = 5$, $x = 2$ and $c = -3$

7   $c = 4p - 3q$; find p when $c = 16$ and $q = 4$

8   $F = 1.8C + 32$; find C when $F = 50$

9   $w = 6(3c + 4)$; find c when $w = 69$

10   $s = ut + 5t$; find u when $s = 100$ and $t = 4$

5.14   Inequalities

We have looked at solving simple equations, for example $4x - 5 = 7$.

$$4x - 5 = 7$$
$$4x = 7 + 5 = 12$$
$$x = 3$$

Cobalt in vitamin B12 protects against anaemia, but only 0.000 002 g per day is needed by the human body.

If, however, we need a value which does *not* satisfy this equation, we need a value of x which is *not* equal to 3. This means that either x is less than 3 or x is greater than 3.

We write x less than 3 as $x < 3$ and x greater than 3 as $x > 3$ (the wider end of the 'arrowhead' points to the greater side), and these are called **inequalities.**
The process of solving inequalities is very similar to that of solving equations.

Example   Solve the inequality $3x + 4 < 19$.

As with equations, we can add or subtract the same value from each side. However we can multiply or divide by *positive* values only.

$3x < 19 - 4$ *Subtract 4 from each side.*

$3x < 15$

$x < \dfrac{15}{3}$ *Divide by 3.*

$x < 5$ *Check: if x < 5, 3x < 15 and 3x + 4 < 19.*

Note: We CANNOT use tip A in inequalities: if x is less than 3 ($x < 3$) then 3 must be *greater* than x ($3 > x$). If we change over the sides of an inequality, we must change the sign (from $<$ to $>$ or from $>$ to $<$).

Example   Solve the inequality $23 - 4x > 7$.

Looking back at the method used for negative terms in equations, we have:

$$23 > 4x + 7 \qquad \textbf{\textit{Adding 4x to each side.}}$$
$$23 - 7 > 4x \qquad \textbf{\textit{Subtracting 7.}}$$
$$16 > 4x$$
$$4 > x$$

So, $x < 4$ **_Look at the note above._**

So if x is less than 4, then $23 - 4x$ will be greater than 7.

Exercise 20   Solve these inequalities.

1 $x + 3 > 5$ 2 $k - 14 < 20$ 3 $5 + 2t > 23$

4 $12 - y < 5$ 5 $8 + 5x < 43$ 6 $3r - 16 > 14$

7 $2y - 6 < 7$ 8 $8p + 25 > -15$ 9 $4z + 13 < 0$

Example   Solve the inequality $12 - x > 3x - 5$.

As with equations, we need to have the 'x' term positive, and on one side.

$$12 > 4x - 5 \qquad \textbf{\textit{Adding x to each side.}}$$
$$17 > 4x \qquad \textbf{\textit{Adding 5 to each side.}}$$
$$\frac{17}{4} > x \qquad \textbf{\textit{Dividing each side by 4.}}$$
$$4\tfrac{1}{4} > x, \text{ i.e. } x < 4\tfrac{1}{4}$$

Exercise 21   Solve these inequalities.

1 $x + 8 > 5 + 2x$ 2 $2k - 5 < 12 + k$ 3 $4 + 3t > 22 - 3t$

4 $9 - y < 15 + y$ 5 $4 - 2x < 12 - 3x$ 6 $4 + 7y < 7 + 4y$

7 $20 - 2n > 3n + 5$ 8 $6x + 20 < 3x$ 9 $2 + 6z < 100 - z$

5.15   Two conditions

'Think of a number between 3 and 12.' This sort of request is asked for when you are trying a riddle on a friend.

If we let the number be n, then we can write $n > 3$ and $n < 12$.

If we write the first condition the other way round, remembering to change the sign, we will have $3 < n$ and $n < 12$.

These two inequalities can be combined into one 'double' condition:

$3 < n < 12$: n has to be *greater* than 3 but *less* than 12.
So $n = 4, 5, 6, 7, 8, 9, 10$ or 11

$\leqslant$ means 'less than or equal to'.

Example   List the possible values of n, where n is a whole number, if

$$1 < n \leqslant 7.$$

The only possible values of n are: $n = 2, 3, 4, 5, 6$ or 7

Example   List the values of x, if x is a whole number, such that $-3 < 2x < 16$.

We must first get x by itself:

$$-\tfrac{3}{2} < x < 8 \qquad \textbf{\textit{Dividing by 2.}}$$

If x has to be a whole number, then: $x = -1, 0, 1, 2, 3, 4, 5, 6$ or 7

Exercise 22   List the values which satisfy each inequality, assuming in all cases that answers are whole numbers.

1 $4 < t < 10$	**2** $0 < x \leqslant 9$	**3** $-5 < s < 2$
4 $6 \leqslant 3n \leqslant 30$	**5** $1 \leqslant 4x \leqslant 20$	**6** $-10 < 3t < 10$
7 $-20 < 2x < -4$	**8** $100 < 10m \leqslant 200$	**9** $-6 < 6n < 60$

Example   Solve the inequality $2n^2 \leqslant 32$.

$$n^2 \leqslant 16 \qquad \textbf{\textit{Dividing by 2.}}$$

Because $n \times n = n^2$ *and* $(-n) \times (-n) = n^2$, we will have *two* inequalities:
$n \leqslant 4$ and $-n \leqslant 4$

Taking the second inequality:

$$0 \leqslant n + 4 \qquad \textbf{\textit{Adding n to each side.}}$$

$$-4 \leqslant n \qquad \textbf{\textit{Then subtracting 4.}}$$

So $-4 \leqslant n \leqslant 4$ **__*Writing both inequalities together.*__**

So if $2n^2 \leqslant 32$, then the value of n lies between -4 and 4.

Exercise 23 Solve these inequalities. There should be two conditions in each case.

1 $x^2 < 9$ **2** $c^2 - 20 < 5$ **3** $72 \geqslant 2s^2$ **4** $\frac{x^2}{2} < 32$

5 $98 > 2x^2$ **6** $25k^2 < 100$ **7** $4x^2 \leqslant 9$ **8** $100 \geqslant \frac{n^2}{4}$

9 $d^2 < \frac{1}{4}$ **10** $x^2 \leqslant 0.01$

Review

Exercise 24 Solve these equations:

1 $x + 3 = 8$ **2** $x - 6 = 7$ **3** $2x + 5 = 21$

4 $5x - 2 = 28$ **5** $3(x - 3) = 12$ **6** $4(x + 9) = 80$

7 $3x - 4 = 2x + 6$ **8** $2x + 17 = 4x - 1$ **9** $5(x + 2) = 7x$

10 $25 - 3x = 1$ **11** $2x + 8 = 0$ **12** $2x + 3 = x - 5$

13 $x + 2x + 3x = 4x + 5$ **14** $\frac{5}{x} = 4$ **15** $\frac{8}{x} + 5 = 9$

Solve these equations, correct to two decimal places, using a 'trial and improvement' process:

16 $x^2 = 13$ **17** $x(x + 1) = 22$

18 $(x - 1)(2x - 1) = 40$ **19** $3x^2 = 40$

20 $\frac{40}{x} = x - 2$ **21** $(x + 3)^2 = 50$

22 $x^2 - 6x = 100$ **23** $\frac{100}{x} = x^2$

Solve these simultaneous equations:

24 $x + y = 12; x - y = 2$ **25** $2x + y = 27; x + y = 17$

26 $x + 2y = 8; x + 5y = 17$ **27** $2x - y = 14; x + 3y = 14$

28 $x - y = 5; 2x + 3y = 15$ **29** $3x - 2y = 19; x + 4y = 18$

30 $x + 3y = 1; x - y = 9$ **31** $x + y = 1; x = 2y$

Rearrange these formulas to make the given letter the subject:

32 $x = 4y: y$ **33** $3h = k - 5: k$

34 $h = 3k - 5: k$ **35** $h = 3(k - 5): k$

36 $m = \frac{n}{3} + 2p: n$ **37** $C = \frac{5}{9}(F - 32): F$

38 $s = 10t^2: t$ **39** $v^2 = u^2 + 2as: u$

Solve these inequalities:

40 $x + 5 > 12$ **41** $x - 3 < 2$ **42** $2x - 3 < 35$

43 $3x + 10 > 100$ **44** $x + 5 < 2x + 1$ **45** $5(x + 4) > 2(x + 16)$

46 $20 - 3x < 5x$ **47** $x < 2(x - 1)$ **48** $2x^2 < 288$

49 $(x - 8)^2 < 9$

Exercise 25   The following questions are all taken from GCSE papers.

1   A kiosk sells two different types of ice cream. The Whopper costs x pence and the Comet costs y pence.
    Wendy buys 7 Whoppers and 5 Comets and pays 391 pence.

(a)   Write down an expression for the total cost, in pence, of the
      7 Whoppers that Wendy bought.   *(1 mark)*

(b)   Write down an expression for the total cost, in pence, of the
      7 Whoppers and the 5 Comets that Wendy bought.   *(1 mark)*

(c)   Hence obtain an equation in x and y.   *(1 mark)*

Jenny buys 4 Whoppers and 9 Comets and pays 377 pence.

(d)   Write down a similar equation in x and y for Jenny's purchase.
                                                                       (1 mark)

(e)   Solve your equations from parts (c) and (d) to obtain the values of x
      and y.   *(4 marks)*

(f)   Ranjit bought 2 Whoppers and 1 Comet.
      How much did his purchase cost?   *(1 mark)*
                                                                       [LEAG]

2   Mrs Hall sets Tony a problem. Her age in six years' time will be twice her
    age nine years ago. What is her age now? Tony writes down the equation

$$x + 6 = 2(x - 9)$$

Solve this equation.   *(3 marks)*
                                                                       [SEG]

3   Jane thinks of a number and gives John the following problem to solve.
    "Three times my number, plus eleven, is the same as five times my
    number, minus seven. What is my number?"

Find Jane's number.   *(3 marks)*
                                                                       [SEG]

4   A bag contains 50 coins all of them either 2p or 5p coins. The value of the
    money in the bag is £1.45.

Find the number of each type of coin in the bag.   *(5 marks)*
                                                                       [SEG]

5 A car is travelling at u m/s. The driver uses the brakes and t seconds later the speed is given by the formula

$$v = u - 2t$$

  (a) When $u = 30$ and $t = 5$, calculate v.   (*2 marks*)

  (b) When the car stops, $v = 0$. Calculate the value of t when $u = 30$ and $v = 0$.   (*3 marks*)

                                             [SEG]

6 Given that

$$t = \frac{2x + y}{3},$$

  (a) find the value of t when $x = 55$ and $y = 28$,   (*2 marks*)

  (b) express y in terms of t and x.   (*2 marks*)

                                            [MEG]

7 Solve these equations:

  (a) $2x = 5$ (*1 marks*)

  (b) $3y + 7 = 1$ (*2 marks*)

  (c) $2(9 - 5z) = 28$ (*3 marks*)

                                            [MEG]

8 A clown is sharing some balloons between a number of children. He gives each child 5 balloons and finds that he has 31 balloons left.

  (a) Assuming that there are x children, write down an expression in x for the total number of balloons.   (*2 marks*)

  (b) The clown continues to share out the balloons. When each child has 7 balloons, there are 5 left over.

    (i) Write down an equation in x.

    (ii) Solve your equation and find how many balloons the clown had altogether.   (*5 marks*)

                                            [MEG]

9 There were x people on a bus when it left Buxton. It then stopped only at Flagg, Monyash and Matlock.

  (a) At Flagg, 7 people got on and nobody got off.
    Write down, in terms of x, an expression for the number of people on the bus between Flagg and Monyash.   (*1 mark*)

  (b) When the bus left Monyash, there were twice as many people on it as when it arrived there.
    Write down, in terms of x, an expression for the number of people on the bus between Monyash and Matlock.   (*1 mark*)

  (c) There were 36 people on the bus when it reached Matlock.
    (i) Write down an equation in x.   (*1 mark*)

    (ii) Find the number of people on the bus when it left Buxton.

                                            (*1 mark*)

                                          [MEG]

10 Solve the equations

(a) $5x = 85$, *(1 mark)*

(b) $3y + 17 = 2$. *(2 marks)*

[MEG]

11 Alex and Pat appeared in a television quiz show.

(a) In the first half of the quiz, Pat scored 15 points more than Alex.
Alex scored x points.
Write down, in terms of x, the number of points scored by Pat.

(1 mark)

(b) In the second half of the quiz, Pat scored another 19 points and Alex
scored twice as many points as he had scored in the first half.

Write down, in terms of x, the number of points scored in the whole
quiz by (i) Pat, (ii) Alex. *(1 mark)*

(c) In the whole quiz, Pat scored the same number of points as Alex. Find
the value of x. *(2 marks)*

[MEG]

12 Solve the simultaneous equations

$5x + 6y = 18$,
$2x + 3y = 3$. *(5 marks)*

[LEAG]

13 The perimeter, P centimetres, of a rectangle is given by the formula

$P = 2(x + y)$

where the lengths of the sides of the rectangle are x centimetres and y
centimetres.

(i) Find the value of P when $x = 2.4$ and $y = 4.8$ *(3 marks)*

(ii) Rearrange the formula so that y is the subject. *(2 marks)*

[LEAG]

14 Statisticians often use the formula $Z = \frac{x - m}{s}$.

Find the value of m and the value of s, if $Z = 1.5$ when $x = 122.5$ and
$Z = 0.4$ when $x = 106$. *(5 marks)*

[MEG]

15 The diagram shows the lines $y = 4x$ and $y = x + 1$.

(a) **Calculate** the coordinates of the point where these lines cross.

(4 marks)

(b) For what values of x is it true that $x + 1 < 4x$? *(2 marks)*

[SEG]

Ideas for investigations

Start

Input N

Let $A = 1$

Divide N by A

Let NEW A become A

Add together $\frac{N}{A}$ and A

Let NEW A $= \frac{1}{2}\left(\frac{N}{A} + A\right)$

Is NEW A = A? (to desired accuracy)   No

Yes

Print A

Stop

1   Follow this flow diagram, starting with (a) 9 (b) 49.

Starting with a number N, what is the output of the flow diagram?

Choose a whole number less than 100.
Investigate the number of times that you need to go round the loop before your answer is correct to two decimal places.

Extension work
(a) Choose any number (e.g. 345.6).
(b) Improve the accuracy to three, or four decimal places.

Further work
Devise a computer program from this flow diagram, to evaluate an answer correct to three decimal places.

2   A. We know that, if $-x = 3$, then $x = -3$.
         But if $-x < 3$, then $x > -3$.

Investigate the rules that apply when inequalities are:
(a) multiplied by (i) a positive number (ii) a negative number,
(b) divided by (i) a positive number (ii) a negative number.

B. We know that, if $\frac{1}{x} = 3$, then $x = \frac{1}{3}$.

But if $\frac{1}{x} < 3$, then $x > \frac{1}{3}$.

Investigate the rules that apply when we are given an inequality with x on the denominator.

Extension work
Investigate the situation when both of the above occur
(e.g. $\frac{-3}{x} > 12$, find an inequality for x).

GRAPHICAL REPRESENTATION

6.1 Coordinates

As a reminder, the first coordinate is the distance across from the origin 0. The second coordinate is the distance up from 0.

The first coordinate is called the x-coordinate, and the second coordinate is called the y-coordinate.

Example The point A has coordinates (3,5).
What are the coordinates of the other points?

A is 3 units across, and 5 units up; its coordinates are, therefore, (3,5).

B is the point (1,4).

C is the point (4,0).

D is the point (0,5).

E is the point (−3,6).

F is the point (5,−2).

G is the point (−4,−3).

Exercise I

1 Copy and complete these statements:

(a) Point H has coordinates (−2,).   (b) Point I has coordinates (,−3).

(c) Point J has coordinates (,).   (d) Point K has coordinates (,).

(e) Point L has coordinates (,).

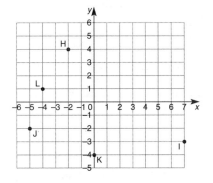

These are called Cartesian coordinates, after a French mathematician of the seventeenth century, René Descartes.

2 Make a copy of the grid on squared paper. Mark these points on your grid.

A = (−5,2), B = (4,−1), C = (−4,1), D = (−1,−4), E = (3,−2), F = (−3,2)

Exercise 2 In these questions you will need to draw a pair of axes on squared paper.

1 Draw a pair of axes, where $-2 \leqslant x \leqslant 5$, and $-3 \leqslant y \leqslant 4$. (See the end of Chapter 5 for the meaning of $\leqslant$.)

(a) Plot the points (4,1), (1,3) and (−1,0).

(b) A fourth point is added to make a square. What are its coordinates?

2 Draw a pair of axes, where both x and y have values from −6 to +8.

(a) Plot the points (7,1), (6,2), (4,4), (2,6) and (0,8).

(b) What is common to all these points? Draw in the line, and write down the coordinates of any other points on the line.

3 Draw a pair of axes, where $-10 \leqslant x \leqslant 8$, and $-3 \leqslant y \leqslant 5$. Join these five sets of points, in order:

(a) (−6,2), (−6,3), (−9,3), (−9,−1), (−6,−1), (−6,1), (−7,1), (−7,0)

(b) (−2,2), (−2,3), (−5,3), (−5,−1), (−2,−1), (−2,0)

(c) (2,2), (2,3), (−1,3), (−1,1), (2,1), (2,−1), (−1,−1), (−1,0)

(d) (6,3), (3,3), (3,−1), (6, −1)

(e) (3,1), (6,1)

Let's hope you improve your grade!

The most deadly poison produced by an animal comes from the skin of the Kokoi frog that lives in Colombia, South America. About 0.00001 grams is enough to kill a human.

6.2 Mappings and plotting graphs

A simple 'function machine' takes one number and **maps** it on to another number. For example, the '−2' machine will take the number 5 and map it on to 3.

We can make a list of inputs, and the corresponding outputs, in a table.

INPUT		OUTPUT
5	→	3
6	→	4
10	→	8
12	→	10
x	→	$x-2$

If we call the input x, then the output will be $x-2$. We can represent this mapping on a graph. Let x be the input and y the output.

This means that the output y is equal to $x-2$.

$$y = x - 2$$

The diagram shows the four points in the table.

*The mapping
$x \to x - 2$
means the same
as the function
$y = x - 2$, since
we are mapping
x on to y.*

Example Draw a graph of the mapping $x \rightarrow x + 3$, for values of x from $x = 0$ to $x = 6$.

First, make a table of x values from 0 to 6; underneath each x value write down its value after the mapping:

x	0	1	2	3	4	5	6
$y = x+3$	3	4	5	6	7	8	9

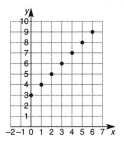

Plot these values on a graph:
clearly the y values range
from 3 to 9.
We can join the points
with a straight line.
This enables us to do two
further things:

(i) we can find what $x = 3.5$ maps on to,

(ii) we can extend the line to show x values that are greater than 6 or less than 0.

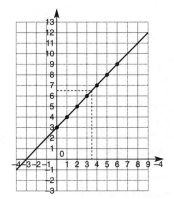

In simple cases, a function is the same as a mapping.

Example Plot the graph of the function $y = 2x - 1$. Take x values from -3 to 5.

As before, make a table of x values from -3 to 5:

Initially, it is easier to work out y values for positive values of x.
When $x = 5$, $2x - 1 = (2 \times 5) - 1 = 9$
When $x = 4$, $2x - 1 = (2 \times 4) - 1 = 7$
When $x = 3$, $2x - 1 = (2 \times 3) - 1 = 5$, etc.
Take care with negatives: $(2 \times -2) - 1 = -4 - 1 = -5$.

The table looks like this:

x	-3	-2	-1	0	1	2	3	4	5
$y = 2x - 1$	-7	-5	-3	-1	1	3	5	7	9

Plot the points, and join them with a straight line.

Exercise 3   Make up a table for these mappings, and plot the graphs. Unless stated otherwise, take values of x from $x = -3$ to $x = 4$.

1 $x \rightarrow x + 2$ **2** $x \rightarrow x - 1$

3 $x \rightarrow 2x + 5$ **4** $x \rightarrow 5 - x$

5 $x \rightarrow 3x - 5$ **6** $x \rightarrow \frac{x}{2} + 7$

7 $x \rightarrow \frac{x}{2} - 1$ **8** $x \rightarrow 15 - 2x, 0 \leqslant x \leqslant 8$

9 $x \rightarrow 10 - x, 0 \leqslant x \leqslant 12$ **10** $x \rightarrow 2x - 2$

Example   Plot the graph of $2x + y = 15$, where $0 \leqslant x \leqslant 10$.

We can rearrange the equation so that we have '$y = ...$', i.e. where y is expressed as a function of x.
Looking back to Chapter 6, we need to subtract $2x$ from each side:

$$2x + y = 15$$

$$y = 15 - 2x$$

In making up the table, an extra line ($2x$) can be added, to help in calculating the values for y.

x	0	1	2	3	4	5	6	7	8	9	10
$2x$	0	2	4	6	8	10	12	14	16	18	20
$y = 15 - 2x$	15	13	11	9	7	5	3	1	−1	−3	−5

Now plot the points.

Exercise 4   Rearrange these equations into '$y = ...$', then make up a table and draw their graphs.

1 $x + y = 8$ **2** $y + 3 = 2x$

3 $y - 2 = x$ **4** $x + y = 12$

5 $x = y - 4$ **6** $2x + 3 = y - 1$

7 $2y + 3 = 4x + 8$ **8** $y - 2x = 3$

9 $3y = 6x - 2$ **10** $2y - x = 8$

6.3 Drawing a line from points lying on it

The speed of sound in air is about 331 m/s.

If you can find *any two* points which lie on a line, then you can join the points to form the line you require. You must be sure that you have worked out the two points correctly, and it is as well to check with a third point, just to make sure that you have not made a slip.

Example Draw the graph of the line given by $3x + 4y = 12$.

One way of finding a point on the line is to make $x = 0$:

$$(3 \times 0) + 4y = 12$$
$$4y = 12$$
$$y = 3$$

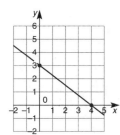

The point $(0,3)$ must lie on the line.
Now try making $y = 0$:

$$3x + (4 \times 0) = 12$$
$$3x = 12$$
$$x = 4$$

The point $(4,0)$ must lie on the line.
This line passes through the point $(2, 1.5)$. Check to ensure that $(2,1.5)$ satisfies the equation: $(3 \times 2) + (4 \times 1.5) = 6 + 6 = 12$.

Example Draw the graph of the line given by $5y = 2x - 3$.

If we let $x = 0$, then $5y = -3$
and $y = \frac{-3}{5}$

This is not very easy to plot. We may be able to find easier points.

Let $y = 0$: $0 = 2x - 3$
$3 = 2x$ *Adding 3 to each side.*
$x = 1.5$ *Dividing by 2.*

The point $(1.5,0)$ is easy to plot. To find another 'easy' point, try $x = 1$, then $x = 2$, etc. until $2x - 3$ is divisible by 5.

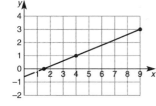

When $x = 4$
             $2x - 3 = 8 - 3 = 5$
Hence $5y = (2 \times 4) - 3 = 5$
So $y = 1$

The point $(4,1)$ lies on the line. We can now draw the line.
The point $(9,3)$ lies on this line. Check that it satisfies the equation:
$5y = 5 \times 3 = 15$, and $2x - 3 = (2 \times 9) - 3 = 18 - 3 = 15$.

129

Exercise 5

By working out two points which satisfy the equation, draw the graph of the line. Check with a third point.

1 $y = x + 3$ 2 $y = 2x - 1$ 3 $x = y - 2$

4 $x = 3y + 1$ 5 $2y = x + 8$ 6 $3x - 1 = y$

7 $x = 12 - y$ 8 $\frac{y}{2} = x + 1$ 9 $x - y = 4$

10 $x + y = 10$ 11 $2y = x - 4$ 12 $2x + y = 16$

13 $x + 3y = 9$ 14 $24 - 2x = 3y$ 15 $4x - y = 16$

6.4 The straight line equation $y = mx + c$

Example   Where do the lines
(a) $y = x + 3$
(b) $y = 2x + 5$
(c) $y = 3x - 2$ cut the y-axis?

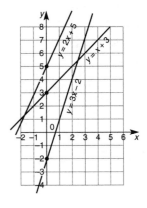

From the graph,
$y = x + 3$ cuts the y-axis at $(0,\mathbf{3})$,
$y = 2x + 5$ cuts the y-axis at $(0,\mathbf{5})$,
$y = 3x - 2$ cuts the y-axis at $(0,\mathbf{-2})$.

Any straight line, written in the form
$y = mx + c$, cuts the y-axis at the point $(0,c)$.

A 'light year', the distance travelled by light in a year, is equivalent to 9 460 528 405 000 kilometres.

Example   Find the coordinates of the point where the line $2y = 3x + 6$ cuts the y-axis.

The answer is *not* $(0,6)$, because we have not made the equation into $y = $ (something).
We must have y by itself:

$2y = 3x + 6$

$y = \frac{3x}{2} + 3.$ *Dividing each side by 2.*

This line will cut the y-axis at $(0,3)$.

Exercise 6

Find the coordinates of the point where each of these lines cuts the y-axis.

1 $y = 4x + 1$ 2 $y = 3x - 4$ 3 $y = 5x - 3$

4 $y = x + 5$ 5 $2y = x - 4$ 6 $3y = 2x + 9$

7 $y = -3x - 1$ 8 $4y = x + 3$ 9 $2y = 5x + 1$

The distance up (or down) from the origin where the line cuts the y-axis is called the **intercept** on the y-axis. It is the y-coordinate of the point where the line cuts the y-axis.

The line $y = 2x + 3$ is drawn. The steepness, or **gradient**, of the line is measured by working out how many units the line rises up, for each unit across.

In this case, the line rises 2 units up for each unit across (in the positive direction).

The gradient of the line $y = 2x + 3$ is 2.

In any equation of the form $y = mx + c$, the **gradient is m**: it is the number of 'x' that there are, (i.e. the **coefficient** of x).

As with the intercept, the line must be expressed in the form $y = $ (something). For example, the line $2y = 4x - 7$ does *not* have a gradient of 4.
$2y = 4x - 7$ is the same as $y = 2x - 3.5$:
the gradient is 2 and the intercept is -3.5.

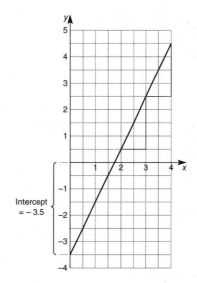

Exercise 7

For each line find (a) the gradient (b) the intercept on the y-axis. Remember to write the equation in the form '$y = mx + c$'.

1 $y = 2x - 1$	**2** $y = 3x + 4$	**3** $y = 5x + 2$
4 $y = x - 7$	**5** $2y = x + 4$	**6** $3y = 2x - 6$
7 $x + y = 3$	**8** $2x + y = 0$	**9** $y = 10 - 3x$

Exercise 8 Work out the gradient, and the intercept on the y-axis for each line. Hence write down an equation for each line.

1

2

3

4

5

6

6.5 Solving simultaneous equations graphically

If we draw two non-parallel lines on the same graph grid, the lines will cross. At the point of intersection, the x and y values will satisfy the equations of *both* lines; the x- and y-coordinates of the point therefore represent the solution when the equations are solved simultaneously.

Example By drawing their graphs, solve the equations
$x + y = 8$ and $x = y + 2$ simultaneously.

Two points on the line
$x + y = 8$ are (8,0) and (0,8).
(Check: (4,4) is a third point.)

Two points on the line
$x = y + 2$ are (2,0) and (7,5).
(Check: (4,2) is a third point.)

From the graph we can see
that the lines meet at the point
(5,3). (Check in each equation:
$x + y = 5 + 3 = 8$ and
$x = y + 2 : 5 = 3 + 2$.)

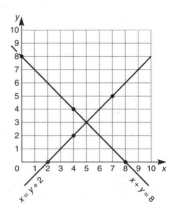

Exercise 9

Find the solution of these pairs of simultaneous equations from the graph. Check that your solution 'works' in both equations.

1

2

3

4

5

6

Exercise 10

By drawing each pair of lines, find graphically the solution of each pair of simultaneous equations.

The Egyptians used geometry for land surveys and for building in about 3000 BC.

1 $x + y = 4$
$\quad y = x - 2$

2 $x + 2y = 6$
$\quad y = x$

3 $y = 2x - 5$
$\quad y = \frac{x}{2} + 1$

4 $x + y = 1$
$\quad y = 2x + 4$

5 $y = x + 5$
$\quad x + y = 5$

6 $x + y = 0$
$\quad y = 2x - 6$

6.6 Curves (I): the quadratic function

Example   Draw the graph of the equation $y = x^2$, for values of x from $x = -4$ to $x = +4$.

The table will be:

x	-4	-3	-2	-1	0	1	2	3	4
$y = x^2$	16	9	4	1	0	1	4	9	16

The graph will look like this:

Remember that $(-4) \times (-4) = +16$.

This is called a **quadratic curve**. Any curve of the form $y = ax^2 + bx + c$ will have this shape.

133

Here are three quadratic curves:

$$y = x^2 + 2x + 6$$

$$y = 2x^2 - 4x$$

$$y = 18 - 2x^2$$

Car headlights and theatre spotlights are in the shape of a quadratic curve, because the light source can be placed at a particular point (the focus) to produce a beam of parallel rays.

All quadratic curves have a symmetry line, which passes through the lowest (or highest) point and is parallel to the y-axis.

All quadratic curves can be transformed into the basic quadratic curve $y = x^2$.

Example Use the graph of $y = x^2$ to solve
(a) the equation $x^2 = 4$ (b) the inequality $x^2 < 9$.

(a) From the graph you can see that there are *two* values of x for which $x^2 = 4$:

$x = 2$ and $x = -2$

(Similarly, if $x^2 = 64$, $x = 8$ and $x = -8$.)

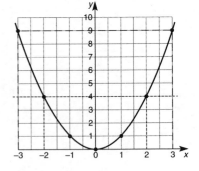

(b) From the graph, if $x^2 = 9$, then the two solutions are $x = 3$ and $x = -3$. Hence, if $x^2 < 9$, then

$x > -3$ and $x < 3$

We can write this more conveniently as $-3 < x < 3$.

6.7 Curves (2): the cubic function

Example Draw the graph of the function $y = x^3$ for $-3 \leqslant x \leqslant 3$.

x		-3	-2	-1	0	1	2	3
$y = x^3$		-27	-8	-1	0	1	8	27

If $x = 4$ then $y^3 = (4)^3 = 64$;
the graph rises quite rapidly as x
increases (e.g. when $x = 10$,
$y = (10)^3 = 1000$). Similarly,
when $x = -10$, $y = -1000$.

Cubic graphs have the general shape
of an 's'.

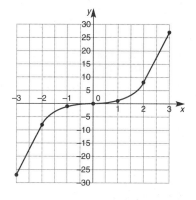

Here are some cubic curves:

$$y = x^3 - 4x$$

$$y = x^3 - 6x^2 + 9x$$

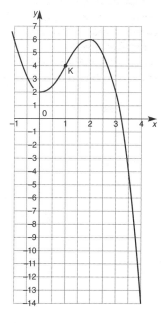

$$y = -x^3 + 3x^2 + 2$$

Imagine a piece of string in the shape of the first cubic curve. The others can
be obtained by 'pulling' each end of the string. Cubic curves have 'half-turn'
rotational symmetry about the point marked K.

6.8 Curves (3): the reciprocal function

Example   Plot the graph of $y = \frac{24}{x}$, for $1 \leqslant x \leqslant 6$.

x	1	2	3	4	5	6
$y = \frac{24}{x}$	24	12	8	6	4.8	4

The graph of this **reciprocal** function is a curve which approaches more closely to the x-axis as values of x become larger, and which approaches the y-axis for small values of x.

The lines which are approached by a reciprocal function are called **asymptotes**.

Here are some reciprocal curves:

$$y = \frac{3}{x+1}$$

$$y = \frac{1-x}{1+x}$$

$$y = \frac{1}{x-2} + 2$$

To be absolutely correct, the curve $y = \frac{24}{x}$ has *two* branches; if we look at negative x values, then the table will be:

x	-1	-2	-3	-4	-5	-6
$y = \frac{24}{x}$	-24	-12	-8	-6	-4.8	-4

Three complete reciprocal curves are drawn below:

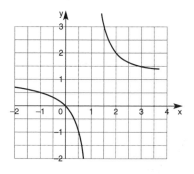

$$y = \frac{1}{x} + 2$$

$$y = \frac{3}{3-x}$$

$$y = \frac{1}{x-1} + 1$$

As with cubic curves, reciprocal curves have half-turn rotational symmetry.

6.9 Plotting simple quadratic functions

The graph of the function $y = x^2$ was drawn earlier:

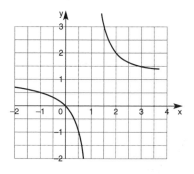

Example Draw the graph of the function
(a) $y = x^2 + 2$ (b) $y = 2x^2$ for
values of x from $x = -4$ to $x = 4$.

(a)

x	-4	-3	-2	-1	0	1	2	3	4
x^2	16	9	4	1	0	1	4	9	16
$y = x^2 + 2$	18	11	6	3	2	3	6	11	18

(b)

x	-4	-3	-2	-1	0	1	2	3	4
x^2	16	9	4	1	0	1	4	9	16
$y = 2x^2$	32	18	8	2	0	2	8	18	32

We could have sketched the graphs without the need to make up a table.
Graph (a) is $y = x^2$ moved up 2 units, and graph (b) is $y = x^2$ 'stretched'
up the y-axis.

137

Exercise 11 Make a sketch of these quadratic graphs. See if you can draw them without having to make up a full table of values.

1 $y = x^2 - 3$ 2 $y = x^2 + 4$ 3 $y = x^2 + 6$

4 $y = x^2 - 1$ 5 $y = 2x^2 + 3$ 6 $y = 2x^2 - 5$

7 $y = 3x^2 - 3$ 8 $y = \frac{x^2}{2} + 4$ 9 $y = x^2 - 4x$

6.10 Regions

Example Draw two axes, each going from 0 to 7, and shade in the region where $x > 3$.

All points which have an x-coordinate *greater* than 3 will be in the required region. The boundary of the region is the line $x = 3$.

Example On the same grid, shade in the region where $y < 4$.

All points with a y-coordinate *less* than 4 will be in the required region. The boundary of this region is the line $y = 4$. Any point in the region with *both* types of shading satisfies *both* inequalities.

Exercise 12 Drawing both axes from 0 to 10, (a) shade in both regions (b) write down the coordinates of *any* point which satisfies *both* inequalities.

1 $x < 6, y < 4$ 2 $x < 3, y > 7$ 3 $x > 5, y > 5$

4 $x > 8, y < 3$ 5 $x < 2, y < 1$ 6 $x > 7, y > 1$

7 $x > 0, y > 8$ 8 $x < 10, y > 7$ 9 $x < 4, y < 6$

Example Draw two axes, each ranging from 0 to 7, and shade in the region where $y < 2x - 2$.

Begin by drawing the boundary line $y = 2x - 2$.

Any point *below* the line will have a y value *less* than $2x - 2$. (Also, any point above the line will have a y value greater than $2x - 2$.)

Originally, a metre was defined as a ten-millionth of the distance between the North Pole and the Equator.

Example   On a grid, shade in the region which satisfies the three inequalities $y < 12 - x$, $x > 2$, and $y > 5$. (Take both x- and y-axes from 0 to 12.)

Begin by working out some points on the boundary line $y = 12 - x$ (e.g. (0,12), (4,8) (6, 6) (12, 0), and then draw the line.

Now draw the lines $x = 2$ and $y = 5$, and shade in the required region.

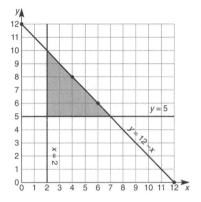

Exercise 13   Drawing both axes from 0 to 10, (a) shade in the required regions (b) write down the coordinates of *any* point which satisfies *all* of the inequalities.

1 $x > 5, x < 8, y < 4$ **2** $x > 6, x < 7, y < 10$

3 $x < 8, x > 3, y > 6$ **4** $x > 4, x < 7, y > 1, y < 5$

5 $x + y < 10, y < 7$ **6** $y < \frac{x}{2} + 6, x < 7$

7 $y > x, y < 8, y > 5$ **8** $y < x + 3, x > 6, x < 8$

Note: In the exercises on regions, we have restricted answers to the positive quadrant, i.e. where $x > 0$ and $y > 0$. The same principles apply in all four quadrants.

6.11   Travel graphs

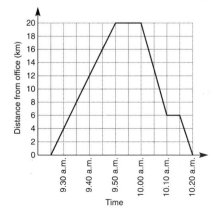

Example   John rides a motorbike, and delivers parcels for a small delivery firm. He has to deliver a package to Mrs Holmes, who lives 20 km away from the firm's main office. The graph represents John's journey to Mrs Holmes's house and back to the office.

(a) At what time did he leave the office?

(b) When did he arrive at Mrs Holmes'?

(c) How long did he stay?

(d) How long did it take him to return?

(e) What was his average speed for the outward journey?

(f) What was his average speed for the return journey?

139

Horizontally each square represents 5 minutes.

(a) John leaves the office at 9.25.

(b) He arrives at Mrs Holmes' at 9.50.

(c) He stays for 10 minutes.

(d) It takes him 20 minutes to return.

(e) Average speed for outward journey

If you drove towards a red traffic light at a speed of 60 000 km/s, the light would appear green.

$$= \frac{\text{total distance}}{\text{total time}}$$

$$= 20 \div \left(\frac{25}{60}\right) \longleftarrow \text{Divide by 60 to convert minutes to hours.}$$

$$= 48 \text{ km/h}$$

(f) Average speed for the return journey

$$= 20 \div \left(\frac{20}{60}\right)$$

$$= 60 \text{ km/h}$$

Exercise 14

1 Alison leaves home at 1300 and drives to the supermarket, which is 60 km away. After shopping, she continues to her aunt's house for a cup of tea. Then she drives back home.

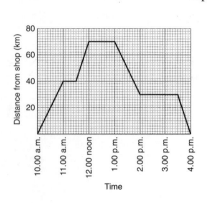

(a) At what time did Alison arrive at the supermarket?

(b) What was her average speed for this journey?

(c) How long did she spend at the supermarket?

(d) How far is it from the supermarket to her aunt's house?

(e) How long did she stay at her aunt's?

(f) How long did it take her to drive home?

(g) What was her average speed for this part of the journey?

2 An electrician is sent out in a van to do three repairs. The travel graph represents the journey made.

(a) At what time did he set out?

(b) He arrived to do the first repair at 11.00 a.m. How long did the repair take?

(c) How far from the shop was the second place that required a repair?

(d) How long did it take to travel from the second to the third repair?

(e) Which repair took longest?

(f) What was the van's average speed from finishing the third repair to arriving back at the shop?

3   Snail A started at 1.00 p.m. to travel across a garden. Snail B started a little later.

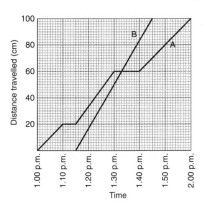

(a) How far had A moved before it stopped at 1.10 p.m.?

(b) At what time did B start?

(c) What was B's average speed in crossing the 100 cm garden?

(d) Between which two times did A move fastest?

(e) What was this fastest speed of A?

(f) At what time did B pass A?

(g) How many minutes did A rest, altogether?

(h) Work out A's average speed for the 100-cm trip.

4   Alan leaves home at 3.00 p.m. for Bruce's house, 200 km away, and drives straight there. At the same time Bruce leaves his house for Alan's, but stops for an hour on the way.

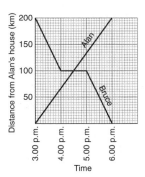

(a) What is Alan's average speed?

(b) What is Bruce's average speed for the first part of his journey?

(c) At what time does Alan pass Bruce?

(d) If Bruce had not stopped, but continued at the same speed, at what time would he have arrived at Alan's?

5   Steve and John, who live 80 km apart, leave at 8.00 a.m. for each other's house. At 10.00 a.m. Steve pulled into a garage and had a fault on his car fixed.

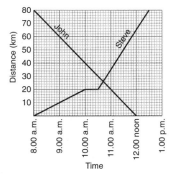

(a) How long did it take to fix his car?

(b) At what time did he stop at the garage?

(c) How far had John travelled when Steve left the garage?

(d) At what time did they pass each other?

(e) Which car went the faster, after Steve's had been fixed?

(f) Steve rang his own house immediately he arrived at John's. How long had John been at Steve's house when he answered the telephone?

Review

1 The points P(−3,2) and Q(5,2) are two corners of a square. What are the coordinates of the other two corners, if:

(a) the square is drawn *above* the side PQ,

(b) the square is drawn *below* the side PQ,

(c) PQ is a diagonal of the square?

2 (a) Draw the line $y + 3x = 12$ on a graph, for $0 \leqslant x \leqslant 4$.

(b) On the same axes, draw the line $y = 3x + 12$, for $-4 \leqslant x \leqslant 0$.

(c) What is the area of the triangle formed by these two lines and the x-axis?

3 Draw the lines $x + y = 16$ and $x + 2y = 20$ on the same graph. (Take both axes from 0 to 20, and make up a table if you wish.)
From your graph, state the coordinates of the points where:

(a) line $x + y = 16$ cuts each axis,

(b) line $x + 2y = 20$ cuts each axis,

(c) the lines meet.

4 On a graph, draw the square ABCD, where A is (0,6), B is (−6,0), C is (0,−6), and D is (6,0).
By looking at the coordinates of points on each side, work out the equation of each of the four sides of the square. (Extend each of the sides of the square if you wish.)

5 By making up a table, or otherwise, draw the graph of the equation $y = x^2 + 4$, for $-4 \leqslant x \leqslant 4$.

(a) What is the least value that y can take?

(b) For what range of values of x is $y < 13$?

6 Make a table of values (take x from 0 to 8), and draw the graph of the equation $y = \frac{30}{x+2}$. Use your graph to find:

(a) the value of y when x is 5.5

(b) the value of x when y is 5.5

(c) the value of y when $x = 298$.

What happens to the value of y as x becomes larger and larger?
Will the value of y ever be zero?

7 Draw axes, where $0 < x < 12$ and $0 < y < 20$.
Draw these four inequalities on your grid:

(i) $2x + y > 10$ (ii) $y < x + 10$ (iii) $x + y < 20$ (iv) $y < 2x - 10$.

What shape is formed by all the points which satisfy these four inequalities?

Exercise 16   The following questions are all taken from GCSE papers.

1 A rectangle has an area of 120 m². Its length is x metres and its width is y metres.

  (a) Show that $y = \frac{120}{x}$.   (*2 marks*)

  (b) Complete the table for the equation $y = \frac{120}{x}$.   (*3 marks*)

x	4	8	12	16	20	24	30
y	30			7.5			

  (c) Draw the graph of $y = \frac{120}{x}$, for values of x from 4 to 30.   (*4 marks*)

  (d) Find the value of y when $x = 18$.   (*2 marks*)

  The paint from a can will usually cover 120 m². A stage manager wishes to paint the largest possible square scenery wall with this can of paint.

  (e) Using the graph, or otherwise, show clearly how you would find the size of this largest wall. What is the length of the wall?   (*2 marks*)
                                                                  [LEAG]

2
Use inequalities to describe the region shaded in the diagram.

                                                                  (*3 marks*)
                                                                  [SEG]

3

Tariff A	Tariff B
£20 plus 15p per mile	40p per mile

Annabel wants to hire a van but decides to check which tariff would be better to use.

She firstly draws a table and works out the cost of some journeys using the two tariffs.

Distance in miles	Tariff A cost	Tariff B cost
0	£20	£0
20		
50		
70		
100	£35	£40

  (a) Complete the table.   (*6 marks*)

  (b) Draw graphs of distance travelled and the cost of the two tariffs. Use a scale of 1 cm to 10 miles on the horizontal distance axis and 2 cm to £5 on the cost axis.   (*5 marks*)

  (c) How many miles would Annabel need to travel before it is cheaper to use Tariff A than Tariff B? Mark this point on your graph.

                                                                  (*3 marks*)
                                                                  [LEAG]

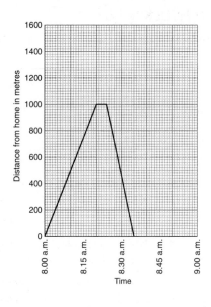

4 On his way to school, Jeremy stops to buy some sweets. He realises that he has forgotten his money and so returns home to collect his dinner money. The distance-time graph for his journey is shown.

(a) How far is the sweet shop from Jeremy's home?

(1 mark)

(b) How long, in minutes, does Jeremy spend in the sweet shop? *(1 mark)*

Jeremy then leaves home at 8.40 a.m. He runs to school which is 1500 m from his home at a constant speed of 9 kilometres per hour.

(c) Copy the graph, and draw the line which represents Jeremy's journey to school. Show your working clearly.

(4 marks)

[LEAG]

5 In an experiment the depth of liquid in a tank is measured over a five minute period. The results are shown on the graph.

(a) What was the depth at the start? *(1 mark)*

(b) What was happening during the first two minutes? *(1 mark)*

(c) What happened 4 minutes from the start? *(1 mark)*

(d) What happened 5 minutes from the start? *(1 mark)*

[SEG]

6 (a) For values of x from 0 to 3, draw and label the graphs of

(i) $y = 2x + 1$, *(2 marks)*

(ii) $y = x^2$. *(2 marks)*

(b) Write down the value of x and the value of y at the point where your graphs meet. *(2 marks)*

[MEG]

7 (a) Write down the coordinates of R.

(b) The points shown are three of the corners of a square PQRS. What are the coordinates of the fourth corner of the square?

(2 marks)

[SEG]

8 The graph below is of $y = \frac{k}{x}$, where k is a constant.

(a) Read from the graph the value of y when $x = 5$. *(1 mark)*

(b) Write down the value of k. *(1 mark)*

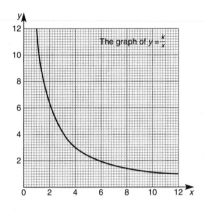

[MEG]

9 In this question the simultaneous equations

$$x + 2y = 8$$

and $\qquad y = \frac{x}{2} - 1$

are to be solved by graphical methods.

(a) Complete the table for the equation $\quad x + 2y = 8$

x	2	4	6	8
y				0

(2 marks)

(b) Complete the table for the equation $\quad y = \frac{x}{2} - 1$

x	2	4	6	8
y	0			

(2 marks)

(c) Draw the straight lines with equations

$$x + 2y = 8$$

and $\qquad y = \frac{x}{2} - 1$

on a square grid, taking both axes from -2 to $+10$. *(4 marks)*

(d) Give the solution of the equations: $x + 2y = 8$, $y = \frac{x}{2} - 1$. *(2 marks)*

[LEAG]

10 Here is a travel graph of a coach trip that Jennifer's aunt took from London to Bath, and back again.

(a) What was the coach doing between 11.00 and 11.30?
(2 marks)

(b) At what time did the coach reach Bath? *(2 marks)*

(c) How long did Jennifer's aunt stay in Bath? *(2 marks)*

(d) (i) How far is it from London to Bath?

(ii) How long did it take the coach to travel from Bath back to London?

(iii) Work out the average speed of the coach on the return journey. *(4 marks)*

[LEAG]

11 The volume, V, of a sealed container is gradually increased.
The pressure, P, of the gas inside is measured for different volumes.
P and V are connected by the equation

$$P = \frac{10}{V}$$

(a) Complete the table of values.

$V(\text{cm}^3)$	1	2	3	4	5	6
$P(\text{N/cm}^2)$	10	5			2	1.7

(2 marks)

(b) Draw the graph of P against V (take both axes from 0 to 12).
(4 marks)

(c) By drawing a line on your graph, estimate the value of P when $V = 3.7$. *(2 marks)*

(d) Does P ever become zero? Explain your answer. *(2 marks)*

[SEG]

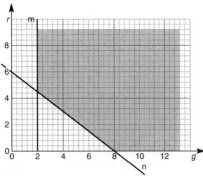

12 In the diagram, the line with the equation $8r + 6g = 48$ is labelled n.

(i) What is the equation of the line labelled m? *(2 marks)*

(ii) Any point inside the shaded region must satisfy the inequality $8r + 6g > 48$.

State another inequality satisfied by any point in the shaded region. *(2 marks)*

[NREB]

Ideas for investigations

1 Make up a table of values for the graphs of:
   (i) $y = x^2$ (ii) $y = x^2 + 3$ (iii) $y = x^2 - 7$

   Draw the three graphs on the same grid.

   What do you notice?

   On your graph, sketch the curve $y = x^2 - 4$, without making up a table.

   What can you say about any graph of the form $y = x^2 + c$ where c is a constant number, positive or negative?

   Extension work
   Make up tables of values for;
   (i) $y = (x + 1)^2$ (ii) $y = (x + 3)^2$ (iii) $y = (x - 7)^2$.

   Draw the graphs. What do you notice?
   What general principles can you deduce?

2 (a) Draw a grid, with $0 < x < 300$ and $0 < y < 300$.

   (b) Draw the line $x + y = 100$.

   (c) Choosing another suitable line, shade in the region where
        $100 < x + y < 200$.

   Draw the line $x + y = 250$.
   What can you say about all lines of the form $x + y =$ (some number)?

   Extension work
   On a grid, as before, draw a line whose equation is of the form
   $2x + y = K$, where K is any number (say 100).

   Now choose some further values for K, and draw the lines.

   What happens to the lines, as the value of K increases?
   What happens if $K = 0$?

   Repeat the process for the equations:
   (i) $x + 2y = K$ (ii) $3x + 2y = K$.

MEASURES 7

7.1 Metric units

'For so it is, O Lord, I measure it. But what it is I measure I do not know.' St. Augustine.

S m a l l e r

B i g g e r

1 kilometre (km) = 1000 metres (m)

1 metre (m) = 100 centimetres (cm)

1 metre (m) = 1000 millimetres (mm)

1 centimetre (cm) = 10 millimetres (mm)

1 kilogram (kg) = 1000 grams (g)

1 gram (g) = 1000 milligrams (mg)

1 tonne (t) = 1000 kilograms (kg)

1 litre (*l*) = 100 centilitres (cl)

1 litre (*l*) = 1000 millilitres (ml)

1 centilitre (cl) = 10 millilitres (ml)

To change from one unit into a smaller unit we multiply.

To change from one unit into a larger unit we divide.

Example   Change (a) 2.46 kg into grams (b) 42 cm into metres.

(a) 2.46 kg × 1000 = 2460 g   *Kg → g: smaller units so multiply.*

(b) 42 cm ÷ 100 = 0.42 m   *Cm → m: larger units so divide.*

Exercise I

The smallest measure of length is the ångström, where 1 millimetre is 10 000 000 ångströms.

Change the following:

1 7 cm into mm	**2** 4 m into cm	**3** 43 m into km
4 62.5 mm into cm	**5** 1250 g into kg	**6** 0.31 *l* into ml
7 1.37 kg into g	**8** 1300 ml into cl	**9** 3 km into m
10 351 cm into m	**11** 0.03 *l* into ml	**12** 2 t into kg
13 200 mg into g	**14** 40 cl into *l*	**15** 700 kg into t
16 3000 mg into kg	**17** 0.498 m into cm	**18** 0.07 *l* into ml
19 11.32 cm into mm	**20** 9.63 m into cm	

Exercise 2

1 A bottle of orange juice is used to fill six cups, each of which holds 175 ml. How many litres of orange juice are in the bottle?

2 A man is running a 5 km race. He has already run 2450 m. How many metres has he yet to run?

3 A lorry load of 3 tonnes of potatoes is to be shovelled into 2 kg bags. How many bags can be filled from this load?

4 A man weighs himself. The scales show 49.5 kg. He then takes off his boots, which weigh 900 g. What weight will now be shown on the scales?

5 How many 30 g servings of breakfast cereal are there in a box containing 0.75 kg?

6 Bobby has used 200 g of flour in making a cake, and 75 g in making buns. How much flour will be left, if he started with a 5 kg bag?

7 If 350 g of minced beef are used in a pie, how many kilograms of minced beef would be needed for 30 pies?

Write each set of measurements in order of size, starting with the smallest:

8 750 mm, 0.4 km, 78 m, 0.072 km, 1.5 km. 550 m, 35 m, 0.3 km

9 400 cl, 0.14 l, 750 cl, 0.012 l, 270 cl, 0.02 l, 1.3 l, 600 cl

10 300 kg, 0.2 t, 875 kg, 0.85 t, 1.4 t, 1500 kg, 112 kg, 0.8 t

7.2 Imperial units

Occasionally you will see the old-fashioned signs " for inches and ' for feet.

1 mile = 1760 yards (yd)

1 yard (yd) = 3 feet (ft)

1 foot (ft) = 12 inches (in)

1 gallon (gal) = 8 pints (pt)

1 pint (pt) = 20 fluid ounces (fl. oz)

1 ton = 20 hundredweight (cwt)

1 hundredweight (cwt) = 112 pounds (lb)

1 pound (lb) = 16 ounces (oz)

1 stone (st) = 14 pounds (lb)

The longest unit of measure is the parsec, a stellar distance that is equivalent to 30 856 776 000 000 km, or 19 173 511 000 000 miles.

Example Change (a) 1 ft 3 in into inches (b) 50 in into feet and inches
(c) $4\frac{1}{2}$ yd into feet (d) 13 ft into yards and feet

(a) 1 ft 3 in = $(1 \times 12) + 3 = 15$ inches
(b) 50 in = $(4 \times 12) + 2 = 4$ ft 2 in
(c) $4\frac{1}{2}$ yd = $(4\frac{1}{2} \times 3) = 13\frac{1}{2}$ ft
(d) 13 ft = $12 + 1 = (4 \times 3) + 1 = 4$ yd 1 ft

Exercise 3

Change the following:

1 $83\frac{1}{2}$ in into ft and in
2 $1\frac{3}{4}$ gal into pints
3 125 lb into st and lb
4 $\frac{3}{4}$ lb into oz
5 65 ft into ft and in
6 $\frac{5}{8}$ mile into yd
7 2 yd 4 ft into feet
8 2 lb 3 oz into oz
9 22 ft into yd and ft
10 $\frac{1}{4}$ pt into fl. oz
11 52 st into cwt
12 $31\frac{1}{4}$ in into ft and in

Exercise 4

1 A man is 5 ft $7\frac{1}{2}$ in tall. His daughter is 4 ft $10\frac{1}{2}$ in tall. Find the difference in their heights, in inches.

2 A length of curtain measures 6 ft 8 in. It also has a folded hem of 6 inches. What is its total length?

3 A petrol tank is filled to a capacity of 10 gallons. How many gallons and pints will be left in the tank, if 3 gallons 3 pints of petrol are then used in a journey?

4 A furlong is $\frac{1}{8}$ of a mile. A horse has run 3 furlongs. How many yards is this?

5 A bag of coal weighs 1 cwt. If 35 bags are loaded onto a lorry, what is the weight of the load in tons and cwt?

6 An athlete drinks $1\frac{1}{2}$ pints of milk each day. How many gallons will the athlete drink in 10 weeks?

7 A man weighs $12\frac{1}{2}$ stone. He loses 21 lb whilst on a diet. How much will he now weigh?

8 A heavyweight boxer weighs 224 lb. How many stones is this?

9 A block of cheese, which weighs 3 lb 9 oz, is to be divided into twelve equal portions. How many ounces will each portion weigh?

10 How many pint bottles of milk can be filled from a 5-gallon milk churn?

7.3 Approximate equivalents

5 miles ≈ 8 kilometres   1 yard ≈ 1 metre   1 foot ≈ 30 centimetres

1 inch ≈ 2.5 centimetres   1 kilogram ≈ 2.2 pounds   1 litre ≈ 1.75 pints

Example Change (a) 30 miles into kilometres (b) 64 km into miles

(a) $30 \text{ miles} \approx 30 \times \frac{8}{5} = \frac{240}{5} = 48 \text{ km}$ *Changing miles → km: 1 mile is the same as $\frac{8}{5}$ km.*

(b) $64 \text{ km} \approx 64 \times \frac{5}{8} = \frac{320}{8} = 40 \text{ miles}$ *Changing km → miles: 1 km is the same as $\frac{5}{8}$ miles.*

Exercise 5

Change the following into their approximate equivalents:

1 10 kg into lb	**2** 6 in into cm	**3** 15 miles into km
4 15.4 lb into kg	**5** $2\frac{1}{4}$ gal into litres	**6** 54 km into miles
7 4 litres into pt	**8** 44 lb into kg	**9** 2 ft into cm
10 25 miles into km	**11** 95 in into cm	**12** 2 lb 10 oz into kg
13 $4\frac{1}{2}$ yd into metres	**14** 1.2 m into ft	**15** 96 km into miles

Exercise 6

Work out the approximate answers to these questions.

1 A scuba diver carries ten lead weights, each weighing $\frac{1}{4}$ lb, in his belt. His air tank weighs 5 kg. What is the total weight of his equipment, in kilograms?

2 A pair of trousers has a waist measurement of 34 inches. What is this in centimetres?

3 Whilst on holiday a family drive 332 km in a day. How many miles is this?

4 In a shop they are selling 3 kg of potatoes for 80p. In another shop they are selling a 5 lb bag for the same price. Which is the better buy?

5 A recipe requires 0.4 kg of flour. How many ounces is this?

6 A roll of carpet is 12 yd long. What is this in metres?

7 A driver buys 30 litres of petrol. Approximately how many gallons is this?

8 A Christmas hamper weighs 8 kg. What is its weight in pounds?

9 A house is estimated to be 24 ft high. Approximately how high is this in metres?

10 A man is 1.8 metres tall. What is his height in feet?

The length of a day is becoming increasingly irregular owing to the moon's tidal drag. Atomic clocks are so accurate they have to be adjusted to fit in with the earth's irregular movements!

7.4 Using units

When measuring, it is important to choose the correct measure for the purpose. For example, it would be no use trying to measure the length of a train with a 30 cm ruler!

Exercise 7   Which *metric* unit would you use use to measure the following:

1 The heaviest weight lifted by a man.

2 The longest fingernail grown by a human.

3 The farthest distance travelled by car on 1 litre of petrol.

4 The diameter of the largest bubble-gum bubble.

5 The largest petrol tank of a family car.

The longest measure of time is the kalpa in Hindu chronology, equivalent to 4320 million years.

6 The length of the largest crystal grown in a week in a chemistry laboratory.

7 The widest head in your class of students.

8 The capacity of an egg cup.

9 A bottle of wine.

10 The longest oil-pipeline.

11 A medicine bottle in common use.

12 The thinnest slice of cucumber.

7.5   Perimeter

The **perimeter** is the distance all around a shape.

Example   Find the perimeters:

(a)

```
        3 m
   ┌──────────┐
2 m│          │
   │          │
   └──────────┘
```

(b)

```
        1 m
      ┌────┐
  1 m │    │
  ┌───┘    │ 2 m
  │        │
  └────────┘
     2 m
```

(a) $2 + 3 + 2 + 3 = 10$ m

(b) $2 + 2 + 1 + 1 + 1 + 1 = 8$ m

7.6   Area

The space contained within a shape is its **area**.
Area is measured in square units: cm^2, m^2, km^2

Area of a **rectangle** = length $\times$ breadth

Area of a **triangle** = $\frac{1}{2}$ base $\times$ height

Example Find the area of each shape:

5 cm

2 cm

5 cm

4 cm

Area $= 5 \times 2 = 10$ cm^2

Area $= \frac{1}{2} \times 4 \times 5 = 10$ cm^2

We can find the area of **combined** shapes by dividing them into separate shapes that we recognise, and then adding them.

Example Find the area:

2 cm

3 cm

7 cm

1 cm

2 cm

3 cm

5 cm

1 cm ***Divide the shape into two separate rectangles.***

The UK has an area of 244 103 km², or 94 249 square miles.

$3 \times 2 = 6$ cm^2
$5 \times 1 = 5$ cm^2
Total area $= 11$ cm^2

Exercise 8 Find (a) the perimeter (b) the area of each shape:

1
5 cm
3.5 cm

2
4.5 cm
4 cm

3
2 m
12 m

4
6 m
1.5 m
2 m   2 m
5 m
2 m

5
2.5 cm
7 cm
7 cm

6
5 cm
6 cm
2 cm
3 cm
2 cm
2.5 cm

7
4.5 cm
5 cm
2 cm
8 cm

Exercise 9   Find the area of each shape:

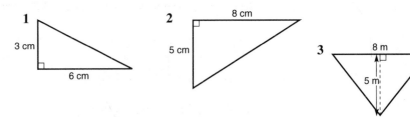

*The surface area
of the earth is
510 065 600 km²,
196 937 400
square miles.*

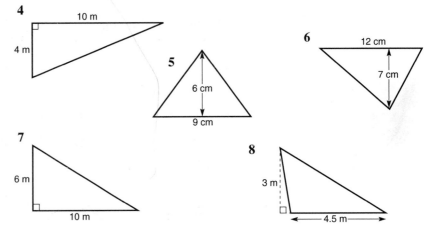

Exercise 10   Copy and complete the tables.

		Rectangles		
	Length	Breadth	Area	Perimeter
1	3 m		6 m²	
2	9 m		45 m²	
3	4 cm			14 cm
4			24 cm²	20 cm
5	10 m			35 m
6	18 cm		81 cm²	
7		12.5 cm		105 cm
8		25 cm	750 cm²	

		Triangles	
	Base	Height	Area
9	4 m		6 m²
10		14 m	70 m²
11	18 cm	12.5 cm	
12		16 cm	192 cm²

To find the areas of other shapes we use simple formulas:

Area of a **parallelogram** = length of base × vertical height

Area of a **trapezium** = $\frac{1}{2}h(a+b)$,
where a and b are the lengths of the two parallel sides, and h the perpendicular distance between them.

Example Find the area of each shape:

Area = $6 \times 4 = 24$ cm^2

Area $= \frac{1}{2} \times 3 \times (7 + 10)$
$= 0.5 \times 3 \times 17 = 25.5$ cm^2

Exercise II   Find the area of each shape:

1

2

3

4

5

6

7

8

9

7.7 The circle

The radius of a circle is half the diameter.
The circumference of a circle is found by using the formula:

$C = \pi \times$ diameter

Some calculators will provide a value for π.
If your calculator does not have a π button, use the value $\pi = 3.14$.

Example   Find the circumference of each shape:

$C = \pi \times$ diameter
$= 3.14 \times 8$ cm
$= 25.12$ cm

$C = \pi \times$ diameter
$= \pi \times (3 \times 2)$ cm
$= 3.14 \times 6$
$= 18.84$ cm

diameter = 2 × radius

Example   Find the radius of a circle if the circumference is 35 cm.

$C = \pi \times d$
$35 = \pi \times d$
So $d = 35 \div \pi = 35 \div 3.14 = 11.14$ cm (to 2 d.p.)
So radius $= d \div 2 = 5.57$ cm

Exercise 12   Find the circumference.

1

2

3

4 cm

4

5

6

Find the circumference of the circle with:

7 $r = 26$ cm   **8** $d = 10$ cm   **9** $r = 3.8$ m
10 $r = 14$ cm

Find the radius of the circle with circumference:

11 40 cm   **12** 85 m   **13** 240 m

Find the diameter of the circle with circumference:

14 150 mm   **15** 90 cm   **16** 63 m

Exercise 13

1 A wheel has a diameter of 60 cm. What is the distance around the rim?

2 The radius of a coin is 5.5 mm. What is the length of the circumference?

3 A mountain bike has a wheel with a diameter of 65 cm. What is its circumference?

4 The radius of the earth is approximately 6370 km. What is the approximate distance around the earth?

In 1897 the General Assembly of Indiana stated that π was 'nearly 4'.

5 A gardener wants to put a fence around a circular pond of radius 150 cm. What length of fence is needed?

6 A lighthouse lower floor has an internal diameter of 6.8 metres. What is the distance around the walls of the lower floor?

The area of a circle is found by using the formula:

$$A = \pi r^2 \quad \text{or} \quad \text{Area} = \pi \times \text{radius} \times \text{radius}$$

Example   Find the area of each shape:

$$A = \pi r^2$$
$$= 3.14 \times 3 \times 3$$
$$= 28.26 \text{ cm}^2$$

3 cm

$$A = \pi r^2$$
$$= \pi \times 4 \times 4$$ *radius* $= \frac{1}{2}$ *diameter*
$$= 3.14 \times 4 \times 4$$
$$= 50.24 \text{ cm}^2$$

8 cm

Example   Find the radius of a circle if the area is 80 cm².

$$A = \pi r^2$$
$$80 = \pi r^2$$
$$r^2 = 80 \div \pi = 80 \div 3.14 = 25.48 \text{ cm}$$

So $r = \sqrt{25.48}$ cm $= 5.05$ cm

Exercise 14   Find the area:

1

2

3

4

5

6

Find the area of each circle with:

7 $d = 4.9$ cm   8 $r = 3.8$ cm   9 $r = 4$ m   10 $d = 10$ cm

Find the radius of each circle with the following area:

11 65 cm^2 12 100 m^2 13 180 mm^2

14 94 cm^2 15 20 m^2

Exercise 15   1 A horse is tied to a stake in a field with a rope 8 m long. What area of the field can be grazed by the horse?

2 A discothèque has a circular dance floor with a diameter of 12 metres. What area is the dance floor?

3 A circular pond has a diameter of 3.5 m. What area of netting is needed to cover the pond?

4 A circular ring has a radius of 1.2 m. What is the area of the ring?

5 A circular pine table has a top with an area of 8 m^2. What is the radius of the top of the table?

6 A circular pond has an area of 16.6 m^2. What is the diameter of the pond?

Find the area:

7

8

9

10

7.8 Volume

Volume is a measure of the space occupied by a solid shape.
Volume is measured in cubic units: cm^3, m^3, km^3

Example Find the volume of the cuboid.

Volume of a **cuboid** = length × breadth × height

Volume = $5 \times 7.8 \times 4.5 = 175.5 \ cm^3$

Example Find the volume of the prism.

Volume of a **prism** = area of cross-section × length

Area of cross-section = $\frac{1}{2} \times 4 \times 5$ ***The cross-section is a triangle.***

$= 10 \ m^2$

Volume   = area of cross-section × length

$= 10 \times 8 = 80 \ m^3$

Example Find the volume of the cylinder.

Volume of a **cylinder** $= \pi r^2 h$ ***The cross-section is a circle.***

$= \pi \times radius \times radius \times height$

Volume $= \pi \times 3 \times 3 \times 5$

$= 3.14 \times 3 \times 3 \times 5 = 141.3 \ cm^3$

Exercise 16   Find the volume of each of the following solids:

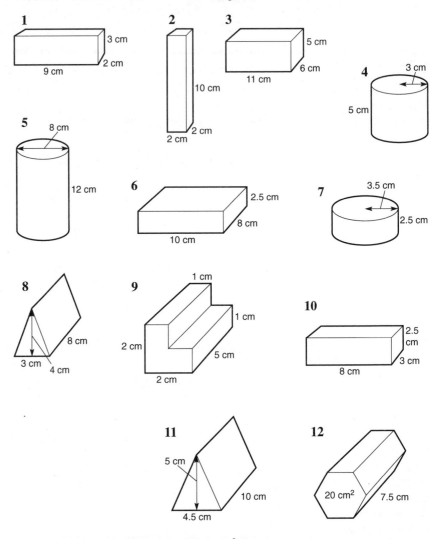

Example   The volume of a box is 24 cm³. Its height is 4 cm, and its width is 3 cm. What is its length?

Volume $=$ length $\times$ breadth $\times$ height

$24 = 4 \times 3 \times h$

So $h = 24 \div (4 \times 3) = 24 \div 12 = 2$ cm

Example   The volume of a cylinder is 62 cm³. Its diameter is 4 cm. What is the height of the cylinder?

Volume $= \pi r^2 h$

radius = half diameter
$= d \div 2 = 4 \div 2 = 2$

$62 = \pi \times 2 \times 2 \times h$

So $h = 62 \div (3.14 \times 2 \times 2) = 62 \div 12.56 = 4.94$ cm

Exercise 17

1 A box has a volume of 50 cm³. It has a length of 8 cm, and a height of 2.5 cm. What is its width?

2 A cylinder has a volume of 100 cm³. Its height is 10 cm. What is its radius ?

3 A box has a height of 3 m, and width of 4 m. Find its length if the volume of the box is 85 m³.

4 A cylinder has a radius of 4 mm, and a volume of 230 mm³. Find the height of the cylinder.

5 A tank in the shape of a cylinder has a height of 4 m. It has a volume of 50 m³. Find the diameter of the tank.

6 A lorry with a skip in the shape of a cuboid contains 7 m³ of sand. The load is 2 m wide and 1 m high. How long is it?

7 A box has a volume of 192 cm³. It is 16 cm long and 4 cm high. What is its width?

8 A cylindrical tank is designed to hold 1000 litres of water. The diameter of the tank is to be 0.5 m. What height will the tank have to be? (1 m³ = 1000 litres.)

7.9 Surface area

The surface area of a solid is the total area of all of its faces.

The combined surface area of all the alveoli inside the human lungs is equivalent to the area of a tennis court.

Example   Find the surface area of each shape:

Each face of each block has an area of 1 cm².

Top: 5 faces = 5 cm²

Around the sides: 12 faces = 12 cm²

Base: 5 faces = 5 cm²

Total surface area = 5 + 12 + 5 = 22 cm²

1 cm cubes

Top face: 5 × 7	=	35 cm²
Base face: 5 × 7	=	35 cm²
Left face: 5 × 2	=	10 cm²
Right face: 5 × 2	=	10 cm²
Front face: 7 × 2	=	14 cm²
Back face: 7 × 2	=	14 cm²
Total surface area	=	118 cm²

The Forth Bridge is the bridge in the UK which has the greatest surface area requiring painting. Once the team of painters have worked their way to one end, they have to start again at the other!

Exercise 18   Find the surface area of these solids:

1

2 m
8 m
5 m

2

13 cm
10 cm
2 cm

3

1 cm³ cubes

4

1 cm³ cubes

5

10 cm
6 cm   6 cm

6

3 cm   5 cm
4 cm   6 cm

7

8

9

85 cm
10 cm   10 cm

10

12 cm
10 cm   15 cm

11

30 cm
10 cm   8 cm

12

12 cm
10 cm
8 cm
18 cm   15 cm

7.10   Direction

There are two common ways of giving a direction:

The earliest navigators at sea used familiar landmarks on the shoreline – this meant they could never sail out of sight of land.

1 **Compass directions**. Face North or South, and turn clockwise or anticlockwise, measuring the angle.

S40°E   N35°E   S70°W

2 **3-figure bearings**. Face North and turn only clockwise, measuring the angle, and giving the answer as a 3-figure number.

140°   035°   250°

Exercise 19

Write the following compass direction as 3-figure bearings:

1 N30°E   **2** N60°W   **3** N50°W   **4** S70°E

5 S45°W   **6** N25°E   **7** S65°E

Write the following 3-figure bearings as compass directions:

8 160°   **9** 185°   **10** 330°   **11** 158°

12 025°   **13** 075°   **14** 295°   **15** 110°

Exercise 20

Can you *draw* directions? Select several compass directions, and several 3-figure bearings from the exercise above. Use your protractor to draw a diagram for each of the chosen directions. Clearly label each diagram.

Unless otherwise stated, direction is normally given as a 3-figure bearing.

Example Find the bearing (a) of Heywood *from* Radcliffe (b) of Radcliffe *from* Prestwich.

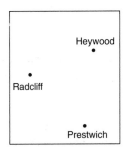

The word *from* tells you where you are standing when you measure the bearing. Always draw a North line at this point.

Then draw in the route. These are the lines you need to use to measure the bearings.

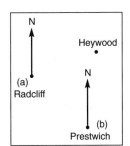

The bearing at (a): Heywood *from* Radcliffe is 070°.

The bearing at (b): Radcliffe *from* Prestwich is 312°.

Measure these bearings on the diagram for yourself.

In giving a **location**, we not only need the **direction**, but also the **distance**. On maps and diagrams we use a scale.

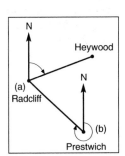

Example   Using the given scale, find the actual distance represented by
(a) 3.5 cm (b) 5.8 cm.

(a) 0   1   2   3   4   km   1 cm →1 km so 3.5 cm →3.5 km

A scale of 1 cm to 1 km.

(b) 0 10 20 30 40 50 60 70 80   km   2 cm → 40 km
5.8 cm → 5.8 × 20 = 116 km

A scale of 1 cm to 20 km.

Exercise 21

In each question give the actual distance for each distance on the map.

1 0   40   80   120   160   km

(a) 2.5 cm   (b) 3.3 cm   (c) 6.9 cm   (d) 7.2 cm

2 0   5   10   15   20   km

(a) 1.5 cm   (b) 2.8 cm   (c) 8.3 cm   (d) 8.4 cm

3 0   25   50   75   100   km

(a) 3.5 cm   (b) 1.2 cm   (c) 9.7 cm   (d) 6.7 cm

4 0   6   12   18   24   km

(a) 0.5 cm   (b) 1.4 cm   (c) 10.1 cm   (d) 12.1 cm

5 0   70   140   210   280   km

(a) 2.5 cm   (b) 0.6 cm   (c) 7.6 cm   (d) 8.8 cm

Exercise 22

Use the map of the Isle of Man to find (a) the 3-figure bearing (b) the direct distance (in km) in each case. All the places are on the coast.

1 From Castletown to Ramsey   **2** From Ramsey to The Cronk

3 From The Cronk to Point of Ayre   **4** From Point of Ayre to Ramsey

5 From Ramsey to Peel   **6** From Peel to Ramsey

7 From Ramsey to Castletown   **8** From Castletown to Peel

9 From Peel to Maughold Head   **10** From Maughold Head to Port Erin

11 From Port Erin to Peel   **12** From Peel to Castletown

7.11   A final word on units

When map scales are given as a ratio, we need to change units to find what 1 centimetre actually represents on the map.

Remember:

10 mm = 1 cm
100 cm = 1 m
1000 m = 1 km

Example   What does 1 cm represent using a map scale of 1 : 50 000?

1 : 50 000 = 1 cm : 50 000 cm = 1 cm : 500 m = 1 cm : 0.5 km

The oldest map is an Iraqi clay tablet dated about 2250 BC, showing part of the river Euphrates.

Example What does 3.8 cm represent using a map scale of 1 : 300 000?

1 : 300 000 = 1 cm : 300 000 cm = 1 cm : 3000 m = 1 cm : 3 km
so 3.8 cm represents 3.8 × 3 km = 11.4 km

Exercise 23

The first printed map of Britain was Ptolemy's outline printed in Italy in 1477. The earliest maps had no scale, as they were merely sketches.

In each question find what the actual distance will be, using the given map scale. Give your answer in an appropriate unit.

1 1 cm using 1 : 3000
2 1 cm using 1 : 500 000
3 1 cm using 1 : 20 000
4 1 cm using 1 : 40 000
5 2.5 cm using 1 : 50 000
6 3.5 cm using 1 : 250 000
7 12.5 cm using 1 : 10 000
8 7.5 cm using 1 : 8000
9 3.2 cm using 1 : 150 000
10 8.7 cm using 1 : 25 000

We have to be clear about the **accuracy** of any measurement. This is because measurements you are given have often been rounded off.

Example You are told a car has travelled 10 km. What is the maximum and minimum distance it might have travelled?

It might have been rounded to the nearest 1 km, so it would lie between 9.5 km and 10.49 km:

Example You are told a snail has travelled a distance of 6.5 cm. What range of distances might it have travelled?

It might have been rounded to the first decimal place, so it could lie between 6.45 and 6.549 cm.

Exercise 24

For each measurement given below, give the minimum and maximum measurements between which it could actually lie.

1 1.7 cm
2 8.3 m
3 10.4 km
4 9.1 cm
5 4.5 m
6 8.0 m
7 3.0 cm
8 4.85 cm
9 2.13 mm
10 7.25 cm
11 8.95 cm
12 2.1 mm
13 14.51 m
14 8.39 m
15 7.12 cm

Review

Exercise 25 Change the following:

1 5 cm into mm   **2** 0.04 *l* into ml   **3** 3.5 t into kg

4 2000 mg into kg   **5** 7.52 m into cm   **6** 700 mm into m

7 How many lengths of wood, each 200 mm in length, can be cut from a piece 3.7 m in length?

8 If 4500 g of potatoes are used in a guest-house kitchen each day, how many kilograms will be needed over a ten-day period?

9 Change $3\frac{3}{4}$ gallons into pints (8 pints = 1 gallon).

10 Change 12 feet into yards (3 ft = 1 yd).

11 What is $1\frac{1}{2}$ lb in ounces (16 oz = 1 lb)?

12 Change 56 ft into feet and inches (12 in = 1 ft).

Change the following into their approximate equivalents:

13 36 inches into cm (1 in ≈ 2.5 cm)

14 10 pints into litres (1 litre ≈ 1.75 pints)

15 40 miles into km (5 miles ≈ 8 km)

Calculate (a) the perimeter (b) the area:

16
4.5 cm
3.2 cm

17
2 cm
6.5 cm
4.5 cm
7 cm

18
12 cm
4 cm
4 cm
4 cm
4 cm
4 cm

Calculate the area:

19
8 cm
10 cm

20
6 cm
7 cm
10 cm

21
6 cm
4 cm
8 cm

22
2.5 cm
7 cm

Calculate (a) the circumference (b) the area of each of these circles:

23
5 cm

24
12 cm

25
1.5 cm

26
7 cm

Calculate the volume:

27   2 cm   4 cm   6 cm

28   2.5 cm   8 cm   Volume = πr²h

29   9 cm   8 cm   12 cm

Calculate the surface area:

30   4 cm   7 cm   5 cm

31   5 cm   3 cm   3 cm

32   15 cm   9 cm   12 cm   10 cm

Write each of these directions (a) as a compass direction (b) as a 3-figure bearing:

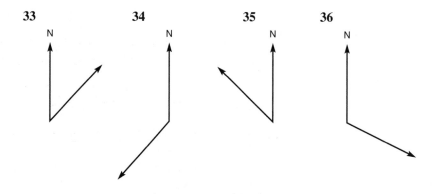

33   N

34   N

35   N

36   N

Exercise 26   The following questions are all taken from GCSE papers.

1 (a) What is the most sensible metric unit to use when measuring the height of a tall building?   (*2 marks*)

   (b) What is the most sensible metric unit to use when measuring the thickness of an exercise book?   (*2 marks*)

   [LEAG]

2 Julie's Ordnance Survey map is drawn to a scale of 1 to 10 000. She measures the distance between two towns as 25 cm on the map.

(a) What is the actual distance between the two towns in
    (i) centimetres?   *(2 marks)*
    (ii) metres?   *(2 marks)*
    (iii) kilometres?   *(2 marks)*

(b) Sarah sets off to walk from one town to the other at an average speed of 5 km per hour. How long does the walk take?   *(2 marks)*
                                                        [LEAG]

3 The diagram shows a circle of diameter 10 cm, with a square drawn outside it. What is the area of

(a) the square?   *(2 marks)*

(b) the circle?   *(2 marks)*

(c) the shaded part?   *(2 marks)*

                                                                [NEA]

4 Sheffield is on a bearing of 110° from Manchester.

(a) Draw a sketch to illustrate this.   *(1 mark)*

(b) What is the bearing of Manchester from Sheffield?   *(2 marks)*
                                                                [NEA]

5 A ship X is 16 kilometres on a bearing 070° from a lighthouse L. Another ship Y is 12 kilometres on a bearing 310° from the same lighthouse L.

(a) Using a scale of 1 centimetre to represent 2 kilometres, construct and label the positions of the two ships, X and Y.   *(4 marks)*

(b) Using your diagram, find the distance in kilometres from X to Y.
                                                          (1 mark)
                                                          [MEG]

6 The area of shapes of this type is given by the formula

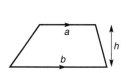

$$A = \tfrac{1}{2}(a + b) \times h.$$

Work out the area of these two shapes of the same type. (All measurements in cm.)

(i) $a = 10$ $b = 12$ $h = 5$ *(3 marks)*

(ii) $a = 2.5$ $b = 3.5$ $h = 1.5$ *(3 marks)*
                                                           [LEAG]

5 cm

6 cm

8 cm

7 The diagram shows a parallelogram.

Calculate

(a) the perimeter of the parallelogram, *(2 marks)*

(b) the area of the parallelogram. *(2 marks)*

[NEA]

8 Pete melted stolen gold and poured it into rectangular moulds as shown here.

He melted the gold in a large cylinder 40 cm in diameter and 60 cm high.

(a) Calculate the volume of this cylinder. *(2 marks)*

(b) The melted gold fills $\frac{3}{5}$ of the cylinder.
Calculate the volume of gold in the cylinder. *(1 mark)*

(c) Each rectangular mould makes a bar 6 cm by 4 cm by 15 cm.
How many of these bars can be made from the stolen gold?

(3 marks)

[NEA]

NOT TO
SCALE

197 m

203 m

9 The diagram shows a rectangular field of length 203 metres and width 197 metres.

(a) Calculate
(i) the perimeter of the field, *(1 mark)*
(ii) the area of the field. *(1 mark)*

(b) 1 hectare = 10 000 square metres.
Write down the area of the field correct to the nearest hectare.

(1 mark)

[MEG]

10 The diagram represents a framework for a Junior Dartboard. It consists of 2 circles of wire and 4 straight pieces of wire.

(a) The radius of the large circle is 20 cm. Calculate the length of wire needed to make it. *(2 marks)*

(b) The small circle has a diameter of 20 cm. Calculate the total length of wire needed for the whole framework. *(3 marks)*

[NEA]

10 cm

h

3 cm   8 cm

11 (a) Calculate the height (h) of the triangle. *(4 marks)*

(b) Calculate the area of the triangle. *(2 marks)*

[NEA]

12 (a) Super Smooth salt is packed in drums. Each drum is a cylinder with radius 15 cm and height 80 cm.

(i) Calculate the circumference of the base of a drum.
Take π to be 3.14 or use the π button on your calculator.

(2 marks)

(ii) Each drum consists of a curved section and two circular ends. The curved section of each drum is made from a rectangular sheet of card.
What are the minimum dimensions of the sheet of card?
(Assume no allowance is made for fixing.) *(2 marks)*

(iii) The salt fills the drum completely. Calculate the volume of salt in a full drum. *(3 marks)*

(b) The same volume of salt can be bought in a container whose shape is a cuboid.

The height of the container is 80 cm. The base is a square.
Calculate the length of the side of the base. *(3 marks)*

[SEG]

13 A set of children's bricks consisted of cuboids with dimensions 5 cm by 8 cm by 12 cm.

(a) Calculate the total surface area of each brick. *(3 marks)*

(b) The bricks were hand-painted with special paint bought in the tin shown here.

How many bricks could be painted with this one tin of paint?

(2 marks)

[NEA]

Ideas for investigations

1 There have been several attempts throughout history to discover an accurate value for π.

1700 BC (Greece): 256 ÷ 81
250 BC (Greece): a maximum of 273 ÷ 71, and a minimum of 22 ÷ 7
AD 100 (China): the square root of 10
AD 300 (China): 142 ÷ 45
AD 500 (China): 355 ÷ 113

How accurate are these ways of finding π? Use values of 3.142, or the π button on your calculator. Find the percentage error in the above methods. Which are the most accurate?

2   Netting is needed to make a 3-sided guinea-pig enclosure. The enclosure needs to be as large as possible, that is, with the largest area.

(a) The total length of the netting is 16 feet. What length and width would give you the maximum area?

(b) Repeat part (a) a number of times, using other lengths of fencing. Can you arrive at an easy way of working out the length and width that will give you the maximum area (that is, a rule)? Can you give the maximum area in terms of a length of fencing of x feet?

3   (a) The volume of the cuboid is $10 \times 20 \times 30 = 6000$ cm^3. What happens when we increase the dimensions by 10%? The volume will become $11 \times 22 \times 33 = 7986$ cm^3. The change in volume is 1986 cm^3. The percentage increase in volume is given by the calculation $\frac{1986}{6000} \times 100 = 33.1\%$.

(b) Try increasing by 10% the volume of cuboids with other dimensions. Find the effect this has on the volume. Do the new volumes have anything in common?

(c) What happens if you *double* the dimensions instead of increasing them by 10%? Investigate other ways of increasing the dimensions, and the effect this has on the volume.

GEOMETRY AND TRIGONOMETRY

8.1 Congruence

Two shapes are **congruent** if they are identical in every way.

Example   Decide whether each pair of shapes is congruent, or not congruent.

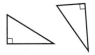 Although these triangles are in different positions, they have exactly the same angles, and the same lengths of sides. They are congruent.

 One rectangle is slightly larger than the other. They are *not* congruent.

Exercise I   Write down whether each pair of shapes is congruent, or not congruent.

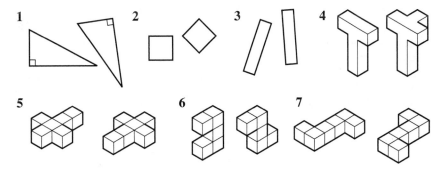

Identify the two shapes in each question which are congruent:

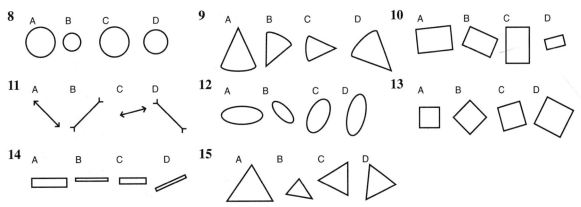

8.2 Angles

There are four main types of angle: acute, right, obtuse and reflex.

Acute angles are less than 90°.
Right angles are exactly 90°.
Obtuse angles are between 90° and 180°.
Reflex angles are more than 180°.

Angles which make
a full circle add up
to 360°.

Angles on a straight
line, that is in a half
circle, add up to 180°.

These angles are
vertically opposite angles.
They are equal in size.

Exercise 2

In each case, (a) find the missing angles indicated by the letters
(b) write down which type of angle it is.

*The mathematician who
has worked most on
geometry is Euclid of
Alexandria, who lived
around 300 BC in Egypt.*

1
a
123°
135°

2
b 141°

3
c
82°

4
d
75°

5
e 146°
146°

6
81°
f 60°

7
64° *g*
80° 74°

8
h
150°

9
120° 120°
i

10
q
70° 85°

11
44° 40°
48° *r*

12
40°
42°
s

8.3 Triangles

There are four main types of triangle: scalene, right-angled, isosceles, and
equilateral.

Scalene
All sides different

Isosceles
Two sides the same
length. Two angles
the same size.

Equilateral
All sides the same
length. All angles
the same size (60°).

Right-angled
One 90° angle.

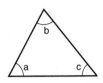

The angles of *any* triangle add up to 180°.

$$a + b + c = 180°$$

Exercise 3

In each question find the missing angles indicated by the letter *x*.

1 184 36° 40°

2 67 78° 35°

3 *x* 53° 70°

4 *x* 48° 45°

5 40° 60° *x*

6 *x* 70° 40°

7 55° 125°

8 *x* 68° 45°

Exercise 4

In each question (a) find the missing angle indicated by the letter *x*
(b) name the type of triangle.

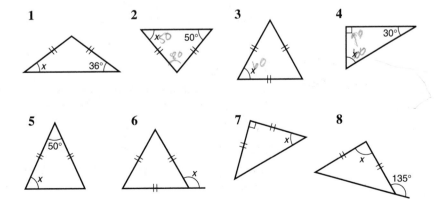

1 *x* 36°

2 *x* 50° 50°

3 *x*

4 30° *x*

5 50° *x*

6 *x*

7 *x*

8 *x* 135°

Exercise 5   In each question find the missing angle indicated by a letter.

1

2

3

4

5

6

7

8

8.4   Parallel lines

Parallel lines are lines which will never meet:

Any line which crosses a pair of parallel lines is called a transversal.
The transversal forms angles, some of which have special names:

Alternate angles

Alternate angles are the same size.

Corresponding angles

Corresponding angles are the same size.

Exercise 6   Copy each diagram, writing in all the angles:

1

2

3

4

In each question find the missing angle indicated by a letter:

5

6

7

8

9

10

11

12

8.5 Quadrilaterals

The angles of any quadrilateral add up to 360°.

Exercise 7 Copy and complete each diagram, writing in the missing angles.

1
76°
80°

2
108° 118°
77°

3
133°

4
87°
95°

There are several different types of quadrilateral. They are listed, each with their properties.

Square
Four sides of equal length.
Opposite sides parallel.
Four right angles.

Rectangle
Opposite sides of equal length.
Opposite sides parallel.
Four right angles.

Trapezium
One pair of opposite sides parallel.

Parallelogram
Opposite sides parallel.
Opposite sides of equal length.
Opposite angles equal.

Rhombus
Opposite sides parallel.
All sides of equal length.
Opposite angles equal.

If we also include the **diagonals** of these quadrilaterals, we can say:

The diagonal bisect each other (square, rectangle and parallelogram).
The diagonals bisect each other at right angles (square and rhombus).

Exercise 8

Write down the name(s) of the quadrilateral(s) to which each statement can be applied.

1   All the sides are of equal length.

2   Only one pair of parallel sides.

3   Diagonals bisect at right angles, and angles are all 90°.

4   The diagonals are of equal length.

5   Both pairs of opposite angles are equal, and are not 90°.

6   None of the angles are equal.

7   Another shape which has all the properties of a parallelogram.

8   Does not have two pairs of sides of equal length.

9   Another shape which has all the properties of a rectangle.

10   Another shape which has all the properties of a rhombus.

8.6 Solids

There are several different types of solids. They are listed below, with some of their properties. Solids have vertices (corners), faces (sides), and edges.

Cube
All edges the
same length.

Cuboid
Opposite edges
the same length.

Pyramid
Square or
rectangular base.

The largest pyramid is the Quetzalcóatl, near Mexico City, which has a volume of 3.3 million m³, compared with 2.5 m³ for the pyramid of Cheops in Egypt.

Tetrahedron
Triangular base.

Cylinder
One curved,
two flat surfaces.

Cone
One curved,
one flat surface.

Sphere
One curved surface.

Ellipsoid
One curved surface.

There are also many different types of prisms:

Triangular   Hexagonal   Octagonal

A **prism** is a solid with a constant cross-section.

Exercise 9

1   For each of the solids (but not prisms or spheres) write down how many (a) faces (b) vertices (c) edges they each have.

2   There is a relationship between faces, vertices and edges for any solid. The relationship is known as Euler's relationship. Can you find it?

3   What is another name for (a) a rectangular prism (b) a square prism (c) a prism with a circular cross-section?

8.7 Nets

A net is a flat shape which can be cut out and folded to make a solid. It is a 2-D representation of a solid.

The simplest net is that of a cube:

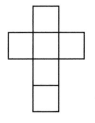

Nets can be drawn to a certain size:

These diagrams show how the various points on the net come together to make the vertices of the solid.

Example Of which solid is this the net?

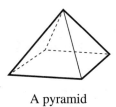

A pyramid

Exercise 10 Which solids can be made from the nets below?

1

2

3

Draw a sketch of the net for each of the following:

4 A triangular prism   **5** An octagonal prism

6 A cone

Draw nets of the cuboids for which the dimensions are given below. Write the lengths on all the sides of your nets.

7 5 cm × 6 cm × 7 cm **8** 3.5 cm × 5 cm × 7 cm **9** 4 cm × 7 cm × 10 cm

Draw a sketch of the net for these solids:

10

42.5 cm
5 cm
30 cm 30 cm

11

0.8 m
1.8 m
2.1 m
2.4 m

12 Which letters will come together to form the vertices of the solid from this net?

8.8 Accurate drawings

To make accurate drawings we need the correct equipment:

Ruler, protractor, a pair of compasses, a sharp pencil, and a rubber.

Exercise II

Draw the following accurately, using your mathematical instruments.

The largest drawings in the world are the ground figures drawn in the Nazca Desert, Peru. Drawn some time between 100 BC and AD 600, they are up to seven miles in length.

1

6 cm
50°
6 cm

2

6 cm
65°
8 cm

3

4 cm
5 cm

4

4 cm 5 cm
100°

5

10 cm
40° 65°
4 cm 3 cm

5 cm
6 cm

6 A rectangle with sides of length 6 cm and 4.5 cm.

7 A square of sides 7 cm.

8 An isosceles triangle with base 6 cm and vertical height 5 cm.

9 A right-angled triangle with sides 3 cm, 4 cm and 5 cm.

10 An isosceles triangle with base 5.5 cm, and sides at angles of 35° to the base.

8.9 Scale drawings

In practical problems it is useful to make a drawing. However, the lengths may actually be in metres, but the drawing cannot be in metres (it would be too big). We need to make a scale drawing in centimetres or millimetres.

Example A room 12 m by 8 m is to have a 1 m work-surface built along a short side. Show this on a scale diagram, using a scale of 1 cm to 2 m.

This is the sketch of the diagram to be drawn, showing the dimensions in centimetres.

12 m ÷ 2 = 6 cm

8 m ÷ 2 = 4 cm

1 m ÷ 2 = 0.5 cm

Exercise 12

Draw the following scale diagrams, to the scale stated in each question.

1

20 cm

25 cm

1 cm to 5 cm

2

55 m

45 m

1 cm to 10 m

3

45°   45°

120 cm

1 cm to 20 cm

4

1 cm to 12 m

18 m

36 m

24 m   24 m

18 m

5

760 mm

800 mm

150 mm

200 mm

1 cm to 100 mm

6

35 km

70°

48 km

1 cm to 8 km

8.10 Loci

A locus (plural loci) is the set of all points which satisfy a rule. When we trace the path made by joining such a set of points, this path is called the **locus** of the points.

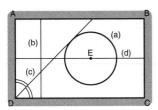

Example Draw the following:

(a) The locus of points 1 cm from point E.

The locus of points at a given distance from a fixed point is actually **a circle**.

(b) The locus of points 1 cm from line AD.

The locus of points at a given distance from a fixed line is two lines **parallel to the first line**.

(c) The locus of points which are the same distance from AD and DC.

The locus of points which are the same distance from two lines is **the bisector of the angle between these two lines**.

(d) The locus of points which are the same distance from B and C.

The locus of points of equal distance from two points is **a line which is at right angles to, and bisects, the line joining the two points**.

Exercise 13

1 Copy the diagram to scale.

(a) A light at A illuminates all points up to a distance of 3 m from the light. Shade the area lit up inside the rectangle.

(b) Draw the locus of points which are at equal distances from AB and BC.

(c) An extension lead is laid across the floor so that it lies an equal distance from corners D and C. Draw the extension lead in the diagram.

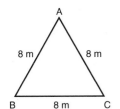

2 Copy the diagram to scale.

(a) Draw the locus of points 5 m from B.

(b) Draw the locus of points 6 m from C.

(c) Shade the region where all points are within 5 m from B *and* 6 cm from C.

(d) Draw the locus of all points which are at equal distances from A and C.

3 Mark a point on your page. Draw the locus of points which are all 3 cm from the point.

4 Draw a square of side 4 cm. Draw the locus of points which are all 1 cm from the sides of the square.

5 Mark any two points A and B on your page. Draw the locus of points which are of equal distance from A and B.

6 ABCD represents a school yard. Lights at points A and B can illuminate objects 10 m away. Another light at D can illuminate objects 5 m away. An illuminated notice board along DC casts light for a distance of 5 m. Draw a scale diagram of the yard, and shade those parts of the yard which are *not* illuminated.

7 Three television transmitters are positioned as shown. The transmitters have a range as follows: A 50 miles, B 55 miles, and C 40 miles. Make a scale drawing and shade the part of the diagram where signals from all three transmitters can be received.

8.11   Pythagoras' theorem

Pythagoras followed the teaching of Buddha, and was also a vegetarian. He was the founder of a private school for mathematics at Crotone, Italy.

Pythagoras was a Greek mathematician who is said to have discovered a rule we can use with right-angled triangles.

In any right-angled triangle

$$c^2 = a^2 + b^2$$

The **hypotenuse** is the longest side in a right-angled triangle.

Example   Find x.

Using Pythagoras' theorem: $x^2 = 4.7^2 + 5.3^2$ ***The hypotenuse is first.***

$$= 22.09 + 28.09$$

$$= 50.18$$

so $x = \sqrt{50.18} = 7.08 \approx 7.1$ cm

Example   Find x.

Using Pythagoras' theorem: $7.8^2 = x^2 + 5.2^2$ ***Put the hypotenuse first.***

$$\text{so } x^2 = 7.8^2 - 5.2^2$$

$$= 60.84 - 27.04$$

$$= 33.8$$

$$\text{so } x = \sqrt{33.8} = 5.8 \text{ cm}$$

When we are *finding* the hypotenuse, we add the square of the other two sides. When we are *given* the hypotenuse, we subtract the square of one of the other two sides.

Note: Pythagoras' theorem is a method of *calculation*. These problems can also be done by accurate/scale drawing. Draw a right-angled triangle to represent that shown in the first example above. Measure the missing side x. Is your measurement as accurate as 7.1 cm?

Which will generally be the more accurate method: calculation, or scale drawing?

Exercise 14   Find the missing sides in each of the following triangles. Give your answers to one decimal place.

1

4.3 cm

x

5.1 cm

2

10.4 cm

7.9 cm

x

3

14.3 cm

8.2 cm

x

4

8.8 cm

8.6 cm

x

5

5.4 cm

x

9.4 cm

6 A BT pole 6.8 m high is held firm by a wire which is fixed to the top of the pole and to a point in the ground 5.9 m horizontally from the foot of the pole. How long is the wire?

7 Calculate the length of a diagonal of a rectangle with dimensions 5.75 m by 6.05 m.

8 A ladder leans against a wall. Its upper end is 3.6 m off the ground. Its lower end is 3.2 m from the foot of the wall. How long is the ladder?

9 Calculate the height of an equilateral triangle with sides 8 cm long.

10 Calculate the length of a diagonal of a square with sides 4.6 m.

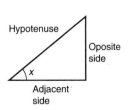

8 cm   8 cm

height

8 cm

8.12   Trigonometry

In any right-angled triangle:

Hypotenuse

Opposite side

x

Adjacent side

$$\sin x = \frac{\text{opposite side}}{\text{hypotenuse}}$$

The opposite side is the side opposite the angle.

$$\cos x = \frac{\text{adjacent side}}{\text{hypotenuse}}$$

The adjacent side is the side next to the angle.

$$\tan x = \frac{\text{opposite side}}{\text{adjacent side}}$$

Sin x means the sine of angle x, cos x the cosine of angle x, and tan x the tangent of angle x.

In solving problems a decision has to be made: which one of the three trigonometrical ratios will be used in the solution?

Example   Find AB.

$$\cos 38° = \frac{AB}{12}$$

$$12 \times \cos 38° = AB$$

$$12 \times 0.7880 = AB$$

So AB = 9.46 cm (to 3 s.f.)

To find AB we need to use the adjacent side and the hypotenuse: we will therefore need cosine.

Press 38 and COS on your calculator to change cos 38° into a decimal.

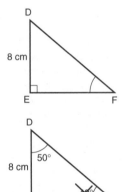

Example   Find EF

$$\tan 40° = \frac{8}{EF}$$ ◄——— *It is difficult to solve the equation when the missing side is on the bottom of the fraction.*

$$\tan 50° = \frac{EF}{8}$$ *Change the problem by using the other angle.*

$$8 \times \tan 50° = EF$$

$$8 \times 1.192 = EF$$

So EF = 9.53 cm (to 3 s.f.)

Exercise 15   In this exercise give your answers to 3 significant figures.
Find the missing side labelled *x*:

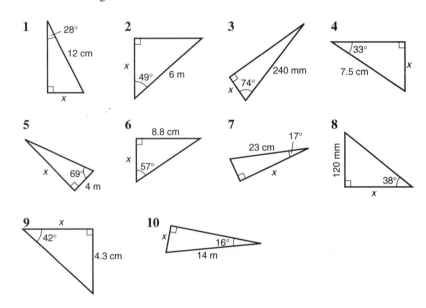

11 A ladder 6 metres long lies against the wall of a house so that it is inclined to the horizontal at an angle of 68°. How far does it reach up the wall?

12 A square has a diagonal of length 8.5 cm. How long is one of its sides?

13 A road is inclined at 15° to the horizontal. A woman walks 100 m up the road. What distance will she have risen *vertically*?

14 A boy looks up to the top of a tree, and estimates the top is inclined at an angle of 30° from where he is standing, 10 m from the foot of the tree. How high is the tree?

15 A diagonal of a rectangle is 10 m long, and is inclined at an angle of 38° to the longer side. Find the length and width of the rectangle.

Trigonometry can also be used to find the missing angles in triangles.

Example Find the angle *x*.

Use inverse tan on the calculator:
0.5357 → 28.2°

$$\tan x = \frac{1.5}{2.8} = 0.5357$$

$$x = 28.2° \text{ (to 1 d.p.)}$$

The two sides that have been given are the opposite side and the adjacent side, so this is a tangent problem.

Note: Some calculators have different ways of finding the inverse of trigonometrical functions: $\tan^{-1}$, 2nd Fct TAN, INV TAN.

Exercise 16 Find the missing angles labelled *x*. Give your angles to 1 decimal place.

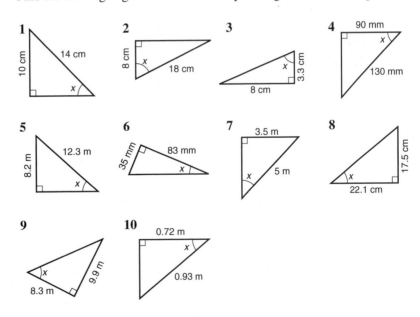

11 A ladder which is 12 m long leans against the wall of a house. The top of the ladder is 9 m off the ground. What angle does the ladder make with the ground?

12 A pipe from a reservoir is 3000 metres long. One end is 100 m higher than the other. At what angle (to the horizontal) is the pipe inclined?

13 A road is 2000 m long, and it climbs 700 m. What is the angle of inclination of the road?

14 The sloping roof of a shed is 4.5 m long. One side of the roof is 2.5 m higher than the other. Find the angle of inclination of the roof.

15 A rectangle has dimensions 12 cm × 8 cm. What are the angles between the diagonals?

Example   Find the hypotenuse AC.

Either:

$$\sin 40° = \frac{4}{AC}$$

$$0.6428 = \frac{4}{AC}$$

$$\frac{1}{0.6428} = \frac{AC}{4}$$

$$\text{So } AC = \frac{4}{0.6428}$$

$$= 6.22 \text{ cm}$$

Or:

$$\tan 50° = \frac{BC}{4}$$ **Find BC first.**

$$BC = 4 × \tan 50° = 4.767 \text{ cm}$$

$$AC = \sqrt{42 + 4.767^2}$$

$$= \sqrt{38.72}$$ **Then find AC using Pythagoras' Theorem.**

$$= 6.22 \text{ cm}$$

Exercise 17   Find the missing hypotenuse labelled x. Give your answers to 3 significant figures.

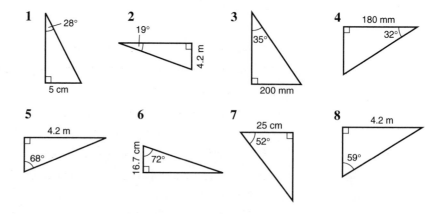

Review

Exercise 18   Find the missing angles indicated by a letter:

1

2

3

4

5

6

7

8

9

10

11

12 How many edges has a hexagonal prism?

13 Which quadrilateral has only *one* pair of parallel sides?

14 Which quadrilaterals have four sides of equal length?

15 Which solid has just *two* flat surfaces?

16 Which solid has just *one* flat surface?

17 Draw a net for a square-based pyramid.

18 Draw the accurate net for a cuboid with length 4 cm, width 2 cm, and height 1.5 cm.

19 This is the net for a solid. Write down the name of the solid.

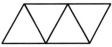

Draw these shapes to the scale given:

20

750 mm

300 mm

1 cm to 150 mm

21

24 cm

15 cm

1 cm to 6 cm

22

120°

17.5 m

30 m

1 cm to 5 m

23 Draw this rectangle to the exact dimensions shown.
Draw the locus of points which are

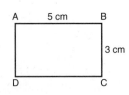

A ——— 5 cm ——— B

3 cm

D ——————————— C

(a) 2 cm from A

(b) of equal distance from sides AB and BC

(c) 2 cm from side DC

(d) of equal distance from corners D and C.

Find the missing side or angle labelled. Give lengths to 3 significant figures,
and angles to 1 decimal place.

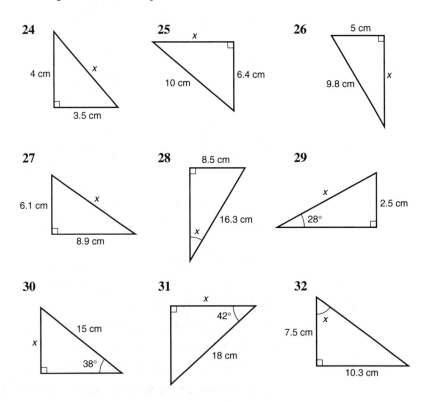

24

4 cm

x

3.5 cm

25

x

10 cm

6.4 cm

26

5 cm

9.8 cm

x

27

6.1 cm

x

8.9 cm

28

8.5 cm

16.3 cm

x

29

x

28°

2.5 cm

30

15 cm

x

38°

31

x

42°

18 cm

32

7.5 cm

x

10.3 cm

_____

Exercise 19   The following questions are all taken from past GCSE papers.

1 (a) Using a protractor, measure and write down the size of angle A.

(2 marks)

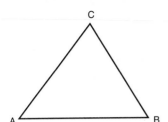

(b) On the diagram, mark a point exactly half-way between A and C.
Label this point D.   *(2 marks)*

(c) Join point B to point D. Measure the length of BD.

(i) Give your answer in centimetres.   *(2 marks)*

(ii) Give your answer in millimetres.   *(2 marks)*
[LEAG]

2 Here is a sketch of the end of a lean-to garden shed.

(a) Make a scale drawing of the end of the shed using a scale of 1 cm to
represent 0.5 m.   *(8 marks)*

(b) Using your scale drawing, measure and write down the length which
represents the slant roof of the shed.   *(2 marks)*

(c) Using your answer, work out the actual length, in metres, of the slant
roof of the shed.   *(3 marks)*
[LEAG]

3 (a) Draw a full size net of this cuboid.   *(4 marks)*

(b) Calculate the volume of the cuboid stating clearly the units in which
your answer is measured.   *(3 marks)*
[LEAG]

4

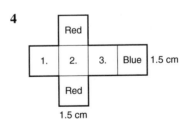

(a) In a game of Ludo, an unbiased die with faces numbered 1 to 6 is
thrown once. Karin needs to score 3 or more in order to win the game.
What is the probability that Karin will win the game with her next
throw?   *(1 mark)*

(b) The diagram shows the net of a cube. The squares are of side 1.5 cm.
Two squares are red, two blue and two white. When the net is folded
to make a cube the same colour squares are opposite each other. Write
down which of the numbered squares is blue.   *(1 mark)*
[SEG]

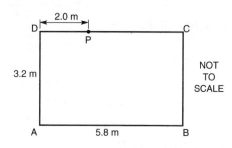

2.0 m

D   C
    P

3.2 m   NOT
                    TO
                   SCALE

A   5.8 m   B

5 In the diagram, the rectangle ABCD represents the floor of a room. P represents a power point at floor level.

(a) Using a scale of 2 cm to represent 1 m, make an accurate scale drawing of ABCD and mark the position of P. *(3 marks)*

(b) Use your scale drawing to find the distance of the power point from the corner B of the room. *(1 mark)*
[MEG]

6 Use the diagram to calculate the value of

(a) x, *(1 mark)*

(b) y, *(1 mark)*

(c) z, *(1 mark)*
[NEA]

7 A ladder is standing on horizontal ground and rests against a vertical wall. The ladder is 4.5 metres long and its foot is 1.6 metres from the wall.

Calculate how far up the wall, correct to 2 decimal places, the ladder will reach. *(3 marks)*
[MEG]

4.5 m

1.6 m

8 In the diagram, ABCD is a rectangle. E is a point on BC such that angle AED = 90°.
Angle EAD = $x°$ and angle DEC = $y°$.

B   E   C
          $y°$

  $x°$

A   D
NOT
TO
SCALE

(a) Label on the diagram

(i) the other angles equal to $x°$,

(ii) the other angles equal to $y°$. *(2 marks)*

(b) Write down a relation connecting x and y. *(1 mark)*
[MEG]

9 A ladder 12 m long leans against the vertical wall of a house.
The foot of the ladder is 2.8 m from the wall on horizontal ground.
Calculate the height of the top of the ladder above the ground.
(3 marks)
[MEG]

12 m

2.8 m

NOT
TO
SCALE

10

The above diagram shows an isosceles triangle.

(a) Calculate the height of the triangle. *(3 marks)*

(b) Calculate the area of the triangle. *(2 marks)*

[NEA]

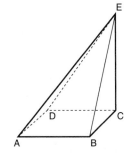

11 The diagram shows the net of a solid.

(a) What name is given to this type of solid? *(1 mark)*

(b) How many edges has the solid? *(1 mark)*

(c) Measure and write down the size of the angle marked x on the net. *(1 mark)*

[MEG]

12 In the diagram AB is parallel to DC.

(a) Calculate the value of

(i) x, *(1 mark)*

(ii) y. *(1 mark)*

(b) Write down a possible pair of values of s and t. *(1 mark)*

[NEA]

13 The figure ABCDE represents a square-based pyramid. The base ABCD is horizontal and the vertex E is vertically above C.

(a) Draw a sketch of a net of this pyramid. *(2 marks)*

(b) Name two congruent faces of the pyramid. *(2 marks)*

[NEA]

14 The diagram shows a field whose shape is a parallelogram.

Lengths are in metres. Angle QST $= 90°$.

(a) Calculate the length QS. *(3 marks)*

(b) Calculate the area of the field. *(2 marks)*

[SEG]

NOT TO
SCALE

15 The diagram shows the plan of a rectangular bedroom which is 3.5 metres long and 2.5 metres wide. Draw a plan of the bedroom using a scale of 4 centimetres to represent 1 metre.

(a) The door FG is hinged at F. Draw accurately the locus of G if the door is opened into the bedroom through 90°. *(2 marks)*

(b) Draw accurately and label clearly the region of the room closer than 1 metre to the window EC. *(2 marks)*

(c) A rectangular bed, 2 metres long and 1 metre wide, is to be placed in the bedroom with at least one edge against a wall. it must also be at least 1 metre from the window and the door must turn through 90°.

Draw accurately a possible position of the bed in the room.

(2 marks)

[MEG]

16

A plane leaves London Airport and flies on a bearing of 050° for 70 miles to Ipswich. The plan then flies due east for 130 miles, landing in Rotterdam.

(a) Calculate how far Ipswich is east of London (the distance marked *x* on the diagram). *(3 marks)*

(b) Calculate how far Ipswich is north of London (the distance marked *y* on the diagram). *(3 marks)*

(c) How far east of London is Rotterdam? *(1 mark)*

(d) What is the bearing of Rotterdam from London? (Give your answer to two significant figures.) *(3 marks)*

(e) Calculate the direct distance of Rotterdam from London. (Give your answer to two significant figures.) *(3 marks)*

[NEA]

Ideas for investigations

1 A model can be built up using several rods and interconnectors.

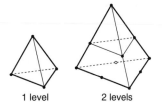

1 level   2 levels

Diagram:	1	2
Number of interconnectors:	4	10

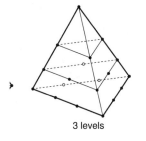

3 levels

How many interconnectors will be needed in the (a) 5th diagram (b) 10th diagram?

2 The numbers 3, 4, 5 form a Pythagorean triple, since they can be used to make the dimensions of a right-angled triangle: $3^2 + 4^2 = 5^2$
There are many other Pythagorean triples: 6, 8, 10
                                                        5, 12, 13
How many Pythagorean triples can you find? Make sure you explain the strategy you use.

3 Copy one of the diagrams. Draw straight lines that join pairs of points which total 13, for example, 3 and 10, 4 and 9, etc. The shape you get is called an envelope. You can vary the type of envelope you get by changing the total you use (e.g. use 11, 9, etc.). You can also change the shape of grid you use. Investigate the various shapes of envelopes you can get by changing the total number and the shape of grid you use.

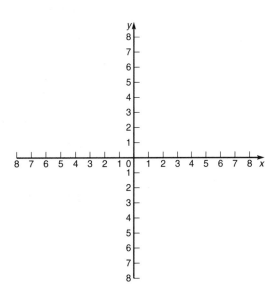

SYMMETRY

9.1 Reflection

The first primitive geometrical designs have been dated at around 25000 BC.

A **reflection** is a type of transformation. The complete shape has line symmetry, and the dotted line is called a **line of symmetry** or mirror line.

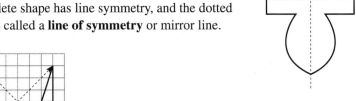

This shape has been reflected in the dotted line, which is also the line of symmetry, or mirror line.

Exercise 1

In each question copy and complete the diagram, and draw the reflection of the shape in the line of symmetry.

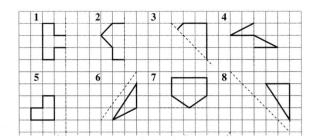

Exercise 2

Copy each shape and draw in *all* possible lines of symmetry. For each question write down the number of lines of symmetry you have found.

Lines on coordinate grids can be used as lines of symmetry:

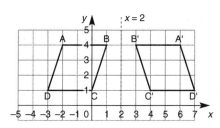

Shape ABCD has been reflected in the line $x = 2$ to give the reflected shape A'B'C'D'

Exercise 3

In each question copy the diagram, and draw the reflections of the shapes as requested.

1 (a) reflected in the x-axis

(b) reflected in the line $x = 1$

(c) reflected in the line $y = 1$

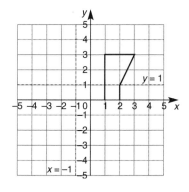

2 (a) reflected in the y-axis

(b) reflected in the line $y = 1$

(c) reflected in the line $x = -1$

3 (a) reflected in the y-axis

(b) reflected in the line $y = x$

(c) reflected in the line $y = -x$

(d) reflected in the line $y = -1$

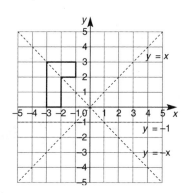

The largest mirror is 6 m, or $19\frac{1}{2}$ ft, in diameter, which is included in a reflector telescope on Mount Semirodriki in the Caucasus Mountains, USSR.

Note: When describing a transformation which is a reflection, always note down in which **line** it is reflected.

9.2 Planes of symmetry

The cube has been divided into two symmetrical halves by a **plane** of symmetry.

This shape has been divided into two by a plane, but the two halves are not symmetrical. The plane is not a plane of symmetry.

Each solid is shown with one plane of symmetry. How many planes of symmetry does each solid have (including the one shown)?

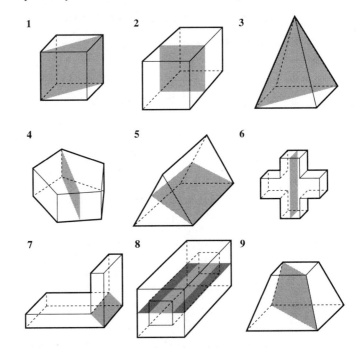

9.3 Rotation

A **rotation** is another type of transformation.
As a shape rotates about a point it will fit on top of itself in certain positions.
The number of times it does this in one revolution is called the **order** of rotational symmetry.

Tracing paper is a useful aid when finding rotational symmetry.

1 Trace the shape onto tracing paper.
2 Place your pen on the centre of rotation.
3 Rotate the tracing paper around the
   point, and through one full turn (360°).
   As you do, count the number of times
   the shapes line up exactly.
4 Your count is the order of symmetry.

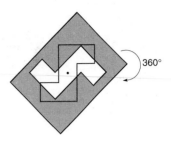

Example Find the order of rotational symmetry.

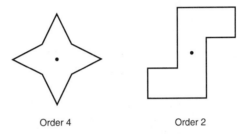

Order 4   Order 2

Exercise 5   For each shape give the order of rotational symmetry.

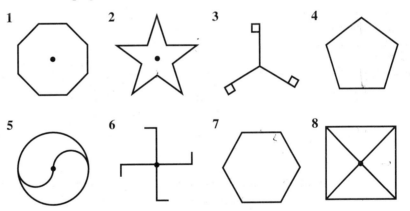

Use the shape given to draw a diagram which has rotational symmetry of the
order stated, using the marked point as centre.

Order 2   Order 6   Order 4   Order 3

Shapes can also be rotated through a given angle about a point.
This shape has been rotated 135° clockwise about point X.

Tracing paper is a useful aid when rotating shapes:
1 Trace the shape onto tracing paper.
2 Place your pen on the centre of rotation.
3 Turn the tracing paper around by the required angle, clockwise or
   anticlockwise.
4 Trace the shape into its new position.

Note: When describing a transformation which is a rotation, always note down
the **angle** (degrees), the **direction** (anticlockwise/clockwise), and the **centre**
of rotation.

Exercise 6

Each shape A has been moved to a new position A'. Describe the rotation
using the point marked X as centre.

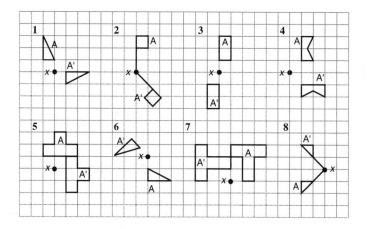

*The highest man-made
rotational speed ever
achieved is 7250 km/h
at Birmingham
University in 1975.*

Exercise 7

Draw each shape A. Rotate the shape about the centre point X, through the
given angle. Label the new position A'.

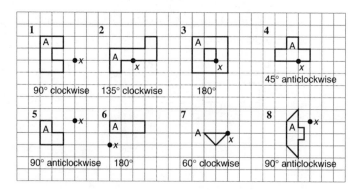

9.4 **Enlargement**

A third type of transformation is an **enlargement.**
Enlargement is a term used frequently in photography.

Shape A' has sides that are twice as long as A: an enlargement of
scale factor 2.

Shape A" has sides that are three times longer than A: an enlargement of
scale factor 3.

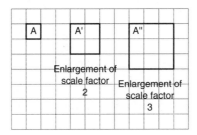

Exercise 8 Draw an enlargement of each diagram to the scale factor indicated.

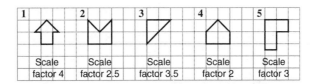

1	2	3	4	5
Scale factor 4	Scale factor 2.5	Scale factor 3.5	Scale factor 2	Scale factor 3

Shape A has been enlarged to become shape A'. In each question write down
the scale factor of the enlargement.

A transformation which is an enlargement has a point from which the shape is enlarged, called the **centre of enlargement**.

ABCD has been enlarged by a scale factor of 2: the distance of each point of the shape from the centre of enlargement X has been increased by a factor of 2, ABCD becomes A'B'C'D'.

ABC has been enlarged by a scale factor of 3. A'B'C' is the enlargement of ABC with the origin (0,0) as centre. A"B"C" is the enlargement of ABC with the point (−3,1) as centre.

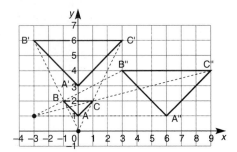

Note: When describing a transformation which is an enlargement always write down two things: the **scale factor**, and the **centre of enlargement**.

Exercise 9

Describe each of the enlargements which transform shape A to shape A', stating the scale factor and the centre of enlargment.

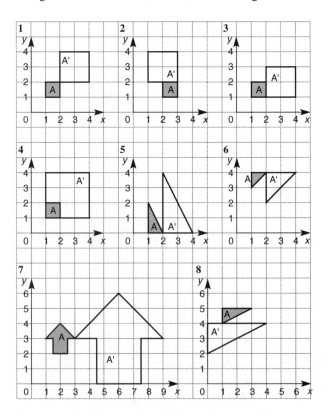

Copy the diagram and draw the enlargement by the given scale factor, from the centre of enlargement. You may need to extend the axes.

 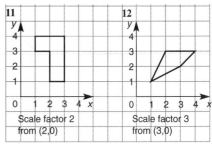

9.5 Similarity

In mathematics, two shapes are **similar** if their dimensions are proportional, that is, if one shape is an enlargement of the other.

If the scale factor of enlargement of **length is** x,
then the scale factor of enlargement for **area is** x^2,
and the scale factor of enlargement for **volume is** x^3,

> *Example* Find the length scale factor of enlargement if the area scale factor of enlargement is 9.
>
> $x^2 = 9$ *x^2 is the scale factor of enlargement for area.*
> So $x = \sqrt{9} = 3$ *x is the scale factor of enlargement for length.*

Exercise 10

1 If the scale factor of enlargement for area is 64, find the scale factor of enlargement for length.

2 If the scale factor of enlargement for area is 81, find the scale factor of enlargement for length.

3 If the scale factor of enlargement for length is 12, find the scale factor of enlargement for area.

4 If the scale factor of enlargement for length is 4, find the scale factor of enlargement for volume.

5 If the scale factor of enlargement for volume is 216, find the scale factor of enlargement for length.

6 If the scale factor of enlargement for volume is 125, find the scale factor of enlargement for length.

7 If the scale factor of enlargement for volume is 27, find the scale factor of enlargement for (a) length (b) area.

8 If the scale factor of enlargement for area is 16, find the scale factor of enlargement for (a) length (b) volume.

Example   A baking tin has a base area of 40 cm², and a volume of 200 cm³. A similar tin has a base area of 160 cm². What is the volume of the larger tin?

Scale factor of enlargement for *area* is $\frac{160}{60} = 4$,
so scale factor of enlargement for *length* is $\sqrt{4} = 2$,
and so scale factor of enlargement for *volume* is $2^3 = 8$.
The volume of the larger tin is $200 \times 8 = 1600$ cm³.

Example   Fertiliser can be bought in two similar containers 15 cm and 60 cm high. The smaller container holds 2 kg of fertiliser. What weight of fertiliser does the larger container hold?

Note: The weight in this question corresponds to the volume.

The scale factor of enlargement for *length* is $\frac{60}{15} = 4$,
So the scale factor of enlargement for *volume* (weight) is $4^3 = 64$.
The weight of the larger container is $2 \times 64 = 128$ kg.

Exercise II

1   Ice-cream is sold to catering colleges in two similar drums, with volumes of 2 litres and 54 litres. The smaller drum has a height of 18 cm. What is the height of the larger drum?

2   Two similar models have heights of 6 cm and 9 cm. The smaller model has a stand with an area of 8 cm². What is the area of the stand of the larger model?

3   A photograph is 20 cm long. A similar, larger photograph is 60 cm long. The area of the smaller photograph is 500 cm². What is the area of the larger photograph?

4   A small tin of cocoa has a height of 6 cm. A similar tin has a height of 8 cm. The volume of the smaller tin is 280 cm³. What is the volume of the larger tin?

5   Two similar tanks will hold 40 litres and 100 litres of water. The height of the larger tank is 75 cm. What is the height of the smaller tank?

6   Two similar barrels hold 1 litre and 125 litres of liquid. The larger barrel is 80 cm high. What is the height of the smaller barrel?

7   Two similar boxes have volumes of 2000 cm³, and 16 000 cm³. The area of the base of the larger box is 60 cm². What is the area of the base of the smaller box?

8   A van has a windscreen of area 4000 cm², and has a capacity of 8 m³. A model of the van has a capacity of 0.5 m³. What is the area of the windscreen in the model?

9   A poster is 96 cm long. A print taken of the poster is 6 cm long. The area of the print is 30 cm². What is the area of the poster?

10   Two similar gas cylinders are used to light motorway repair signs. A large cylinder will last for 800 hours, whilst a smaller one will last for 200 hours. The large cylinder has a height of 200 cm. What is the height of the smaller cylinder?

9.6 Regular polygons

Triangle   Square   Pentagon   Hexagon   Heptagon   Octagon

Exterior angle

Interior angle

Regular polygons are polygons with sides of equal length, and angles of equal size. There are two angles which are useful in calculations involving polygons: the exterior angle and the interior angle.

There are two angle properties which you must know:

Interior angle + Exterior angle = 180° at any vertex of the polygon.

Sum of the Exterior angles = 360°.

The mathematician Gauss, who died in 1814, wanted a 17-sided polygon drawn on his tombstone, but it too closely resembled a circle for the stonemaster to carve.

Example   The interior angle of a polygon is 120°. How many sides has the polygon?

Interior angle = 120°, so exterior angle = 180° − 120° = 60°.

Sum of all exterior angles is 360°,

so the number of angles = number of sides = 360° ÷ 60° = 6 sides.

Example   The sum of the interior angles of a regular polygon is 1260°. How many sides has the polygon?

Sum of exterior anges is 360°,

so sum of interior angles + sum of exterior angles is 1260° + 360° = 1620°.

But 1 exterior + 1 interior angle = 180°,

so the number of sides is 1620° ÷ 180° = 9 sides.

Example   A regular polygon has 30 sides. What is the sum of the interior angles?

Each exterior angle is 360° ÷ 30 = 12°.   *As the sum of exterior angles is 360°.*

So interior angle = 180° − 12° = 168°,   *As interior angle + exterior angle is 180°.*

so 30 interior angles = 168° × 30 = 5040°.

Exercise 12

Find the number of sides of each regular polygon given the following information:

1 Interior angle 135°   **2** Interior angle 108°

3 Exterior angle 40°   **4** Exterior angle 30°

5 Interior angle 144°   **6** Exterior angle 24°

7 Sum of interior angles is 3240°   **8** Sum of interior angles is 2880°

The US Defence Department Building, the Pentagon, has the largest ground area covered by any office building: 604 000 m², and 27 km of corridors.

Find the sum of the interior angles of regular polygons with:

9 16 sides   **10** 25 sides   **11** 32 sides   **12** 36 sides

13 Can a regular polygon be drawn, such that each exterior angle is (a) 20° (b) 16° (c) 15°? If so, state the number of sides,

14 Can a regular polygon be drawn, such that each interior angle is (a) 144° (b) 140° (c) 130°? If so, state the number of sides.

Exercise 13

Use your results from Exercise 12 to help you copy and complete this table:

Regular polygon	Number of sides	Sum of all interior angles	Size of one interior angle	Size of one exterior angle
Triangle (equilateral)				
Quadrilateral (square)				
Pentagon				
Hexagon				
Heptagon				
Octagon				
Nonagon				
Decagon				
Undecagon				
Dodecagon				

9.7 Tessellations

Shapes **tessellate** when they fit together exactly, without any gaps.

Squares tessellate; circles do not tessellate.

We can also have tessellations made up of more than one shape. This tessellation is made using squares and regular octagons.

Exercise 14

1 Show, by drawing a diagram, which of the regular polygons can tessellate.

2 Show, by drawing a diagram, which of these shapes tessellate:

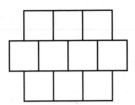

9.8 Moving shapes: translation

A **translation** is another type of transformation. A translation is a way of describing how a shape has been moved by sliding. In the diagams, shape ABCD has been moved to a new position A'B'C'D'. Look at the point C: it has moved 4 spaces across to the right, and 1 space up, to C'. All the points have moved the same amount: A → A', B → B', C → C', D → D'.

ABCD → A'B'C'D' is described by the translation $\binom{4}{1}$

From C to C" is 2 to the left and 1 down.

ABCD → A"B"C"D" is described by the translation $\binom{-2}{-1}$

So a translation is described by: $\left(\begin{array}{c}\text{Moves to the right}\\\text{Moves upwards}\end{array}\right)$

Exercise 15

Describe the translations which map:

1 A onto C   2 A onto B

3 B onto A   4 B onto C

5 C onto A   6 C onto B

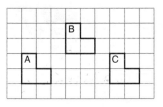

Describe the translations which map:

7 A onto C   8 B onto A

9 D onto B   10 D onto F

11 F onto D   12 E onto B

13 F onto C   14 D onto A

15

Draw this shape on a square grid.
Draw and label the translations of this shape as follows:

(a) A $\begin{pmatrix} 1 \\ 2 \end{pmatrix}$ (b) B $\begin{pmatrix} 3 \\ -2 \end{pmatrix}$ (c) C $\begin{pmatrix} 4 \\ 1 \end{pmatrix}$ (d) D $\begin{pmatrix} -2 \\ -3 \end{pmatrix}$

16

Draw this shape onto a squared grid.
Draw and label the translations of this shape as follows:

(a) A $\begin{pmatrix} -3 \\ -2 \end{pmatrix}$ (b) B $\begin{pmatrix} 4 \\ 0 \end{pmatrix}$ (c) C $\begin{pmatrix} 3 \\ -2 \end{pmatrix}$ (d) D $\begin{pmatrix} -3 \\ 0 \end{pmatrix}$

9.9 Vector notation

In decribing a transformation which is a translation, the notation $\begin{pmatrix} 3 \\ 2 \end{pmatrix}$ is called a **column vector**. This can also be shown as a diagram indicating the movement:

Vector **a** is $\begin{pmatrix} 3 \\ 2 \end{pmatrix}$.

Vectors were developed relatively recently, in the nineteenth century, as a new branch of mathematics.

The vector which is the opposite to **a** is $-\mathbf{a} = \begin{pmatrix} -3 \\ -2 \end{pmatrix}$

Vectors are equal if they are the same size, and have the same direction. In the diagram AB = GH.

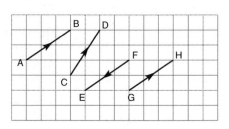

Exercise 16   State whether the following are true or false:

1 m = n   **2** a = h   **3** m = −b   **4** e = p
5 p = e   **6** k = 3a   **7** k = 2a   **8** g = p
9 n = 2d   **10** m = b   **11** l = −c   **12** g = ½k

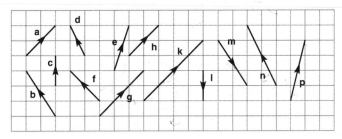

13 Write each of the following vectors as a column vector,
for example $\mathbf{a} = \binom{2}{2}$:

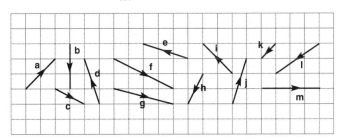

14 On a square grid draw each of the following vectors.

$$\overrightarrow{AB} = \binom{4}{3} \quad \overrightarrow{CD} = \binom{1}{2} \quad \overrightarrow{EF} = \binom{-1}{3} \quad \overrightarrow{GH} = \binom{1}{-2} \quad \overrightarrow{IJ} = \binom{0}{2}$$

$$\overrightarrow{KL} = \binom{-1}{-2} \quad \overrightarrow{MN} = \binom{-3}{-1} \quad \overrightarrow{OP} = \binom{3}{-1} \quad \overrightarrow{QR} = \binom{-2}{3} \quad \overrightarrow{ST} = \binom{3}{0}$$

$$\overrightarrow{UV} = \binom{4}{-3} \quad \overrightarrow{WX} = \binom{0}{-2} \quad \overrightarrow{YZ} = \binom{-1}{-3}$$

9.10   Positions in 3-D

3-D coordinates are used extensively in writing the programs for automated manufacturing equipment, and for navigating space vehicles.

A position in 3-dimensional space is shown using 3-D coordinates. The diagram shows a cuboid of dimensions 5 × 3 × 2. The coordinates of the corners of the base are written as:

A (0,0,0)   B (0,5,0)   C (3,5,0)   D (3,0,0)
        ↑↑↑

x-y-z- coordinate

Can you write down the coordinates of the corners of the top?

For each of the diagrams below:

(a) write down the coordinates of all the points (corners)

(b) write down the dimensions of the cuboid

(c) calculate the volume of the cuboid.

1

2

3

4

5

6
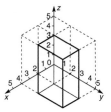

Draw a 3-dimensional grid for each of the questions below.

Draw a cuboid as decribed:

7 With base 2 × 5 and height 3

8 With base 3 × 3 and height 4

9 With base 4 × 2 and height 2

10 With base 5 × 4 and height 3

11 With one corner at (2,1,0), and base 3 × 3 and height 4

12 With one corner at (1,1,1), and base 4 × 3 and height 2

13 With one corner at (3,0,4), and base 2 × 2 and height 1

14 With one corner at (0,2,2), and base 2 × 3 and height 3

Review

Exercise 18 **1** Reflect this shape in the dotted line.

2   Reflect this shape in the dotted line.

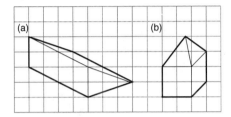

3   Reflect the triangle as follows:

(a) in the *x*-axis, and label it A

(b) in the *y*-axis, and label it B

(c) in the line *y*=1, and label it C

(d) in the line *y*=—*x*, and label it D.

4   How many planes of symmetry have each of these solids?

(a)   (b)

5   Write down the order of rotational symmetry:

(a)   (b)   (c)   (d)

Copy the shape and complete the rotation about the marked point as centre.

6   7   8

180°

135° clockwise   45° anticlockwise

9   Enlarge the shape using (0,1) as centre, and using a scale factor of 3.

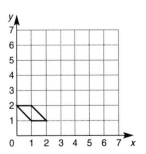

10 Can a regular polygon be found such that the interior angle is 136°?

11 A regular polygon has an interior angle of 165°. How many sides has it?

12 A regular polygon has an exterior angle of 45°. How many sides has it?

13 Describe the translation which maps:

    (a) A → C   (b) C → D

    (c) D → B   (d) B → A

14   Copy the diagram, and in it draw vectors **b**, **c**, and **d**, where **b** = **a**, **c** = 2**a**, **d** = −**a**.

15 A cuboid has a base of length 5 cm, width 2 cm, and height 3 cm. A corner of the base is at the position given by the 3-D coordinate (0,2,1). Draw the cuboid using 3-dimensional axes, and work out the 3-dimensional coordinate of the corner of the cuboid diagonally opposite (0,2,1).

16 A photograph has an area of 8 cm². The dimensions of the photograph are enlarged so they are nine times as big. What is the area of the enlarged photograph?

17 Two similar bottles of wine contain ½ litre and 4 litres. The smaller bottle has a height of 18 cm. What will be the height of the larger bottle?

Exercise 19   The following questions are all taken from GCSE papers.

1 A toy brick is in the shape of a cuboid measuring 2 cm by 3 cm by 4 cm. State how many planes of symmetry the toy brick has.   *(1 mark)*

    [NEA]

2 Complete the diagram below so that is has line symmetry in XY.

    (3 marks)

    [LEAG]

3 Describe fully three different single transformations which will each map the square **A** to the square **B** on the grid shown.   (*6 marks*)

[NEA]

4 ABCDEFG is a regular seven-sided polygon called a heptagon.

Calculate the size of angle GAB, the interior angle of the heptagon. (Give your answer to one decimal place.)   (*4 marks*)

[NEA]

5 (a) calculate the size of one interior angle of a regular dodecagon (12 sides).   (*2 marks*)

(b) A square, a regular hexagon and a regular dodecagon can be tessellated. The diagram shows part of the tessellation. Only four sides of the dodecagon have been drawn.

Add two more squares and one more hexagon to the diagram to show how the tessellation will continue.   (*3 marks*).

[MEG]

6 (a) In a diagram, rotate triangle ABC anticlockwise through 90° about A. Label the image T.   (*2 marks*)

(b) In a diagram, rotate triangle ABC anticlockwise through 90° about C. Label the image S.   (*2 marks*)

(c) Describe fully the single transformation which will map T onto S.   (*2 marks*)

[MEG]

7 (a) Describe fully the transformation that takes Triangle A to Triangle B.   (*2 marks*)

(b) Describe fully the transformation that takes Triangle B to Triangle C.   (*4 marks*)

[LEAG]

213

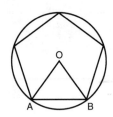

8 A regular pentagon is drawn inside a circle of radius 8 cm with centre O, as shown.

(a) Show how the angle AOB can be calculated to be 72°. (*1 mark*)

(b) State the size of angle OAB. (*2 marks*)

(c) On the diagram, draw the line of symmetry of the triangle AOB. (*1 mark*)

[NEA]

9 ABCD is a quadrilateral whose four sides have length 6 cm.
Angle ABC = 120°.

(a) Draw an accurate diagram of ABCD. (*2 marks*)

(b) What is the mathematical name for quadrilateral ABCD? (*2 marks*)

[SEG]

10 Complete the shading in the diagram so that the broken lines AB and CD are lines of symmetry. (*3 marks*)

[MEG]

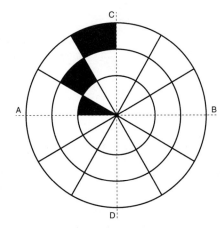

11 The diagram below shows shapes A, B and C.

State fully

(a) the single transformation that moves shape A to shape B, (*3 marks*)

(b) the single transformation that moves shape A to shape C. (*2 marks*)

[NEA]

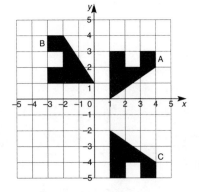

Ideas for investigations

1

The first line has been enlarged by a scale factor of 2, and 3.

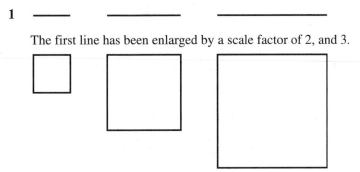

The dimensions of the first square have been enlarged by a scale factor of 2, and 3. By what factors has the area been enlarged?

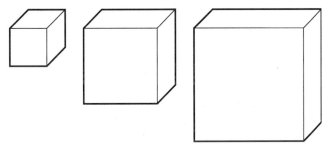

The dimensions of the first cube have been enlarged by a scale factor of 2, and 3. By what factors has the volume been enlarged?

Can you describe a rule connecting scale factor of enlargement of distances (lengths), scale factor of enlargement of areas, and scale factor of enlargement of volumes?

2 In snooker a ball hits the cushion and rebounds. The second part of its path is a reflection of the first part of its path. Draw a scale diagram of a snooker table, 6 ft × 3 ft, and use this idea of reflections to plot the path of snooker balls as they rebound off the cushion.

Try a few examples with the ball starting in different places on the table.

3

Triangle	Quadrilateral	Pentagon
180°	2 triangles:	3 triangles:
	2 x 180°	3 x 180°

The diagram shows how polygons can be divided up into triangles to help find the total of all the interior angles.

Total for a triangle (3 sides) = 180°.

Total for a quadrilateral (4 sides) = 180°× 2 = 360°.

Total for a pentagon (5 sides) = 180° × 3 = 540°.

Can you use this method to help find a rule linking the number of sides of the polygon with the total of the interior angles?

COLLECTING AND PROCESSING

The heaviest rainstorm recorded occurred in 1952 on the Island of Reunion in the Indian Ocean: 1870 millimetres of rain fell in 24 hours.

Statistical information required for processing can be gathered in a number of ways of which two of the more common ones are:
(1) from data collecting sheets (e.g. questionnaires),
(2) from tables and lists (e.g. train timetables).
In the next chapter we shall look more closely at representing and interpreting information, but in this chapter we will concentrate on the collection and processing of information.

10.1 Data collecting sheets

Example A hot-drinks machine in a college canteen sells tea, coffee, chocolate, tomato soup and vegetable soup. As part of a survey, information has been collected on the data sheet shown.

Copy and complete the 'Total' column.

(a) How many coffees were sold?
(b) How many soups?
(c) If one of the drinks had to be withdrawn, which one would you choose? Why?

(a) There were 26 coffees sold.
(b) There were $16 + 23 = 39$ soups sold.
(c) Based only on the survey information, you would choose tomato soup, because it had fewest sales.

With further information from other days and from other times in the day, your choice may be different.

A good data collecting sheet:
(1) has a clear heading, with dates, times where necessary,
(2) is clear in what it is asking for,
(3) is easy to complete, with ticks or simple numbers.

Survey Sheet
HOT DRINKS

Start: 10.30 a.m.   Finish: 12.30 p.m.

DRINK	TALLY	TOTAL
Tea	‖‖ ‖‖ ‖‖ ‖‖ ///	23
Coffee	‖‖ ‖‖ ‖‖ ‖‖ ‖‖ /	
Chocolate	‖‖ ‖‖ ‖‖ ‖‖ ‖‖ ‖‖ //	
Tomato soup	‖‖ ‖‖ ‖‖ /	
Vegetable soup	‖‖ ‖‖ ‖‖ ‖‖ ///	
	Total	

Exercise 1

The purpose of each data sheet is given. Say what aspects of each of these data collecting sheets you think could be improved. Write down your improvements in each case.

Lunch survey

Date:

Customer	Meal	Cost
1.	Pizza + chips	1.20
2.	Baked potato	0.85
3.		
4.		
5.		
6.		
7.		
8.		
9.		
10.		

1 To see how many occupants there are in cars travelling into a town in the morning, as part of a survey into public transport facilities.

2 To survey the lunches provided in a canteen, with a view to improving the meals service.

Cars

Car No.	No. of passengers
1	
2	
3	
4	
5	
6	
7	
8	
9	
10	

Newspaper Survey

Date:

From 9.30 – 10.30 a.m.

Paper	No. bought	Total
Mirror		
Express		
Mail		
Sun		
Today		
Times		
Guardian		
Telegraph		
Independent		

3 To look into which morning newspapers are the most popular with students by surveying the papers bought at the college bookshop in a morning.

4 To look into the car parking provision in a supermarket car park by checking the number of vacant spaces.

Car parking

Date:

Time	Empty spaces
13.00	
13.15	
13.30	
13.45	
14.00	
14.15	
14.30	
14.45	
15.00	

As with data collecting sheets, questionnaires need to be carefully worded, otherwise the information collected could be confusing or biased.

Exercise 2

The following questionnaires attempt to gather information for the purpose stated. Criticise each of these questionnaires, and rewrite them so as to remove as much of the confusion or bias as you can.

Lecturer questionnaire

Please rate the lecturers in order of preference, entering a number from 1 to 5 in the box beside the name

Mr N. James
Mr B. Anderson
Mrs K. Robson
Mr M. Islam
Mrs L. Oates

Signed (if desired): ....

1 To ascertain the effectiveness of the five college lecturers who teach on a mathematics course.

2 To look into making the menu in the college canteen more acceptable to students.

Canteen Questionnaire

(a) Which of these meals do you eat?

Sausage	Vegetarian
Pizza	Baked potato
Stir-fry	Hamburger
Roast meat	Other

(b) Which meal would you prefer to eat?

Name: ....
(not compulsory)

Where do you go on holiday?
Are you male/female?
Please indicate your holiday destination last year.
France   Germany
Spain   Greece
Belgium   U.S.A
Other – please name
Signed: ....

3 To investigate foreign holidays.

4 To look into destinations, having completed a one-year course.

Leavers' destinations	Date: _____	
Which course have you recently completed?	What are you Intending to do?	
Male/female	Age:	16 19 22 over 17 20 23 24 18 21 24

10.2 Information from tables and lists

There are more than 12 000 different species in the 'pea' family (leguminosae).

Holidays of 1–3 nights	Holidays of 4 nights or more	Charge
2–14 days	2–14 days	60%
15–21 days	15–28 days	45%
22–28 days	29–42 days	30%
28+ days in advance	42+ days in advance	deposit only

Example A holiday company makes a charge if a previously booked holiday is cancelled. The charge depends on how many days' notice is given, before the holiday is due to begin. The rates are shown in the table.

Find the charge for cancelling a holiday which should have lasted:

(a) 6 nights, costing £300, with 25 days' notice,
(b) 1 night, costing £55, with 3 days' notice,
(c) 8 nights, costing £840, with 32 days' notice.

(a) The charge is 45% of £300, which is £135.
(b) The charge is 60% of £54, which is £32.40.
(c) The charge is 30% of £840, which is £252.

Exercise 3 Use the information in the tables or lists to answer the questions.

Element	Density (g/cm^3)	Melting point (°C)	Boiling point (°C)
Aluminium	2.7	660	2470
Copper	8.9	1084	2570
Gold	19.3	1064	3080
Iron	7.9	1540	2750
Lead	11.3	180	1340
Magnesium	1.7	650	1110
Silver	10.5	961	2212
Tin	7.3	232	2270
Zinc	7.1	419	907

1 The table gives the density, melting point and boiling point of some metallic elements.

(a) What is the melting point of silver?

(b) What is the boiling point of copper?

(c) Which metals are denser than iron?

(d) Which is the least dense metal?

(e) Which metal has the highest boiling point?

(f) Brass consists of 60% copper and 40% zinc. Will its density be more than, or less than, 8g/cm³?

INTERCITY	
Newcastle–London Mondays to Fridays	
Newcastle depart	King's Cross arrive
1500	1808
1535	1840
1600	1918
(P) 1622	1903
1700	2015
1730	2045
1845	2159
1905	2222
2039	0023

2 The train times for travelling between Newcastle upon Tyne and London are shown, from 3.00 p.m. onwards.

(a) At what time does the 1700 arrive at King's Cross?

(b) If I arrive in London just after 7.15 p.m., at what time did the train leave Newcastle?

(c) How long is the journey on the 1730?

(d) The fastest train is the First Class Pullman service (P). How long is this journey?

(e) At what time does the last train arrive at King's Cross?

3 The monthly repayments for personal loans from an insurance company are shown in the table.

	Number of payments		
Amount	12	24	36
£7500	713.98	396.66	292.93
£5000	475.98	264.44	194.61
£3000	286.25	159.34	117.45
£2000	190.83	106.22	78.30
£1000	95.42	53.11	39.15
£500	47.71	26.56	19.58

(a) What is the premium for a loan of £3000 over 24 payments?

(b) I wish to borrow £5000 over three years. What are the monthly repayments?

(c) What loan can I have, if I can afford to pay up to £80 a month for three years?

(d) What would the premium be for a loan of £1500 over 12 payments?

4 A table of continental quilts from a mail-order catalogue shows the size, catalogue number, price, and weekly payments over 20 weeks.

Size	Cat. No.	Price	20 weeks
54 × 78	MQ 23 56	£49.99	£2.50
54 × 78	MQ 23 59	£59.99	£3.00
78 × 78	MQ 23 57	£69.99	£3.50
78 × 78	MQ 23 60	£84.99	£4.25
90 × 86	MQ 23 58	£79.99	£4.00
90 × 86	MQ 23 61	£94.99	£4.75

(a) What is the price of the quilt MQ 23 59?

(b) What is the weekly payment for quilt MQ 23 58?

(c) What size is the quilt which is priced at £84.99?

(d) I buy two of the large MQ 23 61 quilts. What will be my weekly payments?

(e) I would like one each of the two 54 × 78 quilts. What will be the weekly payments for these two quilts?

10.3 Ordering data

When information is collected, by whatever means (questionnaires, data collection sheets, set of test results, etc.), it needs to be put into some sort of **order**, if further work is to be done.

WALKER'S GARAGE

Repairs, MOT, service.
Phone: 729 401

brown red red blue
white blue blue green
red brown red green
red yellow red white
blue green red red red
blue blue brown grey
red yellow blue green
yellow brown

Example A garage worker was asked to note the colours of cars passing through the garage over a period of half an hour. From his figures he was asked to work out:

(a) the most popular colour,
(b) the least popular colour,
(c) the total number of cars seen,
(d) the percentage of cars of the most popular colour.

From his sheet, it is not clear what the answers are to any of the questions. We need to rearrange the information into some order.

Firstly, make a list of all the colours seen. Now count how many of each colour there were. The safest way to ensure that you do not miss any out is to go through the list of colours one by one, making a **tally mark** under the appropriate colour.

The complete **tally table** looks like this:

brown	red	blue	white	green	yellow	grey
////	++++	++++	//	////	///	/
	++++	//				

Note: We usually draw the fifth tally mark *across* the previous four marks, to help us count in 5's, especially when there are many tally marks to add up. We can now answer questions (a) and (b) easily: the most popular colour was red and the least popular colour was grey.

To answer (c) we can add up the tally marks for each colour:

brown	red	blue	white	green	yellow	grey	
4	+ 10 +	7 +	2 +	4 +	3 +	1	= 31

(d) The percentage of red cars is $\frac{10}{31} \times 100 = 32\%$, approximately.

It would have been much more convenient if the garage worker had planned his data collecting sheet rather more carefully in the first instance.
This sheet would have been much better; he does not need to write down each colour, only a tally mark.

WALKER'S GARAGE

Repairs, MOT, service.
Phone: 729 401

Colour	Tally	Frequency
brown	////	4
red	++++ ++++	10
blue	++++ //	7
white	//	2
green	////	4
yellow	///	3
grey	/	1
	Total	31

Exercise 4

For each of these sets of data, make up a suitable tally table, and complete it, showing the totals in the 'Frequency' column.

1 A set of 40 marks obtained by students in a test, with a maximum score of 10.

3	6	7	2	8	5	9	6	4	8
0	9	5	7	10	3	5	6	0	7
6	4	8	2	6	9	2	10	1	4
7	8	4	9	6	7	3	0	6	8

The column headings should be: Mark, Tally, Frequency.

2 A survey on the favourite fruit eaten by a group of students.

apple	apple	grape	melon	orange	orange
apple	banana	apple	orange	pear	grape
pear	apple	kiwi	banana	melon	apple
orange	pear	apple	apple	orange	melon

The column headings should be: Fruit, Tally, Frequency.

3 The number of minutes a local train is late, over a period of 35 weekdays.

3	0	0	8	5	1	1	2	0	4	0	0
1	4	0	0	2	2	9	3	0	1	2	1
0	5	7	0	0	3	1	4	4	0	2	

4 The National Curriculum level in mathematics attained by students wishing to follow a science course at a college.

The strongest surface wind was 372 km/h recorded at Mt. Washington in the USA in 1934.

8	6	9	7	6	6	7	6	5	9	7	7	6
7	5	9	8	8	6	7	6	6	7	6	5	8
7	8	6	7	6	5	7	8	7	6	7	7	7
6	7	6	5	6	7	6	6	9	6	8		

10.4 Grouping data

Example The marks scored by 28 students in a test (marked out of 100) are given.

(a) Make up a tally table.
To reach grade B a score of 60 was needed.
To reach grade A a score of 80 was needed.
(b) How many grade A's were there?
(c) How many grade B's were there?

43	47	88	76
52	66	49	68
92	77	37	65
49	71	91	62
83	74	71	70
57	19	37	90
50	85	66	75

(a) A tally table would be tedious to produce for these figures as they stand, as the mark range is from 19 to 92, and most scores occur only once. A more useful method would be to **group** the scores, into tens.

Mark	Tally	Frequency
0–9		0
10–19	/	1
20–29		0
30–39	//	2
40–49	////	4
50–59	///	3
60–69	##+	5
70–79	##+ //	7
80–89	///	3
90–100	///	3
	Total	28

We can represent this information in a diagram – there are more examples in the next chapter.

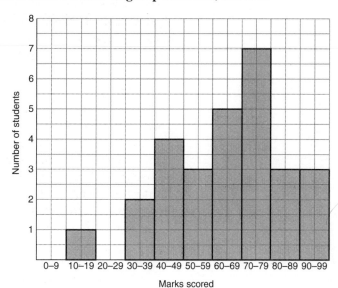

(b) From the table, there were $3 + 3 = 6$ grade A's.

(c) From the table, there were $5 + 7 = 12$ grade B's.

Exercise 5

For each set of data, make up a tally table, using the groupings suggested, and complete the frequency column.

1 The number of tomatoes picked from 24 tomato plants:

18	31	25	16	21	20	34	7
19	18	24	26	30	21	26	18
28	31	11	25	33	23	17	24

0–4, 5–9, 10–14, 15–19, ...

2 The number of words in each line of a page in a book:

12	8	9	15	2	14	10	9
7	15	9	11	13	12	5	14
7	10	11	1	11	13	9	3
8	10	8	11	12	11	3	11
10	8	8	6	14	12	10	4

0–2, 3–5, 6–8, 9–11, 12–14, 15–17, ...

How many lines altogether are there on this page?

3 The number of books on 27 of the shelves in a college library:

35	42	43	31	27	39	30	45	37
33	36	26	30	29	38	36	34	43
23	35	43	34	30	26	37	44	37

21–25, 26–30, 31–35, 36–40 ...

10.5 Discrete and continuous data

So far we have considered numbers of objects: items which can be **counted**, e.g. test marks, tomatoes, words, and books. If data has been counted, then the values are **discrete** – they can be only whole numbers. (In the examples above, there are no half-marks, and no half-tomatoes!)

The groupings are quite arbitrary: it is normal to have between six and ten groups. In question 3 of exercise 5 we could just as easily have chosen our groups as 20–23, 24–27, 28–31, ...

Discrete = countable
Continuous = measurable

If, however, the information has been **measured**, then there must have been some degree of approximation, depending on the accuracy of the measuring instrument, whether it be a stopwatch, a set of weighing scales or a ruler. If data has been measured, then the values are **continuous** – they can have *any* values (within a certain range).

Example   The ages of people taking out a policy with an insurance company is shown. Make up a suitable grouped frequency table.

34	42	19	26	30	23	18	20	53	38
23	27	49	29	34	36	19	22	45	31
20	20	28	29	22	24	19	26	40	38

Firstly, we need to identify exactly what each figure represents. The range of ages for anyone aged '34' will be any age from the day of their 34th birthday up to the day before their 35th birthday. We can use inequality signs to help us here:

$34 \leqslant$ age < 35 will mean anyone aged 34.

We can now choose groupings (between about 6 and 10 is suitable).

Age (y)	$15 \leqslant y < 20$	$20 \leqslant y < 25$	$25 \leqslant y < 30$	$30 \leqslant y < 35$
Tally	IIII	HHI III	HHI I	IIII
Frequency	4	8	6	4

Age (y)	$35 \leqslant y < 40$	$40 \leqslant y < 45$	$45 \leqslant y < 50$	$50 \leqslant y < 55$
Tally	III	II	II	I
Frequency	3	2	2	1

Along the horizontal axis the scale is continuous, so we can mark it quite easily.

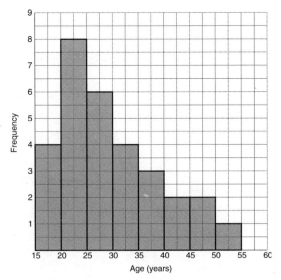

Exercise 6

For each set of data, decide on your groupings, make up a tally table, and complete the frequency column. State whether or not the information is discrete or continuous. (A possible grouping is suggested for question 1.)

1 The amount £A spent in a supermarket by customers passing through a particular till.

£15.76 £52.63 £24.53 £8.92 £16.02 £10.70 £33.57 £19.46
£12.72 £21.80 £40.52 £28.88 £36.63 £13.29 £2.99 £18.49
£38.62 £42.73 £31.74 £11.24 £14.80 £20.66 £17.04 £36.29
£10.63 £18.20 £6.46 £16.33 £29.05 £25.81 £58.31 £22.77
£45.62 £38.01 £10.42 £18.62 £33.38 £28.01 £5.74 £44.77

£0 ≤ A < £10, £10 ≤ A < £20, £20 ≤ A < £30, ...

2 The weights, in kilograms, of baskets of raspberries picked at a 'pick-your-own' fruit farm.

2.32 0.67 1.62 1.95 0.79 1.21 2.31 1.98
1.58 1.53 1.83 1.42 2.70 1.20 1.58 1.87
2.88 1.03 1.16 0.80 1.44 1.35 2.20 2.35
1.79 1.76 1.09 1.59 0.82 2.34 2.67 1.92
0.83 1.43 1.71 1.18 1.22 1.88 2.61 1.43

3 The duration of films, in minutes, on video from a video-hire shop.

93   106 104 89   92   90   115 89
111 126 96   98   100 102 120 114
100 91   123 110 81   87   102 93
96   105 85   91   109 99   100 86
90   128 116 97   92   119 113 88

10.6 Mode and median

In the year 1583, Pope Gregory instructed that 5th October should become 15th October, thus losing ten days.

The mode and the median of a set of numerical data are measures of a single average value. They are usually, but not always, central values, i.e. somewhere in the middle of the range of numbers.

The **mode** is easiest to work out – it is the most popular, or frequently occurring value in the set of data.

The **median** requires the figures to be written in order – it is the middle value when the figures are written in order of size.

Example In its first eleven games in a season, a rugby team scored these points: 15, 12, 20, 8, 12, 16, 14, 17, 23, 16, 12. What is (a) the mode (or modal number of points) (b) the median?

(a) We can see, by merely looking at the figures, that the mode is 12 points, because 12 occurs more often than any other number of points (12 occurs three times).

If there is an even number of figures, then the median is halfway between the middle two numbers.

(b) To find the median, we first put the numbers in order:

8, 12, 12, 12, 14, 15, 16, 16, 17, 20, 23

The median is 15 points, because it is the middle value.

Exercise 7

In questions 1 to 7, work out the mode, and the median, of each set of figures.

1 3, 4, 4, 4, 5, 6, 6, 8, 9

2 13, 15, 20, 13, 16, 15, 18, 13, 12

3 8, 5, 6, 6, 4, 7, 7, 4, 7, 5, 6, 7

4 52, 51, 53, 66, 55, 46, 51, 52, 51

5 4, 8, 5, 8, 8, 5, 6, 8, 6

6 24, 24, 24, 27, 29, 29, 32, 35

7 4, 7, 8, 8, 11, 11, 11, 14, 15

8 Students were asked to estimate the height of the college sports hall, in metres. Their guesses were:

14, 13, 11, 13, 16, 15, 15, 12, 13, 12, 16, 14, 14, 15, 13

(a) What is the modal guess at the height?

(b) Work out the median guess at the height.

9 In a test out of 20, the marks for a class of 22 students were:

8, 15, 14, 17, 10, 6, 9, 16, 16, 15, 20, 10, 15, 18, 3, 12, 16, 17, 12, 19, 9, 16.

Find (a) the modal mark (b) the median mark.

10 A student says that she has solved the problem of writing down seven whole numbers, from 3 to 9 inclusive, which have a mode of 4 and a median of 6. Work out her seven numbers.

10.7 Mode and median for grouped data

Example The mass of apples produced by each tree in an orchard is recorded. The table shows the result for 50 apple trees:

Weight of apples (kg)	0–9.9	10–19.9	20–29.9	30–39.9	40–49.9
Number of trees	4	11	18	10	7

(a) What is the modal mass? (b) Work out the median mass.

(a) We cannot say exactly what the mode is here, because we have a **range** of masses for each group, and do not have the mass of apples produced by each individual tree. What we can say is that the **modal group** is the most popular, which is the 20–29.9 kg group.

(b) As there are 50 trees, the median mass will be midway between the mass of apples produced by the 25th and 26th trees, when put in order. There is a broad 'order' already – the lightest 15 masses are under 20 kg (4 + 11). As with the mode, we do not know the mass of apples produced by any individual tree; all we can say for certain is that the median mass is between 20 kg and 29.99 kg.

Mass (kilograms)

However, we can make an assumption that the 18 trees in the 20–29.9 kg group are more or less evenly distributed throughout this range.

Hence the mass increase per tree $= \frac{10}{18}$ ⟵ *Mass in range 20–29.9.*

⟵ *Number of trees in range.*

As we need the mass halfway between the 25th and 26th mass, and as there are 15 masses below 20 kg, we need

$\frac{10}{18} \times 10.5$ ⟵ *25.5 – 15*

$= 5.8$ kg approximately

We can estimate, therefore, that the median mass is about 25.8 kg. Bear in mind, however, that this is only an approximation to the median mass.

COLLECTING AND PROCESSING

Exercise 8   State the modal group, and estimate the median value, in each case.

1 The heights of 35 saplings in a market garden nursery.

Height of saplings (mm)	0–99	100–199	200–299	300–399	400–499
Number of saplings	2	10	12	9	2

2 The lengths of cable bought in a DIY shop.

Length of cable (m)	0–1.99	2–3.99	4–5.99	6–7.99	8–9.99
Number bought	12	15	8	5	3

3 The points scored by a snooker player in the 11 frames in a competition.

Score	0–19	20–39	40–59	60–79	80–99	100–119
Number of frames	3	0	2	4	1	1

4 The amount of money taken daily (Monday–Friday) over the counter in a college bookshop during a period of six weeks.

Money taken	£0–£29.99	£30–59.99	£60–89.99	£90–£119.99	£120–£149.99
Number of days	3	6	10	7	4

10.8 Bar graphs

The highest recorded temperature in the shade was 58°C, in Libya in 1922.

A **bar graph**, or **block graph**, gives a picture of a set of data which has been collected. It does not matter whether or not there is a gap between the blocks.

Example   Draw a bar graph for the colours of cars in Walker's Garage (see the example in section 10.3)

Colour	Brown	Red	Blue	White	Green	Yellow	Grey
Number of cars	4	10	7	2	4	3	1

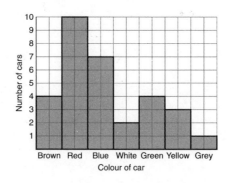

The diagram gives a clearer picture of the information than the figures in the table. Sometimes it is more convenient to draw a block graph 'on its side'.

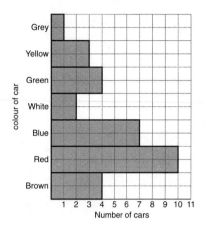

Exercise 9

Draw a block graph for the data in each question. Choose a suitable scale, and decide which way you wish to draw the diagram.

1 The number of horses, diary cattle, beef cattle and sheep on a large collection of Russian farms.

Animal	Horses	Dairy cattle	Beef cattle	Sheep
Number	500	1100	1600	4600

2 The daily takings, over a week, on a stall in a market (taken to the nearest £).

Day	Monday	Tuesday	Wednesday	Thursday	Friday	Saturday
Takings	£45	£76	£26	£68	£88	£136

How much money did the stall take in the week?

3 The number of players in different sections of an orchestra.

Section	String	Brass	Woodwind	Percussion
Number of players	40	12	18	6

How many players are there in the orchestra?

4 The results of an assignment given to a group of students.

Result	Distinction	Credit	Pass	Fail
Number of students	8	19	15	6

How many students did not fail?

5 The annual sulphur dioxide emissions from factories and power stations during the 1980s (in millions of tonnes).

Country	UK	Spain	West Germany	Italy	France	Belgium
SO$_2$ emission	3.9	2.5	2.2	2.1	1.5	0.6

10.9 Frequency diagrams for discrete data

A **frequency diagram** is a particular type of bar graph. The vertical scale shows the **frequency** with which each value occurs.

Example Draw a frequency diagram of scores when two dice are thrown 100 times.

Score	2	3	4	5	6	7	8	9	10	11	12
Frequency	3	7	5	8	13	24	16	13	6	3	2

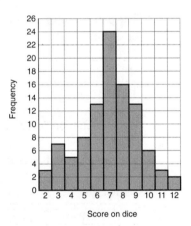

Score on dice

The mode is very easy to see from a frequency diagram – it is the highest bar. In this case the mode is 7, as 7 occurs more often than any other score.

The median is obtained by working out the average of the 50th and 51st score when placed in order. Adding the frequencies, there are 36 (3 + 7 + 5 + 8 + 13) scores of 6 or below. The 50th and 51st scores are both 7, as there are 24 scores of 7 – hence the median is 7.

Exercise 10   Draw a bar graph of the information. Work out the mode and the median in each case.

1 The number of hits on a target by 39 marksmen each firing six shots.

Number of hits	0	1	2	3	4	5	6
Frequency	1	3	4	10	8	9	4

2 The number of no-score draws during a football season of 41 weeks.

Number of no-score draws	3	4	5	6	7	8
Frequency	7	13	8	5	6	2

3 The number of GCSEs gained by students beginning a course of further education.

Number of GCSEs	4	5	6	7	8	9	10	11
Number of students	2	5	8	16	19	11	7	1

4 The number of faulty packets per minute produced by a packaging machine, in a one-hour period.

Number of faulty packs per minute	0	1	2	3	4	5	6	7
Frequency	23	2	9	6	10	6	3	1

10.10   Frequency diagrams for grouped data

Example   Draw a frequency diagram for the information in exercise 8, question 4.

Money taken	£0–£29.99	£30–59.99	£60–£89.99	£90–£119.99	£120–£149.99
Number of days	3	6	10	7	4

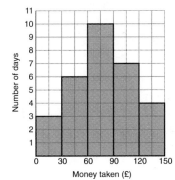

There is no problem in deciding where to draw the bars, as the information is given to the nearest penny (i.e. the fourth or fifth significant figure).
The mode or modal group is the £60–£89.99 group.
The median can be calculated in the same way as before.

Example   The times (to the nearest minute) taken by students to complete a piece of homework is given in the table. Draw a frequency diagram.

Time taken (min)	5–9	10–14	15–19	20–24	25–29	30–34
No. of students	2	5	6	5	5	1

Every snowflake is hexagonal in form.

In this case the bars are drawn at 9.5 min, 14.5 min, 19.5 min, etc. because the two students in the 5–9 min column could have taken up to 9.5 minutes. Similarly, the 5 students in the 10–14 min column could have taken any time between 9.5 and 14.5 minutes.

Exercise II   Draw a frequency diagram for each of questions 1, 2 and 3 of exercise 8.

10.11   Mean value

The mode and median provide a simple type of average measure for a set of data. However neither take into account all of the data. The mode looks at the most popular value, and the median looks at the middle one, when put in order.

When people talk about the 'average value' of a set of numerical data, they are usually referring to the **mean** value (more correctly, the arithmetic mean).

The **mean** value of a set of N numbers is calculated by *adding* the numbers, and *dividing* this total by N.

Example   Find the mean value of
          (a) 3, 6, 7, 8   (b) 24, 25   (c) 2, 4, 4, 5, 5, 6, 7, 9.

(a)   mean value is $(3 + 6 + 7 + 8) \div 4 = \frac{24}{4} = 6$
(b)   mean value is $(24 + 25) \div 2 = 24.5$
(c)   mean value is $(2 + 4 + 4 + 5 + 5 + 6 + 7 + 9) \div 8 = \frac{42}{8} = 5.25$

COLLECTING AND PROCESSING

Example Two dice were thrown, and the higher score noted (if both dice showed the same number, then that number was noted).
The frequency table shows the results of 100 throws of the two dice. What was the mean score?

Score	1	2	3	4	5	6
Frequency	4	7	14	22	25	28

The frequency table shows that there were 4 ones, 7 twos, 14 threes, 22 fours, 25 fives and 28 sixes.

The total of the 100 scores was

$$(4 \times 1) + (7 \times 2) + (14 \times 3) + (22 \times 4) + (25 \times 5) + (28 \times 6)$$
$$= 4 + 14 + 42 + 88 + 125 + 168 = 441$$

The mean score is therefore $\frac{441}{100} = 4.41$.

In general, to work out the mean value from a frequency table:

1 Multiply each value by its frequency.
2 Add these numbers.
3 Divide this total by the sum of the frequencies.

Exercise 12

1 My gas bills for the last four quarters were £121.53, £142.74, £85.39 and £124.06. What was my average quarterly bill?

2 The eight forwards in a rugby side weigh 103 kg, 104 kg, 96 kg, 88 kg, 98 kg, 104 kg, 98 kg and 107 kg. What is the mean weight?

3 Sandra sat six tests and Tracey sat seven tests. Their percentage scores were:

Sandra	64	72	66	38	49	60	
Tracey	47	49	86	71	36	50	56

Who has the higher mean score?

4 An office thermometer was read at 9.00 a.m. each day for a week.
The temperatures, in °C, were 16, 19, 14, 14, 10, 13, 12.
What was the mean temperature over the week?

5 The number of winning horses backed by a gambler each day, over a period of 24 days, is shown.
Calculate the mean number of winners per day.

Number of winners	0	1	2	3	4	5
Number of days	8	7	6	2	0	1

233

6 Mrs Hunter noted the number of minutes that the 0745 train was late in arriving at the station, over a a period of 20 days. She claimed that the train was over three minutes late every day, on average.

Minutes late	0	1	2	3	4	5	6
Number of days	6	3	2	0	1	5	3

(a) Calculate the mean number of minutes late per day.

(b) Was Mrs Hunter correct in her claim?

7 A pigeon fanciers' club has 23 members. The frequency table shows the number of pigeons that these members have.

Number of pigeons	9	10	14	15	16	17	18	20	21
Number of members	3	2	3	5	1	2	3	2	2

What is the mean number of pigeons per member?

8 The table shows the number of students enrolled in science classes at a college.

Number of students in class	12	13	14	15	16	17	18
Number of classes		2	3	2	5	4	3	1

Work out the mean class size (average number of students per class).

10.12   Mean value of grouped data

Example   Find the mean daily takings at the college bookshop in exercise 8, question 4.

Money taken	£0–£29.99	£30–£59.99	£60–£89.99	£90–£119.99	£120–£149.99
Number of days	3	6	10	7	4

The frequency diagram is drawn in the first example of section 10.10.
We can only *estimate* the mean value, because we do not know each value; we only know the limits within which each value lies. The only reasonable assumption to make is that each value is in the *centre* of its range; in this case these central values are £15, £45, £75, £105 and £135.
These **mid-interval** values can be shown in an extra row in the table:

Money taken	£0–£29.99	£30–£59.99	£60–£89.99	£90–£119.99	£120–£149.99
Mid value	£15	£45	£75	£105	£135
Number of days	3	6	10	7	4

The best estimate of the mean value is:

$[(3 \times £15) + (6 \times £45) + (10 \times £75) + (7 \times £105) + £4 \times £135)] \div 30$

$= (£45 + £270 + £750 + £735 + £540) \div 30$

$= £2340 \div 30 = £78$

Exercise 13

Find the best estimate of the mean value for these grouped data.

1   The lengths of cable bought in an electrical wholesale shop.

Length (m)	0–4.99	5–9.99	10–14.99	15–19.99	20–24.99
Mid value (m)	2.5	7.5	12.5	17.5	22.5
Frequency	3	6	12	4	5

2   The number of free-range eggs laid by a farmer's hens.

Number of eggs	10–14	15–19	20–24	25–29	30–34
Mid value	12	17	22	27	32
Number of hens	4	7	6	9	7

3   The points scored by a snooker player in the eleven frames of a competition.

Score	0–9	10–19	20–29	30–39	40–49	50–59	60–69
Mid value	4.5	14.5	24.5	34.5	44.5	54.5	64.5
Number of frames	3	1	0	3	1	2	1

4   The number of faulty components in each batch of 100.

Number of faulty components	0–1	2–3	4–5	6–7	8–9	10–11
Mid value	0.5	2.5	4.5	6.5	8.5	10.5
Number of batches	8	5	0	1	1	2

10.13 Range

The **range** of a set of figures is: (highest value) − (lowest value). For example, when two dice are thrown and the highest score is 12 and the lowest is 2, then the range of scores is $12 - 2 = 10$.

If a machine is filling cans with lemonade, the manufacturer will want the range to be as small as possible, so that (a) there is the stated volume in the can (440 ml, say) but (b) there is as little extra as possible.

Exercise 14

These questions require you to understand the mean and the range of a set of numerical information.

1 My first three telephone bills this year were £89.67, £95.62 and £107.94. If I want my mean telephone bill for the year to be under £100, what is the maximum amount that I can allow my fourth bill to be?

2 Dean's scores in his last ten innings were: 68, 2, 19, 126, 51, 88, 5, 17, 62, and 103. Ian's last seven innings were: 46, 27, 1, 133, 94, 50 and 74.

   (a) What is the range of each batsman's scores?

   (b) Which batsman had the better average (i.e. mean score per innings)? (*Note:* Both batsmen were 'out' in every innings.)

3 In her last six rounds of golf, Betty's scores were 81, 83, 84, 79, 77, and 82. Moira has played eight rounds recently, with scores of 74, 73, 92, 81, 74, 93, 88 and 73.

   (a) Work out the mean score per round for each lady.

   (b) What is the range for each lady?

   (c) Which lady is the more consistent?

   (d) The golf club has one place left in the team to play in a tournament. Which lady would you choose? Why?

4 The average (mean) attendance for the first five days of a six-day tennis tournament was 743. The average attendance for the whole six days was 750. How many people attended the tournament on the last day?

5 Edwin ran a market stall on Monday, Tuesday and Wednesday, and Edwina took over the stall for Thursday and Friday. Edwin's mean takings were £45.62 per day, and Edwina's mean takings were £52.32 per day.

   (a) How much did Edwin take altogether?

   (b) Work out the mean takings for the five days.

   (c) They both work on the stall on Saturday. How much, at least, will they have to take, in order to make the mean daily takings for the six days come to over £55?

Review

Mark	Tally	Frequency
0	I	1
1	III	3
2	I	
3	III	
4	ꙇꙇꙇ II	
5	ꙇꙇꙇ IIII	
6	ꙇꙇꙇ II	
7	IIII	
8	II	
9		
10	III	
	Total	

1 The tally table shows the number of marks scored in a test that was taken by 40 students. Copy and complete the table, showing the frequencies of each mark scored.

(a) What was the modal mark?

(b) The 'pass' mark was 7. How many passed the test?

(c) If you scored 3 or fewer marks, you had to resit the test. How many students had to resit?

Mark	Tally	Frequency
1–10	ꙇꙇꙇ I	6
11–20	ꙇꙇꙇ III	
21–30	ꙇꙇꙇ ꙇꙇꙇ II	
31–40	ꙇꙇꙇ ꙇꙇꙇ I	
41–50	ꙇꙇꙇ III	
	Total	

2 For a teacher-assessed piece of coursework the marks (out of 50) for a group of students are shown in the tally table.

Copy and complete the frequency column.

(a) Draw a bar chart of this information.

(b) A score of more than 30 marks was considered satisfactory. For how many students was the coursework satisfactory?

(c) A score of 15 marks or fewer was considered 'ungraded'. Estimate the number of 'ungraded' students.

3 The registration letters of 30 cars entering a seaside car park were noted. Make up a tally chart and frequency table. Draw a bar chart from this information.

H	K	A	T	D	D	E	G	Y	C
G	H	B	B	D	F	K	F	X	J
E	J	F	D	D	A	D	G	Y	H

(a) What was the modal registration letter?

(b) What was the registration letter of the oldest car?

(c) How many cars were older than 'G' registrations?

4 The opening bowler in a cricket team noted the number of wickets he had taken in each game throughout the season:

3	6	3	4	1	5	2	8	6	4	2	0
1	3	4	4	6	3	1	7	4	3	4	5
4	2	0	4	6	5	4	6	3	4	2	

Make up a tally chart, and frequency table. Draw a bar chart.

(a) In how many games did he take no wickets?

(b) What was his modal number of wickets taken per game?

(c) In how many games did he take five or more wickets?

(d) How many wickets did he take all season?

(e) What was his mean number of wickets per game?

Work out the mode, the median, the mean, and the range, for each of the sets of figures in questions 5, 6 and 7.

5 5, 7, 9, 9

6 28, 30, 30, 30, 30, 31, 34, 34, 35, 38, 43

7 14, 16, 17, 17, 18, 18, 18, 23, 30

8 Estimate the mean height of these students from the grouped frequency table. Use mid values of 155 cm, 165 cm, etc.

Height (cm)	150–160	160–170	170–180	180–190	190–200
Frequency	5	8	20	16	11

9 After applying a certain fertiliser, a fruit grower measured the total weight of apples collected from each tree in his orchard.

Weight of apples (kg)	2–4	4–6	6–8	8–10	10–12	12–14	14–16	16–18
Number of trees	4	3	6	10	10	5	6	2

(a) Draw a frequency diagram.

(b) How many apple trees were in the orchard?

(c) How many trees yielded at least 12 kilograms of apples?

(d) Using mid values of 3 kg, 5 kg, etc., estimate the mean weight of apples per tree.

10 A new process for manufacturing long-life batteries was being evaluated. Sixty of these new batteries were tested for continual use, and the number of hours that each lasted is shown in the table.

Life (hours)	0–10	10–20	20–30	30–40	40–50	50–60
Number of batteries (frequency)	12	2	4	12	20	10

(a) Draw a frequency diagram.

(b) What was the modal frequency?

(c) Estimate the median life, to the nearest hour.

(d) Using mid values of 5 h, 15 h ..., estimate the mean life of a battery.

The following questions are all taken from GCSE papers.

1 The table shows the numbers of piglets in some litters.

9	10	13	12	10	11	12	9	10	9
9	11	12	11	12	13	11	10	10	11

Calculate the mean number of piglets in a litter.   (*5 marks*)

[LEAG]

2 When Kylie went on work experience to the local junior school, she decided to find the average height of a class of eleven-year-olds. Their heights, in metres, were

1.20	1.25	1.21	1.40	1.30	1.25	1.36	1.43
1.25	1.34	1.15	1.20	1.18	1.25	1.40	1.30
1.25	1.50	1.26	1.54	1.30			

(a) Work out the mean height.   (*3 marks*)

(b) Which height occurred most often?   (*2 marks*)

(c) Find the median value of the heights.   (*3 marks*)

[LEAG]

3 Claire conducted a survey on the hourly rates of pay at 10 local stores. The rates were:

£3.90, £3.80, £3.50, £3.70, £3.50, £3.20, £3.90, £3.80, £3.50, £3.70

Find:

(a) the modal rate,   (*1 mark*)

(b) the median rate,   (*1 mark*)

(c) the mean rate,   (*2 marks*)

(d) the range.   (*1 mark*)

[SEG]

4 The eleven members of a hockey team were asked what size of boot they wore. The replies were:

3, 6, 2, 7, 6, 4, 5, 4, 6, 3, 7.

For these sizes, find

(a) the mode   (*1 mark*)

(b) the median.   (*2 marks*)

[MEG]

5 Here is part of a ferry company's price list.

Dates of Sailing	Tariff
Jan 1 – March 16	E
March 17 – June 30	D
July 1 – July 16	B
July 17 – Sept 10	C
Sept 11 – Dec 31	E

TARIFF

All fares are for single journeys unless otherwise stated.

Drivers and vehicle passengers	E	D	C	B
Adults	12.50	12.50	12.50	12.50
Children – 1st child (under 14)	FREE	FREE	FREE	FREE
Additional children	6.50	6.50	6.50	6.50
Vehicle rates				
Cars, Motorised Caravans, Minibuses and Motorcycle combinations				
Up to 4.0 m in length	22.00	33.00	49.00	59.00
Up to 4.5 m in length	22.00	40.00	59.00	67.00
Up to 5.5 m in length	22.00	43.00	61.00	70.00
Additional metres or part thereof	13.00	13.00	13.00	13.00
Caravans, Baggage Trailers				
Up to 3.0 m in length	6.50	6.50	7.50	9.50
Up to 6.0 m in length	13.00	13.00	15.00	19.00
Additional metres of part thereof	13.00	13.00	13.00	13.00
Motorcycles	11.00	12.00	14.00	15.00

(a) How much does it cost for a car of length 3.5 m to travel by this ferry on June 16th? *(2 marks)*

(b) How much does it cost for a car and trailer, each of length 4.4 m to travel by this ferry on August 20th? *(3 marks)*

(c) How much does it cost in total for a car of length 3.8 m with a driver, another adult and two children both under 14 years old to travel by this ferry on September 20th? *(4 marks)*

[LEAG]

6 Tracey is captain of the Year 10 girls athletics team.
She needs to pick her best runner for the 200 m.
The choice is between Ela and Sharon.
Here are their last few times for running 200 m.
All the times are in seconds.

Ela	29.5	32	27.5	31.5	27	29.5
Sharon	29.5	27.5	30.5	29.5	30.5	

(a) Calculate the average 200 m times for each girl. *(3 marks)*

(b) Find the range of each runner's times. *(2 marks)*

(c) Who would you pick for the race? *(2 marks)*
Give reasons for your choice. [MEG]

7 (a) Write in the totals in this tally table. *(5 marks)*

Type of Shop	Tally	Total
Clothing	ℍℍ ‖	
Electrical	‖‖	
Stationery	‖‖	
Shoe	ℍℍ ‖	
Toy	ℍℍ	

  (b) Draw a fully labelled bar chart of the results obtained. *(6 marks)*

[LEAG]

8 The table shows the results when a square spinner was spun 100 times.

  (a) What is the mode of the 100 scores? *(1 mark)*

  (b) Calculate the mean of these scores. *(2 marks)*

[MEG]

Score	Frequency
1	17
2	31
3	24
4	28

9 Foresters have loaded a trailer with 20 logs. They have estimated the average diameter of each log in centimetres and written it on the log.

  (a) Calculate the mean of the numbers written on the logs. *(3 marks)*

Each log is approximately 5 m long. A forester needs to work out an estimate, in cm³, for the volume of wood on the trailer. To do this, he assumes that all the logs have the mean diameter.

  (b) Work out his estimate, in cm³, for the volume of wood on the trailer. *(3 marks)*

The wood weighs 0.5 g per cm³. The trailer can safely carry up to 5000 kg.

  (c) Estimate the largest number of such logs that the foresters can safely load on the trailer. *(4 marks)*

[MEG]

10 The chess team at Grange Mount School plays several matches each year. Each match is either won, drawn or lost. The table shows the results for 1985 to 1989.

	Number of matches			Total number of matches played
	won	drawn	lost	
1985	9	2	1	12
1986	14	0	3	17
1987	12	4	1	
1988	10		2	16
1989	14	1		15

(a) Fill in the missing numbers in the table.   (*3 marks*)

(b) Describe the standard of the Grange Mount team compared with the other teams.   (*1 mark*)

(c) In which year was the team most successful?   (*1 mark*)

(d) How many matches did they play altogether during these years?   (*2 marks*)

(e) Calculate the mean number of matches played per year.   (*2 marks*)

(f) Mr. Rook watched one match during 1985. Calculate the probability that the team won this match. Write your answer as a fraction or a decimal.   (*2 marks*)

[SEG]

11 Each symbol represents 2 hours of sunshine during a particular day at Bournemouth.
How many hours of sunshine were there on the day represented below?

(*2 marks*)

[NEA]

12 The amount of milk bought each day for a week by the Evans' is shown in the table.

(a) Find the average (mean) number of pints bought per day.   (*2 marks*)

(b) A pint of milk costs 32 pence.
    What is the Evans' milk bill for the week?   (*2 marks*)

[NEA]

Day	Number of pints
Sunday	3
Monday	3
Tuesday	3
Wednesday	5
Thursday	5
Friday	3
Saturday	6

13 The numbers of tomatoes on 24 tomato plants is given below.

18	24	23	23	26	20	24	27
22	23	21	25	19	23	27	25
25	20	20	23	24	23	22	22

(i) Make a tally chart for the number of tomatoes per plant.   (*3 marks*)

(ii) Complete the frequency diagram below.

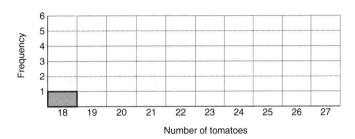

(3 marks)

(iii) What is the modal number of tomatoes per plant?   (*1 mark*)

[NEAB]

14 The diagram shows the number of pets owned by the pupils in a group.

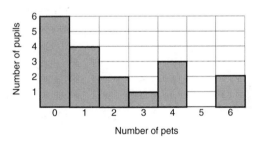

(i) How many pupils have 4 pets only?   (*1 mark*)

(ii) How many pupils have 2 pets or less?   (*2 marks*)

(iii) How many pupils are in the group?   (*2 marks*)

[NEAB]

15 The number of newspapers delivered to each of 17 houses in a street during one week is given below:

6, 0, 6, 6, 1, 0, 1, 3, 3, 0, 1, 2, 6, 5, 5, 6, 0.

(i) Complete the frequency table:

Number of newspapers	0	1	2	3	4	5	6
Frequency	4						

(3 marks)

(ii) How many houses receive 3 newspapers? *(1 mark)*

(iii) What is the model number of newspapers? *(1 mark)*

(iv) How many newspapers are delivered altogether in one week?

(2 marks)

[NEAB]

Ideas for investigations

1 When there are quite a large number of results (e.g. the marks scored in a test by 70 students, say), we have usually grouped the marks into ranges: 1 to 9, 10 to 19, 20 to 29, etc.

Choose a set of results (from one of the questions in the chapter, if you wish).
Investigate what differences occur in (a) the estimated mean value (b) the bar chart, when you change the groupings, for example, from 1 to 6, 7 to 12, 13 to 18, 19 to 24, etc. or from 1 to 8, 9 to 16, 17 to 24, etc.

2 For a set of results, there is an approximate rule which states that:

mean − mode = 3(mean − median)

Choose four or five sets of results, and investigate the accuracy of this 'rule'.

REPRESENTING AND INTERPRETING

11.1 Decision-tree diagrams

Example   There are six teams in a local badminton league. They are Grange, Swans, Whiteburn, Anglers, Wings and Old Town. Each team has a distinctive T-shirt; the diagram shows how to identify the shirts.

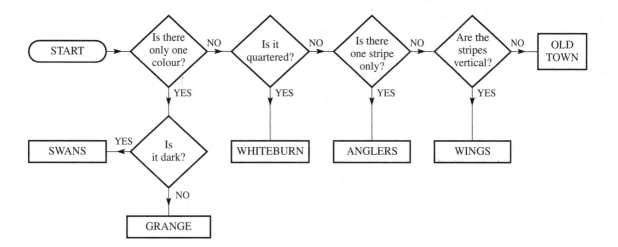

Identify which team wears these shirts:

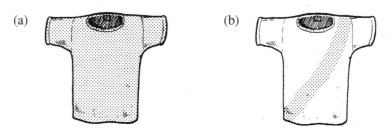

(a)

(b)

(a) This shirt belongs to the SWANS, as it is *one* colour, and it *is* dark. We follow the YES path out of the first decision box, and the YES path out of the second 'Is it dark?' box.

(b) This shirt belongs to the ANGLERS, it has more than one colour, is not quartered, and has only *one* stripe.

In a decision-tree diagram, we must make a 'YES/NO' decision at each box, and follow the path through the diagram until we reach an end point.

Exercise I

1 Photofit pictures of suspects with moustaches and/or beards are kept in boxes S, T, U and V. Use the decision-tree diagram to decide into which of the boxes each of these pictures should go.

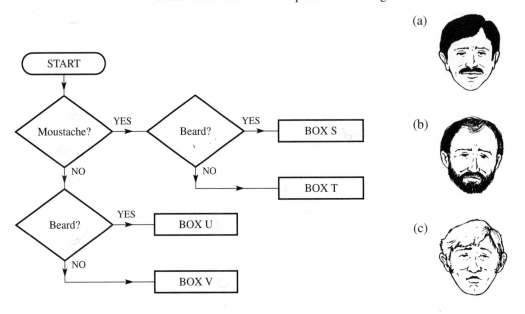

(a)

(b)

(c)

2 Pairs of jeans are hung on rails E, F, G and H, depending whether or not they have rear pockets and belts.
On which rail will these jeans be hung?

(a)

(b)

(c)

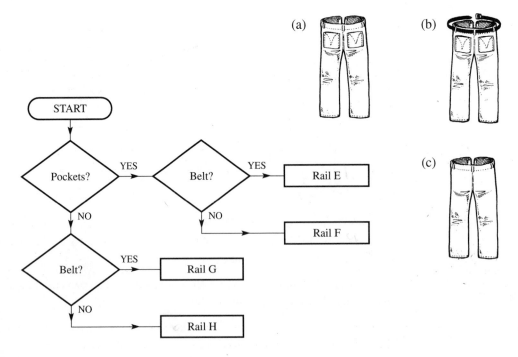

3 Use the decision-tree given in the first example to find to which team each of these shirts belong.

(a)   (b)   (c)

4 A number of circular metal discs have been found in an archeological dig. They have dark and light triangular marks on them. Which type of disc is each of these?

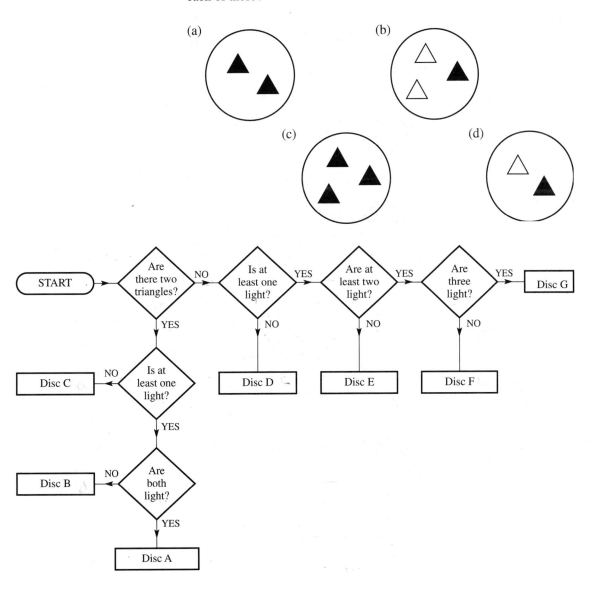

247

5   Each card in a set has three shapes on it, chosen from triangles, circles and squares. Use the decision-tree diagram to find out which type of card each of the following is.

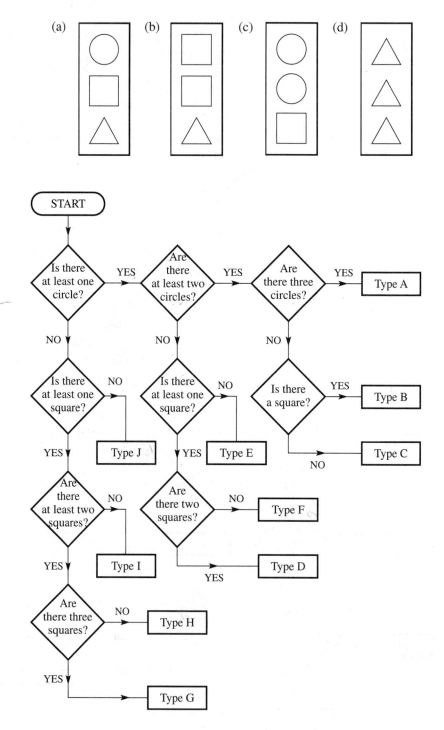

11.2 Line graphs

Example A patient's temperature is taken every two hours.

Time	0600	0800	1000	1200	1400	1600	1800	2000	2200
Temperature (°C)	39.4	39.8	37.6	38.1	37.4	37.4	37.1	36.9	36.9

(a) Plot the points on a graph.
(b) Draw a line graph.
(c) Estimate the patient's temperature at 1100 and at 1700.

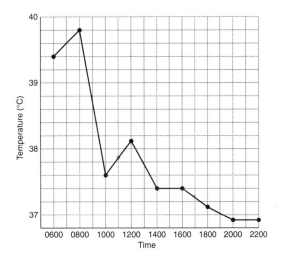

It is reasonable to join the points and complete the line graph, because the patient's temperature at intermediate times can be estimated.

(c) The patient's temperature at 1100 is estimated at 37.9° and at 1700 is 37.3°C.

In some line graphs, values along the lines themselves have no meaning; they can, however, show a trend.

Example The profits of a company are issued every three months in the company's quarterly account statement. The table shows the figures for a two-year period during 1990 and 1991.

Date	Mar 90	Jun 90	Sept 90	Dec 90	Mar 91	Jun 91	Sept 91	Dec 91
Profit (£M)	18	21	16	14	18	15	10	2

(a) Plot the points and join them to make a line graph.

(b) What can you say about the company's prospects?

(a)

(b) Any values *along* the line graph are meaningless, because the points represent profits over a three-month period, not at any one time. The June 1990 figure of £21M could mean £7M in April, £9M in May and £5M in June, for example. The **trend** however, can be seen more easily from the line graph than from either the table or just plotting the points. For example, the rate of profit over the last year has declined more and more steeply during each quarter; it would appear that the company will make a **loss** in the next quarter.

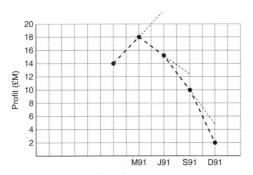

Exercise 2

1 The value of a share index at the end of trading on each day of one week is given in the table.

Day	Monday	Tuesday	Wednesday	Thursday	Friday
Share index	1788	1800	1806	1794	1790

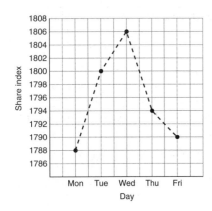

Use the graph to answer these questions;

(a) What was the lowest index? On which day?

(b) On which day was the rise from the previous day the greatest?

(c) What was the greatest fall, from one day to the next?

(d) Work out the mean index for the week.

2 The number of customers who visited 'X & Y Superstore' each day is given in the table.

Day	Mon	Tue	Wed	Thu	Fri	Sat
Number of customers	107	143	68	206	153	294

Plot these figures on a graph (similar to question 1) and join the points to form a line graph (dotted).

(a) The superstore was closed for one half-day during the week, and stayed open until 9.00 on one week night. Which was the half-day, and which night did it stay open?

(b) Why do you think Saturday had most customers?

(c) Work out the mean number of customers per *hour*, given that the store is open for 52 hours per week.

3 The temperature in a garden centre greenhouse was taken at hourly intervals, as shown in the table.

Time	0700	0800	0900	1000	1100	1200	1300	1400	1500	1600	1700	1800
Temperature (°C)	21.5	21.7	22.6	23.4	25.9	26.6	23.3	23.5	24.2	23.0	22.2	21.8

(a) Draw a line graph of the temperature through the day.

(b) Between which two times was the fall in temperature greatest?

(c) At what time, approximately, was the temperature 25°C and rising?

(d) Estimate for how long the temperature was above 25°C.

4 Andrea's savings account balance at the end of each month is given in the table.

Month	Jan	Feb	Mar	Apr	May	June	July	Aug	Sept	Oct	Nov	Dec
Balance (£)	120	91	84	101	160	252	326	69	75	195	211	72

Draw a line graph of the balance on Andrea's account.

(a) During which month did she withdraw most money?

(b) What was the increase in the balance from the end of February until the end of May?

(c) During which months did she spend more than she saved?

11.3 Pie charts

There are deep underground streams beneath some parts of the Sahara desert. People digging for fresh water have been known to catch live fish.

Example Michael has recently started to collect stamps from France, Germany, Spain and the UK. The table shows how many stamps he has. Represent this information in a pie chart.

Country	France	Germany	Spain	UK
Number of stamps	33	49	31	67

In a **pie chart**, the 'slices' of the 'pie' are in proportion to the numbers of stamps.

Michael has 180 stamps altogether. As there are 360° in one revolution, each stamp will be represented by 2°, and we can add another row to the table:

Country	France	Germany	Spain	UK
Number of stamps	33	49	31	67
Angle of sector	66°	98°	62°	134°

The pie chart can now be drawn. The order in which the sectors are drawn does not matter.

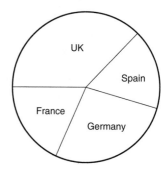

11.4 How to work out the angles in a pie chart

Example The students in a flower-arranging class were asked to state the colour of their favourite rose. Their replies are given in the table.

Colour	Red	White	Yellow	Pink
Number of replies	8	5	3	4

(a) Calculate the angles required for a pie chart.

(b) Draw a pie chart of the colours.

(a) $8 + 5 + 3 + 4 = 20$ *Finding the total number of replies.*

$\frac{360}{20} = 18$ *Dividing 360 by this total.*

Angle of sector for red   *Multiplying each value by this number*
$= 18° \times 5$ *to give the required angle.*
$= 144°$

Colour	Red	White	Yellow	Pink
Number of replies	8	5	3	4
Angle of sector	144°	90°	54°	72°

Check: total = 360°

(b) The pie chart can now be drawn

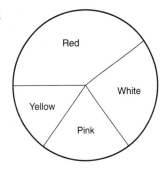

Exercise 3 For each question, calculate the required sector angles, and then draw a pie chart of the information.

1 The number of times the letters E, A, S and T occur in a paragraph from a book.

Letter	E	A	S	T
Number of occurrences	38	23	19	10

2 The number of items that are sold with chips in a fish and chip shop.

Item	Fish	Sausage	Pie	Fishcake	Spring roll
Number sold	24	26	17	32	21

3 The amount from £10 000 that is allocated to three projects and the administration in a charity.

Project	A	B	C	Administration
Money allocated	£5000	£3000	£1500	£500

4 A shop sold 90 packets of crisps in each of two weeks. The pie charts show the sales of four types of crisps for these two weeks.

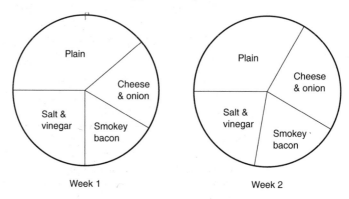

Week 1   Week 2

(a) Which was the most popular flavour over the fortnight?

(b) Which flavours had a reduction in sales?

(c) By measuring angles in the diagrams, estimate the number of packets of plain crisps that were sold each week.

5 The pie chart shows which TV channel was watched by 600 people one evening. Estimate, by measuring angles in the pie chart, the number of people who watched each channel.

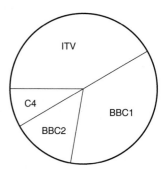

6 The number of various makes of car sold by a second-hand car dealer in a week is given in the table. Draw a pie chart of the information.

Make of car	Ford	BL	Renault	Vauxhall	Others
Number of cars sold	10	8	4	3	5

7 Stainless steel is made of 72% Iron, 19% Chromiun, 8% Nickel and 1% Carbon. Draw a pie chart to represent the proportions of each element in stainless steel.

8 A pie chart has four sectors. Three are equal, and the fourth is 50% larger than each of the other three.

(a) What are the angles of the sectors?

(b) Draw the pie chart.

11.5 Scatter graphs

If it is claimed that two *separate*, *variable* quantities are connected, then one way of testing the claim is to plot a **scatter graph**.

Example   The scores of 12 students in a Numeracy test and a Literacy test are given in the table.

Student	A	B	C	D	E	F	G	H	I	J	K	L
Numeracy score	26	18	20	17	16	10	12	22	19	19	23	18
Literacy score	18	14	15	12	10	12	7	17	14	12	15	16

Draw a scatter diagram, and from the diagram decide whether there is a connection between Numeracy score and Literacy score.

To draw a scatter graph, we take the two scores for each student as **coordinates**. (The points are identified by the letter corresponding to each student.)

As higher Numeracy scores tend to match with higher Literacy scores, there seems to be some evidence to suggest that there *is* a **correlation** between these two scores.

The first electronic computer, built in 1945, weighed 30 tonnes, filled a hall of 140 square metres, and contained over 18 000 valves.

Example   A non-golfer borrows his friend's iron clubs, from a 3-iron to a 9-iron, and hits a golf ball with each of the seven clubs. The distance travelled by the ball after each hit is measured.

Iron club used	3	4	5	6	7	8	9
Distance (metres)	85	72	90	46	26	35	28

(a) Plot the points on a scatter graph.

(b) Is there a connection between the number of the club, and the distance the ball travelled?

(a)

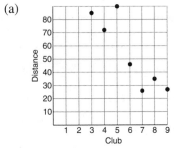

(b) From the graph, there appears to be a trend that the *higher* the number of the club used, the *shorter* the distance travelled by the ball.

There are three general types of scatter graph; they are shown below.

Positive trend

Negative trend

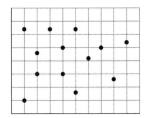

No trend

Exercise 4

1 The table shows the handicap, and the score for a round of golf, for eight golfers in a competition. Plot a scatter diagram.

Golfer	John	Ann	Matt	Rena	Judy	Henry	Shaidul	Ellen
Handicap	6	7	12	1	6	8	14	6
Score	81	84	90	75	78	77	92	83

Is there a connection between the handicap and the score for a round?

2 Two judges rate eight contestants in a 'knobbly knees' competition from 1 to 8. Plot a scatter graph.

Contestant	A	B	C	D	E	F	G	H
Judge X	1	2	3	4	5	6	7	8
Judge Y	6	2	5	7	8	1	4	3

Do the judges have similar opinions?

3 The table states the marks scored in a science assignment (out of 50) and a technology assignment (out of 40) by 11 students.

Student	A	B	C	D	E	F	G	H	I	J	K
Science	42	28	40	44	30	37	42	38	33	37	45
Technology	33	26	32	29	20	24	26	26	26	30	35

Draw a scatter diagram. Does your diagram suggest that there is a link between science marks and technology marks?

4 The heights and weights of seven junior badminton players are given in the table. Draw a scatter graph.

Player	Amanda	Sally	Jim	Donna	Cliff	Suzy	Harry
Height (cm)	152	144	158	168	150	139	148
Weight (kg)	44	43	48	49	45	40	43

For these players, does taller mean heavier, in general?

11.6   Line of best fit

Look again at the scatter diagram in the previous example.

A '**trend**' line is drawn on the graph, so that it passes close to as many points as possible. This is called the **line of best fit**.

We can use the line to help us with further estimates.

Example   A student scored 24 marks in the Numeracy test. What mark would the student expect to score in the Literacy test?

From the 'line of best fit' we can estimate that the student would score about 18 marks in the Literacy test.

Exercise 5

1 The marks scored by ten students in Papers 1 and 2 of a mathematics examination are shown.

Student	1	2	3	4	5	6	7	8	9	10
Paper 1	35	56	87	43	52	94	23	35	48	56
Paper 2	43	69	72	62	51	88	24	40	40	60

(a) Draw a scatter diagram.
(b) Draw the line of best fit.
(c) Maria scored 60 marks on Paper 1, but was ill for Paper 2. What mark might she have been expected to score on Paper 2?
(d) Daniel's Paper 1 script is missing. He scored 57 on Paper 2. What is his Paper 1 mark likely to have been?

2 The mass of eleven paperbacks, and the number of pages in each, is given in the table.

Number of pages	79	90	100	104	116	127	140	140	148	158	166
Mass (g)		158	180	180	202	232	263	265	291	320	330	349

(a) Draw a scatter diagram and line of best fit.
(b) A paperback has 135 pages. What is its likely mass?
(c) Another paperback has a mass of 190 g. How many pages is it likely to have?

3 On Sports Day there were nine competitors who had entered for both the men's 100 m race and the long jump. Their times and distances are given in the table.

100 m (time in seconds)	12.3	12.3	12.5	12.6	12.9	13.4	13.7	13.7	14.3
Long jump (length in metres)	6.03	5.95	5.40	4.93	5.04	4.69	4.66	4.12	3.87

(a) Draw a scatter diagram and line of best fit.
(b) Sean ran the 100 m in 13.1 s. If he had entered the long jump, how far might he have been expected to jump?

The Romans built the first known road tunnel in 36 BC. It was near Naples, and was nearly a mile long (about 1600 m).

4 Ten members of 'Weightwatchers' have been following a diet. The number of kilograms lost over various periods of time is shown in the table.

Number of weeks	3	4	5	7	7	8	8	10
Weight loss	6	6	8	9	12	15	14	16

(a) Draw a scatter graph, and the line of best fit.
(b) Does this diet seem useful, if you wish to lose a specific number of kilograms?
(c) About how many weeks would it take Susan to get her weight down from 65 kg to 52 kg?

11.7 Cumulative frequency

Example Make up a cumulative frequency table from the group frequency table, which gives the marks scored by 80 students in an examination, in groups of ten marks.

Mark	0–9	10–19	20–29	30–39	40–49	50–59	60–69	70–79	80–89	90–99
Frequency	2	4	9	13	20	14	8	6	3	1

Cumulative frequency means the frequency of that group **together** with any lower group. It gives the 'running total'. The cumulative frequency for the 10–19 group is therefore 6, as there are 6 (2 + 4) students whose marks were in the 10–19 group or any lower group (i.e. those who scored 19 or fewer). Similarly, there are 15 (2 + 4 + 9) students who scored 29 marks or fewer. The complete cumulative frequency row is added to the bottom of the table:

Mark	0–9	10–19	20–29	30–39	40–49	50–59	60–69	70–79	80–89	90–99
Frequency	2	4	9	13	20	14	8	6	3	1
Cumulative frequency	2	6	15	28	48	62	70	76	79	80

This confirms that there were 80 students who took the examination, because all 80 students scored 99 marks or fewer.

Example From the frequency table, which shows the heights (to the nearest centimetre) of tomato plants in a market garden, (a) make up a cumulative frequency row (b) draw the cumulative frequency diagram.

Height (cm)	0–4	5–9	10–14	15–19	20–24	25–29
Frequency	1	4	10	19	12	4

(a) A row for the cumulative frequency has been added:

Height (cm)	0–4	5–9	10–14	15–19	20–24	25–29
Frequency	1	4	10	19	12	4
Cumulative frequency	1	5	15	34	46	50

(b) The cumulative frequency scale is drawn on the *vertical* axis, as it is in a frequency diagram.

The figure 34 in the cumulative frequency row represents those plants whose heights were in the 15–19 group or any lower group. We can only be sure that the *tallest* of any of these 34 plants is 19 cm, to the nearest centimetre.

On the cumulative frequency diagram, we have to mark the cumulative frequency of 34 at *19.5 cm*, because any plant whose height is *19.5 cm or less* will be included in the figure of 34.

The complete cumulative frequency diagram is drawn.

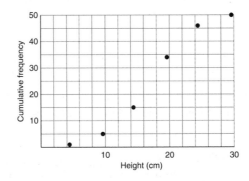

There are only two types of regular polygon that you can make using rubber bands round the pins on a rectangular pin-board: squares and octagons.

The points can be joined, either by straight lines to make a cumulative frequency polygon, or by a smooth curve to make a **cumulative frequency curve**.

Exercise 6   For each frequency table:

(a) Make a cumulative frequency row.

(b) Draw a cumulative frequency diagram.

(c) State the sum of the frequencies (the last number in the cumulative frequency row).

(The next exercise will require you to extract some information from these cumulative frequency diagrams.)

1 A radar speed detector measured the speeds of 100 cars moving along a road, to the nearest km/h.

Speed	0–9	10–19	20–29	30–39	40–49	50–59	60–69	70–79
Number of cars	1	4	11	27	38	12	4	3
Cumulative frequency								

2 A market gardener has Christmas trees for sale. He classifies them by height: less than 4 feet, from 4 to 5 feet, from 5 to 6 feet, etc.

Height (feet)	up to 4	4 to 5	5 to 6	6 to 7	7 to 8	8 to 9
Number of trees	4	8	15	22	18	14
Cumulative frequency						

These points will have to be plotted at 4 ft, 5 ft, 6 ft etc. Why?

3 At a 'Guess the weight of the cake' stall at a Fayre, the range of guesses was noted. (Each guess was to the nearest gram.)

Weight (g)	450–499	500–549	550–599	600–649	650–699
Frequency	5	10	22	18	11
Cumulative frequency					

Why does it make little difference whether the points are marked at (a) 499.5, 549.5, 599.5, etc. or (b) 500, 550, 600, etc.?

4 The amount spent by a group of students on cassettes, albums or CDs in a month.

Amount	0–£4.99	£5–9.99	£10–£14.99	£15–19.99	£20–24.99	£25–29.99
Frequency	4	7	18	12	7	3

Why does it make little difference whether the points are marked at (a) £4.99. £9.99, £14.99, etc or (b) £5, £10, £15, etc.?

11.8 Median value from a cumulative frequency diagram

Example Estimate the median height of tomato plants in the previous example.

The **median value** is the halfway value, when the heights are put in order. In this case it is the height midway between the heights of the 25th and 26th tomato plant. The cumulative frequency scale puts the heights in order, so we can estimate the median by drawing a line across from 25.5 mark on the cumulative frequency scale until it meets the graph, and then read off the value on the horizontal axis.

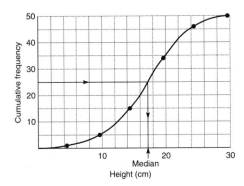

In this case the **median height** is approximately 17 cm.

In many cases, as the values will be approximate, it is reasonable to take the halfway value up the cumulative frequency axis, i.e. 25 in this case.

Exercise 7

From the cumulative frequency diagrams, estimate the median value for questions 1 to 4 in exercise 6.

11.9 Quartiles, interquartile range

Another name for the median value is the **50th percentile**. If the frequency is expressed as a percentage, then the median, or halfway value, will be obtained by taking the reading on the horizontal scale which corresponds to the value that is 50% of the way up the cumulative frequency axis.

The **lower quartile** is the value of the 25th percentile.

Also, the **upper quartile** is the 75th percentile.

Example What are the upper and lower quartiles of the heights of tomato plants in the previous example?

Drawing lines across from 12.5 ($\frac{1}{4}$ of 50) and 37.5 ($\frac{3}{4}$ of 50), and down to the horizontal scale, the lower quartile is 13 cm approximately, and the upper quartile is about 21 cm.

The **interquartile range** is the range between the two quartiles, and is the difference between these two values.

For example, the interquartile range for the tomato plants is 21 cm − 13 cm = 8 cm

Exercise 8

From these cumulative frequency tables and diagrams, estimate the lower and upper quartiles. State the interquartile range in each case. (You will need to draw the cumulative frequency diagrams for questions 4 and 5.)

1 The lengths of metal rods in a batch, measured to the nearest centimetre, was recorded.

Length (cm)	8	9	10	11	12	13	14	15
Cumulative frequency	14	50	105	187	267	328	362	372

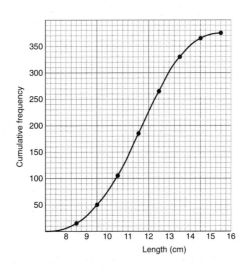

2 The value of each of the houses in a village was estimated by an estate agent, to the nearest £1000.

Value (£1000)	up to 40	40 up to 60	60 up to 80	80 up to 100	100 up to 120	120 up to 140	140 up to 160
Cumulative frequency	6	13	29	43	54	60	64

3 A library issued fines for overdue books. The cumulative frequency of each range of fines is given in the table.

Fine (pence)	0–39	40–79	80–119	120–159	160–199	200–239
Cumulative frequency	8	14	25	49	67	76

4 The tomatoes collected from each plant in a greenhouse were weighed, to the nearest 0.1 kg. The table shows the cumulative frequency of weights.

Weight (kg)	1.7 up to 1.9	1.9 up to 2.1	2.1 up to 2.3	2.3 up to 2.5	2.5 up to 2.7	2.7 up to 2.9
Cumulative frequency	3	11	21	34	36	37

5 The length of telephone calls from the students' telephone was recorded over a period of a fortnight.

Length (min)	0 up to 1	1 up to 2	2 up to 3	3 up to 4	4 up to 5	5 up to 6	6 up to 7	7 up to 8	8 up to 9	9 up to 10
Cumulative frequency	5	22	54	92	123	147	170	188	197	202

Review

1 Children who enter a play park are given a badge to help to identify them. The decision-tree diagram shows how to identify which badge belongs to which group.

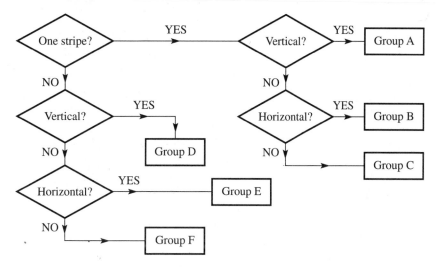

Three children are brought to the 'Lost Children' room. There badges are:

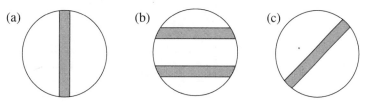

(a)   (b)   (c)

To which group does each child belong?

2 The line graph shows the money taken in the college bookshop on each day of a week.

(a) On which day were the takings the highest?

(b) What were the takings on Friday?

(c) On which days were the takings greater than £50?

(d) How much was taken altogether in the week?

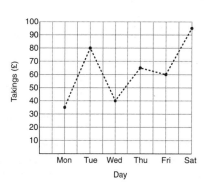

3 The table shows the number of copies made by a photocopier on each day during a week.

Day	Mon	Tue	Wed	Thu	Fri
Number of copies	138	154	86	208	134

(a) Draw a line graph of this information.

(b) How many copies were made on Tuesday and Wednesday?

(c) On which day was there a fault that prevented the use of the machine for three hours?

(d) How many copies were made in the week?

4 The pie chart shows the distribution of the 36 'A' level grades (A,B,C,D and E) gained by a group of students.

By measuring the angles, estimate the number of each grade obtained.

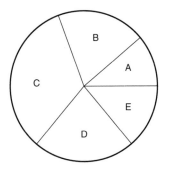

5 A pie chart is to be drawn to show the number of photocopies in question 3. Copy and complete the table which shows the angles for each sector in the pie chart.

Day	Mon	Tue	Wed	Thu	Fri	Total
Number of copies	138	154	86	208	134	
Angle	69°				67°	360°

Draw the pie chart, labelling each sector (Mon, Tue, etc.).

6 The ages of the 24 members of an under-25 athletics team are shown in the table. Copy and complete the table to show the angles required for each sector of a pie chart.

Age	19	20	21	22	23	24
Number of athletes	6	3	2	4	4	5
Angle	90°					

(a) Draw the pie chart.

(b) What fraction of the students are aged 22 or 23?

7 The height and weight of ten of the athletes in question 6 are shown in the table.

Height (cm)	163	167	170	170	175	178	180	183	185	187
Weight (kg)	65	68	69	73	72	75	79	80	84	88

(a) Draw a scatter graph.

(b) Draw in a line of best fit.

(c) Another athlete joins the team. She is 173 cm tall. Estimate her weight from the graph.

(d) John, a reserve athlete, weighs 82 kg. How tall is he likely to be?

8 The girth (circumference) and height of a set of eight conifer trees is shown.

Girth (cm)	25	26	28	30	32	32	35	36
Height (cm)	220	240	270	275	290	305	320	340

(a) Draw a scatter graph and line of best fit.

(b) Another tree is 300 cm high. What is its likely girth?

(c) How tall will a tree be, which has a girth of 27 cm?

9 The table shows the scores gained by a group of 50 students in a test. Copy the table and complete the cumulative frequency row.

Score	0–10	11–20	21–30	31–40	41–50	51–60	61–70	71–80	81–90	91–100
Frequency	1	3	4	6	10	8	6	5	4	3
Cumulative frequency	1	4	8	*	*	*	*	*	*	*

(a) Draw a cumulative frequency curve.

(b) Estimate the median score.

(c) Estimate the lower and upper quartiles.

10 The weights of boxes of waste paper returned to a pulp mill over a ten-week period are shown in the frequency table.

Weight (kg)	0–20	20–40	40–60	60–80	80–100	100–120	120–140
Frequency	5	18	33	52	42	26	8
Cumulative frequency	5	23	*	*	*	*	*

(a) Draw a cumulative frequency curve.

(b) Estimate the median weight.

(c) Estimate the lower and upper quartiles, and the interquartile range.

Exercise 10 The following questions are all taken from GCSE papers.

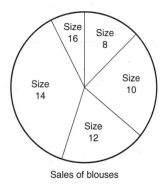

Sales of blouses

1 A shop sells a certain type of blouse in five sizes. The sales for one month are illustrated in pie chart.

   (a) Which size was the mode?   (*1 mark*)

   (b) (i) Measure the angle for size 10.   (*2 marks*)

        (ii) The total number of blouses sold during the month was 150. Calculate the number of size 10 blouses which were sold.
                                                                         (*2 marks*)
                                                                         [SEG]

2 All pupils in 5N took Mathematics. Their results are shown in the table below.

Grade	C	D	E	F
Number of pupils	5	12	5	2

   Using a circle of radius 6 centimetres, draw a pie chart to illustrate these results, showing clearly how you work out the angles.   (*5 marks*)
                                                                         [MEG]

3 In each of the 3 flow diagrams below, find the output result when the input number is 4.

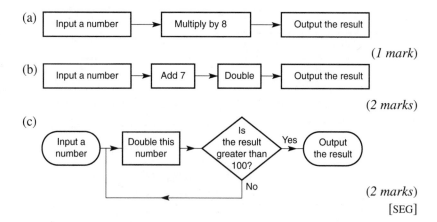

   (a)   (*1 mark*)

   (b)   (*2 marks*)

   (c)   (*2 marks*)
                                                                         [SEG]

4 Pickering's Principle gives scores for the 'Natural Environment' and 'Human Impact' of places. The scores are on a scale from 0 to 10. The table gives these scores for some places.

Situation	Natural Environment	Human Impact
Private garden	4.3	5.0
Public urban park	6.7	4.4
High density houses	1.6	8.6
Nature reserve (closed)	9.9	0.0
Playing fields	6.4	3.6
Motorway	3.7	6.6
Gravel workings (active)	5.6	3.4
Rural footpath	3.9	5.6
Private camp site	6.7	4.9
Lorry park	1.5	8.7
City open space	5.2	6.2

(a) Draw a scatter diagram of these scores. Take both axes from 0 to 10. *(6 marks)*

(b) Comment on the scatter diagram. *(2 marks)*

[MEG]

5 Use the flow chart below to classify the patterns found on these three pieces of pottery.

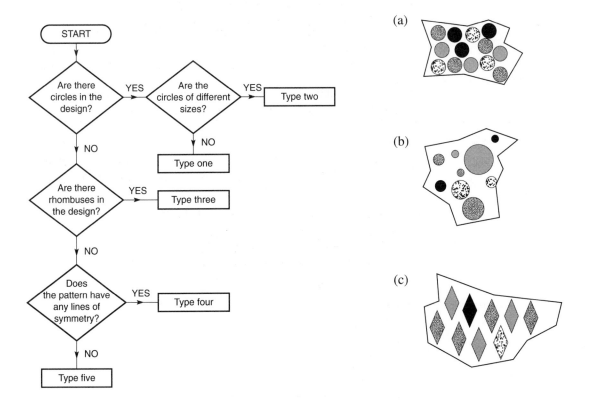

(a)

(b)

(c)

(6 marks)

[MEG]

Variety	Number of packets sold
Salt and Vinegar	64
Smoky Bacon	48
Cheese and Onion	45
Roast Chicken	23

6 A school tuck shop sells four varieties of crisps. The number of each variety sold one day last week is shown in the table.

This information is to be illustrated on a pie chart.

(a) Calculate the sizes of the angles of the four sectors in the pie chart.

(3 marks)

(b) Draw the pie chart. Label the sectors *(2 marks)*

[MEG]

7 The ages of 40 children who attend the local playgroup are shown in the histogram.

(a) Complete the table of results.

Age in years	1–2	2–3	3–4	4–5
Frequency		17	18	

(1 mark)

(b) Calculate the mean age of the children *(4 marks)*

The results can also be displayed on a pie chart.

(c) What is the angle of the sector representing the modal age group? Do not draw the pie chart. *(3 marks)*

[SEG]

8 Pieces of processed cheese are made to weigh 30 g. The table shows the weight of 30 pieces sampled during one morning's production.

```
28.3  29.6  30.8  33.2  34.0  28.8  31.7  33.1  30.9  34.1
27.6  31.3  38.8  27.4  31.7  30.0  32.1  30.8  31.4  28.6
30.1  27.8  28.0  31.7  26.7  29.9  29.9  29.8  29.2  29.6
```

(a) Complete the tally and frequency table below.

	Tally	Frequency
26.5–27.5		2
27.5–28.5		
28.5–29.5		
29.5–30.5		
30.5–31.5		
31.5–32.5		
32.5–33.5		
33.5–34.5		
Total		30

(3 marks)

(b) Complete the bar chart started for you below.

Weight of piece of cheese

(3 marks)

(c) Write down the modal weight of the pieces of cheese. *(2 marks)*

(d) The manager of the factory selects one of the 30 pieces of cheese at random to check its weight. What is the probability that he will select a piece of cheese which weighs less than 29.5g? *(2 marks)*

(e) The 30 pieces of cheese are packed into five boxes each of which holds six pieces of cheese. What is the maximum possible weight of cheese in one of these boxes? *(2 marks)*

[LEAG]

9 In a competition, 160 people successfully solved crossword puzzles in the four hours allowed. The table below shows the cumulative frequency of solving times, in minutes.

Solving time (minutes)	under 30	under 60	under 90	under 120	under 150	under 180	under 210	under 240
Cumulative frequency	0	10	36	70	106	136	154	160

(a) On graph paper draw a cumulative frequency diagram for this information. Use a scale of 1 cm to represent 20 minutes on the horizontal axis, and a scale of 1 cm to represent 10 people on the vertical axis. *(7 marks)*

(b) From your diagram estimate:

   (i) the median solving time;

   (ii) the number of people who took over 200 minutes;

   (iii) the number of 'Superbrains', who took under 75 minutes.

(5 marks)

(c) The first 40% of entrants who finished were eligible to continue to the second round. What was the longest time taken to qualify for the second round? *(4 marks)*

(d) (i) Copy and complete the table below.

Solving time (minutes)	Mid-value	Frequency	Total
0 – under 30	15	0	
30 – under 60	45	10	
60 – under 90	75	26	
90 – under 120			
120 – under 150			
150 – under 180			
180 – under 210			
210 – under 240			*(2 marks)*

(ii) Calculate an estimate of the mean solving time.   *(6 marks)*

[NREB]

10 In a forest 160 trees were felled. The length of each tree trunk was measured correct to the nearest centimetre. The cumulative frequency table shows the results.

Length of tree trunk (metres)	5 m or less	6 m or less	7 m or less	8 m or less	9 m or less	10 m or less	11 m or less
Cumulative Frequency	20	32	60	96	130	154	160

(i) How many tree trunks were between 10 m and 11 m in length?

(2 marks)

(ii) From the table draw on graph paper a cumulative frequency curve. Use a vertical scale of 2 cm to 20 tree trunks and a horizontal scale of 2 cm to 1 m.   *(6 marks)*

(iii) From your diagram find the values of the upper and lower quartiles.

(4 marks)

(iv) Tree trunks which are between 7.2 m and 9.7 m in length are suitable for telegraph poles. Use your diagram to find the percentage of tree trunks which could be used to make telegraph poles.   *(6 marks)*

(v) The table shows the lengths of the 34 tree trunks which were between 8 m and 9 m long. Estimate the mean length of these 34 tree trunks, correct to the nearest centimetre.   *(6 marks)*

[NEAB]

Length (metres)	Mid-interval value	Frequency
from 8.00 to 8.10	8.05	2
from 8.10 to 8.20	8.15	0
from 8.20 to 8.30		2
from 8.30 to 8.40		6
from 8.40 to 8.50		5
from 8.50 to 8.60		3
from 8.60 to 8.70		7
from 8.70 to 8.80		4
from 8.80 to 8.90		2
from 8.90 to 9.00		3

11 A local district council has three sources of income: taxes (60%), rates (30%) and charges (10%). You are asked to represent this information by a pie chart.

(i) Calculate the angle of each sector of your chart. *(4 marks)*

(ii) Draw the pie chart, writing the words 'taxes', 'rates' and 'charges' in the appropriate sectors. *(3 marks)*

[NEAB]

12 When 30 people were asked to name their favourite fruit, 10 chose apples, 7 chose bananas, 5 chose cherries, 2 chose pears and 6 chose oranges. These choices are to be illustrated on a pie chart.

(a) Calculate the angle of the sectors representing those who chose:
(i) apples; (ii) bananas; (iii) cherries; (iv) pears; (v) oranges.

(6 marks)

(b) Complete the pie chart accurately, and label each sector. *(4 marks)*

[NEAB]

13 This pie chart represents the sales of packets of sweets in a shop during one particular day.

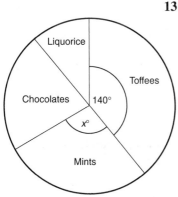

(a) 28 packets of toffees were sold during the day.
How many degrees represent 1 packet of sweets? *(2 marks)*

(b) (i) Measure and write down the size of the angle marked $x°$.

(ii) How many packets of mints were sold during the day?

(3 marks)

(c) What was the total number of packets of sweets (of all four types) sold during the day? *(2 marks)*

[NEA]

Ideas for investigations

1 Some people say a bar graph is better than a pie chart for presenting information.

By choosing examples from colour supplements, finance sections, etc. of newspapers and magazines, investigate the advantages and disadvantages of each type of diagram.

2 Investigate ways of improving the 'line of best fit' on a scatter graph, to ensure that the sum of the distances of each point from the line is the least that it can be.

PROBABILITY

12.1 Probability scales

How likely is it that these three events will happen?

A: You will find a 20p coin on the ground next week.
B: You will watch more than two hours of television next week.
C: You will buy a cassette next week.

The origins of probability came about when a French gambler started to lose money on what he thought was a winning bet.

Event A is most unlikely, while B is very likely. Event C will depend on a number of factors, and you just might buy a cassette.
We can put these events in order of likelihood, by marking their positions on a scale.

In order to express these likelihoods in mathematical terms, we can give them a number from 0 to 1. The likelihoods are then called **probabilities**.
Event A has a very small probability – possibly 0.01.
Event B has a high probability – it could be 0.95.
Event C could have a probability of between 0.4 and 0.5.

Probabilities can be expressed as percentages as well as decimals, as is shown on this scale.

The probability of event A is 1%, the probability of event B is 95%, and the probability of event C could be between 40% and 50%.

Exercise I For each of the events P, Q, R, S and T,
(a) estimate its probability (as a decimal and as a percentage)
(b) mark its letter in the appropriate place on a probability scale.

P: a coin land 'tails' when it is spun.
Q: two coins both land 'tails' when they are spun.
R: it will snow next winter somewhere in Great Britain.
S: you will back the winner of the Grand National horse race.
T: the first four cards you are dealt from a pack are all the same suit.

12.2 Certainty, impossibility

An event which is **certain** to occur has a probability of 1 (or 100%).
An event which is **impossible** has a probability of 0 (or 0%).
All other events must have a probability of between 0 and 1.

The number 0.99999... is equal to 1.

For example, the probability of 'throwing a total of 14 with two dice' is 0, because it is impossible to have a score of 14 with only two dice.

Also, the probability that 'the day of your birthday is a number less than 32' is 1, because it is certain that the day is less than 32, as the longest months have only 31 days.

12.3 Calculating probabilities

Example Four sweets, coloured red, green, brown and yellow, are wrapped in the same way so that they all look the same. If you pick one sweet, what is the probability that it is green?

On a probability scale, we might guess at between 20% and 30%. We can work out the probability accurately, by a method which uses fractions. Firstly, find out how many possible equally likely outcomes there are. In this example there are *four*, because there are four sweets to pick from. Secondly, work out how many of these are asked for in the question. In this example, we are asked for the probability of a green sweet, and there is only *one* of these.

'The probability of picking a green sweet is therefore:

$\frac{1}{4}$ *The number of ways the event can occur.*
The total number of possible outcomes.

Example The red sweet is exchanged for a green sweet. Now what is the probability that you pick a green sweet?

There are *two* ways in which the event can occur, out of a total of *four* possible outcomes.
The probability of a green sweet is $\frac{2}{4} = \frac{1}{2}$. **Simplifying the answer.**

Example Another yellow sweet is now added. What is the probability of picking (a) a green sweet (b) a brown sweet (c) a black sweet (d) either a yellow or a brown sweet?

(a) The probability of picking a green sweet $= \frac{2}{5}$ **Two green sweets. A total of five sweets.**

(b) The probability of picking a brown sweet $= \frac{1}{5}$ **One brown sweet. A total of five sweets.**

(c) The probability of picking a black sweet $= 0$ **None of the sweets is black.**

(d) The probability of picking either a yellow or a brown sweet

$= \frac{3}{5}$ **Three sweets are either yellow or brown.**

Exercise 2

1 In his bag, Colin has three similar notebooks. Two are for science and one is for technology. If he picks one notebook from his bag, what is the probability that it is (a) one of the science notebooks (b) the technology notebook?

2 Mandy has seven pieces of paper. She writes 'Monday' on one piece, 'Tuesday' on another, and so on, up to 'Sunday' on the last piece. Each piece is folded up, and then Brenda picks one of them. What is the probability that Brenda picks (a) Wednesday (b) Monday or Thursday (c) neither Saturday nor Sunday?

3 Harriet has two ordinary dice. One falls on to the floor. What is the probability that it lands showing (a) a four (b) either a two or a three (c) an odd number (d) any number except five?

4 There are five blue and seven black pens in a drawer. One pen is picked out. What is the probability that it is (a) blue (b) black (c) red (d) either black or blue?

5 Ian is playing a board game in which there are twelve counters. Three are red, four are white and five are green. He shakes the twelve counters in a cup, and then picks one out. What is the probability that it is (a) green (b) white (c) either green or red (d) not red (e) brown?

6 I buy ten raffle tickets at a village fête. Altogether there are 200 tickets sold.

(a) What is the probability that I have the winning ticket?

(b) Of the 200 tickets, how many would I need to buy to ensure that my probability of winning is greater than $\frac{1}{4}$?

7 There are 37 possible numbers on a roulette wheel (0, 1, 2, ..., 36). What is the probability that I win if I bet on:

(a) 8   (b) 12 or 13

(c) 17, 18, 19, or 20   (d) 30 or over

(e) a multiple of 3   (f) an even number?

12.4   **Estimating probabilities**

In the examples in section 12.3, we have been able to work out probabilities by knowing beforehand all the equally likely possible outcomes. There are some situations, however, where we can only make **estimates** of probabilities based upon experimental results.

P(A) is a shorthand for 'the probability of the event A occurring'.

Example   A cube has one of the three letters A, B or C on each of the six faces. You do not know how many faces are 'A's, 'B's or 'C's. The cube is thrown; the results of the first ten throws are: two 'A's, six 'B's and two 'C's.

(a) What are the **experimental** probabilities of each letter?

(b) How many faces are likely to be 'A's, 'B's or 'C's?

(a) $p(A) = \frac{2}{10} = \frac{1}{5}$, $p(B) = \frac{6}{10} = \frac{3}{5}$ and $p(C) = \frac{2}{10} = \frac{1}{5}$.

(b) As just over half of the results are 'B's, it is likely that, based on these ten throws, there are either 3 or 4 faces with a 'B'.

If 3 faces are 'B', then there must be *either* 2 'A's and a 'C' *or* an 'A' and 2 'C's.

If there are 4 'B's, then there is one 'A' and one 'C'.

Clearly the information is not enough to enable you to be reasonably sure how many of each letter is on each face of the cube. With more throws, you should be able to be more accurate in your guesses.

Example   The next 20 throws produce three 'A's, thirteen 'B's and four 'C's. Looking at all 30 results so far:

(a) *Now* what are the experimental probabilities of each letter?

(b) How many faces are likely to be 'A's, 'B's or 'C's?

The results so far are five 'A's, nineteen 'B's and four 'C's.

(a) $p(A) = \frac{5}{30} = \frac{1}{6}$, $p(B) = \frac{19}{30}$ and $p(C) = \frac{6}{30} = \frac{1}{5}$

(b) It would appear that the cube is likely to have one 'A', four 'B's and a 'C'.

Exercise 3

1 There are 24 eggs on a tray. 23 are used, of which three are found to have double yolks. What is the probability that the remaining egg is a 'double-yolker'?

2 In her last 30 shots, Judi, a shooter at netball, has scored 22 times. What is the probability that she scores with her next shot?

3 Colin shuffles a pack of playing cards and deals Syeda the first eight cards. She picks one card at random from these eight and makes a note of its suit. She then returns it to the other seven, shuffles the eight cards, and again picks one at random, noting its suit. After 12 turns she has noted a heart six times, a club four times, and a diamond and a spade once each.

   (a) What is the probability of a heart?

   (b) How many cards of each suit do you think make up Syeda's eight cards?

4 A plastic bottle contains coloured beads. When it is turned upside down, one bead is visible through the bottle top. Brian shakes the bottle, and turns it upside down 20 times, noting the colour of the bead each time.

Colour of bead	White	Red	Black
Frequency	12	3	5

   (a) Using these figures, what is the probability that, when Brian again turns the bottle upside down, the bead is (i) red (ii) black (iii) white (iv) blue?

   (b) If there are 60 beads in the bottle, how many are likely to be (i) red (ii) black (iii) white (iv) blue?

12.5 Comparing probabilities as decimals, fractions and percentages

In the example in section 12.4, where a cube had the letters A, B and C on its faces, the probabilities after 30 throws were:

$$p(A) = \tfrac{1}{6}, \; p(B) = \tfrac{19}{30} \text{ and } p(C) = \tfrac{1}{5}$$

Changing these fractions into decimals,

Dividing the top number by the bottom number.

$p(A) = \tfrac{1}{6}$	$p(B) = \tfrac{19}{30}$	$p(C) = \tfrac{1}{5}$
$= 0.1666...$	$= 0.6333...$	$= 0.2$
$= 0.167$	$= 0.633$	$= 0.2$

Rounding to three decimal places.

Changing these into percentages,

$$p(A) = 16.7\%, \; p(B) = 63.3\% \text{ and } p(C) = 20\%$$ *Multiplying by 100.*

All probabilities *must* lie between 0 and 1; hence probabilities (other than certainty) expressed as:

- **fractions** must have the numerator *smaller* than the denominator
- **decimals** must begin with 0. ...
- **percentages** must be *less* than 100%

Exercise 4   In each question, write down the probability of each of the two events as a fraction. By converting to a decimal (or a percentage), decide which of the two events is more likely to happen.

1   (i) Choosing a girl from a group of eight girls and twelve boys.
    (ii) Choosing a girl from a group of six girls and eight boys.

2   (i) Picking a green sock from three green and five red socks.
    (ii) Picking a white sock from two white and three black socks.

3   (i) Picking a club from a pack of cards.
    (ii) Picking a red pen from a bag with one red and four blue pens.

4   (i) Choosing a 2p piece from a purse with five 2p pieces and two 10p pieces.
    (ii) Choosing a £5 note from a wallet with three £5 notes and £10 note.

5   (i) Winning a raffle, if you have bought four of the 100 tickets sold.
    (ii) Winning a raffle, if you have bought fifteen of the 350 tickets sold.

12.6   Combined events

Example   What is the probability of a score of 11 when two dice are thrown?

There are two ways of scoring 11: either 6–5 or 5–6.
The probability that the first die scores a 6 is $\frac{1}{6}$.
The probability that the second die scores a 5 is $\frac{1}{6}$.
The probability of this *combined* event is $\frac{1}{6} \times \frac{1}{6} = \frac{1}{36}$.
Similarly, the probability of a 5 on the first die
and a 6 on the second is $\frac{1}{6} \times \frac{1}{6} = \frac{1}{36}$.

As these are the only two ways of scoring 11, then
the probability of a score of 11 is $\frac{1}{36} + \frac{1}{36} = \frac{2}{36} = \frac{1}{18}$.

With 'two–dice' problems, it is often easier to work out probabilities by showing all 36 possibilities in a 6 × 6 square.

				second score			
		1	2	3	4	5	6
first score	1	2	3	4	5	6	7
	2	3	4	5	6	7	8
	3	4	5	6	7	8	9
	4	5	6	7	8	9	10
	5	6	7	8	9	10	(11)
	6	7	8	9	10	(11)	12

$$p(11) = \frac{2}{36} = \frac{1}{18}$$

Exercise 5   Find the probability of each event, when two dice are thrown:

1 a score of 6   2 a score greater than 9

3 an even number   4 either 3 or 4

5 a score of 13

If the outcomes of two events are **independent**, i.e. the results of one are not affected by the results of the other, then the probability of a **combined event** is obtained by *multiplying* the two separate independent probabilities.

Example   A boy and a girl are chosen from a group of four boys, Alan, Bablus, Colin and Damian, and three girls, Judith, Kathleen and Maureen. What is the probability that the chosen pair are (a) Alan and Kathleen (b) Bablus and not Judith (c) neither Colin nor Maureen?

(a) P(Alan) $= \frac{1}{4}$ and p(Kathleen) $= \frac{1}{3}$.

Hence p(Alan and Kathleen) $= \frac{1}{4} \times \frac{1}{3} = \frac{1}{12}$.

(b) P(Bablus) $= \frac{1}{4}$ and p(not Judith) $= \frac{2}{3}$ *As 2 of the girls are not Judith.*

Hence p(Bablus and not Judith) $= \frac{1}{4} \times \frac{2}{3}$

$= \frac{2}{12} = \frac{1}{6}$.

(c) P(not Colin) $= \frac{3}{4}$ and p(not Maureen) $= \frac{2}{3}$

Hence p(neither Colin nor Maureen) $= \frac{3}{4} \times \frac{2}{3}$

$= \frac{6}{12} = \frac{1}{2}$.

Exercise 6

1 When I toss two coins, what is the probability that they both land 'heads'?

2 In a game, I have to toss a coin and pick a card from the four aces. If the coin lands 'heads', and I pick the ace of hearts, I win. What is the probability that I win?

3 Pens are packed in boxes of ten, of which eight are black and two are red. Kate picks a pen from a box, and Emma picks a pen from another box. What is the probability that they both pick (a) a black pen (b) a red pen?

4 The probability that the No.33 bus is late at Harry's bus stop is $\frac{1}{5}$.
(a) What is the probability that the next No.33 is on time?
(b) What is the probability that the next two No.33's are on time?

5 One of the four batteries in Samantha's personal stereo is flat. Also, one of the three batteries in Clive's torch is flat. If two batteries are chosen, one from Samantha and one from Clive, what is the probability that neither is flat?

12.7 Bar graphs

One gram of gold can be drawn out into a wire 2 kilometres long.

In earlier chapters we have drawn bar graphs of the results of experiments. We can make the heights of the bars represent probabilities if we change the scale from frequency to **relative frequency**. This we can easily do by dividing *each* outcome by the *total number* of outcomes.

Relative frequency = estimate of probability

Example Two dice are thrown 100 times. The table shows the results. Draw a relative frequency diagram. What is the probability that the outcome is (a) 8 (b) less than 5 (c) an odd number?

Score	2	3	4	5	6	7	8	9	10	11	12
Frequency	3	6	7	10	13	18	15	14	8	5	1

The relative frequency row is worked out by *dividing* each frequency by 100:

Score	2	3	4	5	6	7	8	9	10	11	12
Frequency	3	6	7	10	13	18	15	14	8	5	1
Relative frequency	0.03	0.06	0.07	0.1	0.13	0.18	0.15	0.14	0.08	0.05	0.01

The diagram can now be drawn.

(a) p(8)   = 0.15
(b) p(less than 5)   = 0.03 + 0.06 + 0.07
                      = 0.16
(c) p(odd)   = 0.06 + 0.1 + 0.18 + 0.14 + 0.05
                      = 0.53

Exercise 7

1 The relative frequency of medals awarded at a sports meeting to a college athletic team is shown in the diagram. The ribbon attached to one of the medals is faulty.

What is the probability that the faulty ribbon is attached to a medal which is (a) gold (b) not bronze (c) either silver or bronze?

2 The diagram shows the relative frequency of heights of sunflowers grown by a group of science students. What is the probability that a sunflower was: (a) between 1.6 m and 1.8 m, (b) taller than 1.8 m, (c) shorter than 1.4 m?

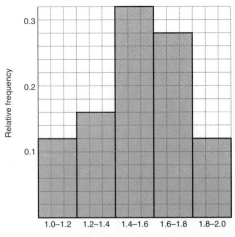

3 A darts player's scores were noted after each throw of three darts. The table shows the relative frequency of scores.

Score	under 20	21–40	41–60	61–80	81–100	over 100
Relative frequency	0.15	0.3	0.25	0.1	0.1	0.1

(a) Draw a relative frequency diagram.

(b) What is the probability that, on the next throw of three darts, the player scores (i) 40 or less (ii) over 80 (iii) more than 60?

4 Fifty students following a statistics course are grouped by age. The table shows the number in each age band.

Age band	under 20	20 to 29	30 to 39	40 to 49	over 50
Number	27	13	6	3	1

(a) Add a relative frequency row, and draw a relative frequency diagram.

(b) If a statistics student is selected at random, what is the probability that the student is (i) under 20 (ii) 30 or over (iii) under 50?

12.8 Adding probabilities

In an experiment, if two outcomes cannot both happen together, then the probability of either result occurring is the *sum* of the probabilities of the two individual outcomes.

You have been using this principle in answering some of the questions in the previous exercise, because the diagrams separate the outcomes into events that cannot occur simultaneously.

Outcomes like this are said to be **mutually exclusive**.

Example What is the probability of throwing either a 3 or a 5 with an ordinary die?

$P(3) = \frac{1}{6}$ and $p(5) = \frac{1}{6}$.

$p(3 \text{ or } 5) = \frac{1}{6} + \frac{1}{6}$ *These outcomes cannot both occur together.*

$= \frac{2}{6} = \frac{1}{3} (= 0.33 \ldots)$

Example I have been dealt these eight cards. I ought to have been dealt seven cards, so my partner removes one card from these eight. What is the probability that the card removed is either a 6 or a 7?

$p(6) = \frac{3}{8}$ and $p(7) = \frac{2}{8}$.

$p(6 \text{ or } 7) = \frac{3}{8} + \frac{2}{8}$ ***The outcomes are mutually exclusive.***

$= \frac{5}{8} (= 0.625)$

Exercise 8

1 There are three green, four white and five red counters in a jar. One is picked out. What is the probability that it is (a) either red or white (b) either green or red?

2 Barbara has six coins in her purse. Three are 10p pieces, one is a 20p piece and the other two are 2p pieces. She picks one coin out of her purse. What is the probability that it is (a) either a 2p or a 10p piece (b) either a 10p or a 20p piece?

3 Twelve of Marie's cassettes fall out of their boxes on to the floor. She knows that five are Queen tapes, four are Julian Lennon, two are INXS and one is Simply Red. What is the probability that the first cassette she picks up is (a) either Queen or INXS (b) Julian Lennon or Simply Red?

4 The table shows the handicaps of 16 golfers entering a competition.

Handicap	10	9	8	6	5	3
Number of players	6	4	1	1	3	1

What is the probability that the first person drawn will have a handicap of (a) ten (b) five or six (c) eight or more?

5 Gerald is dealt a hand of thirteen cards, in which five are hearts, four are diamonds, one is a club and three are spades.
He picks a card at random.
What is the probability that the card is (a) a heart or a spade (b) a club or a diamond (c) a red card?

12.9   P(A) = 1 – p(not A)

Example   When a die is thrown, what is the probability that the number is
(a) a 4 (b) not a 4?

(a) $p(4) = \frac{1}{6}$

(b)   This can be worked out in two ways.

Method 1
If the number is *not* a 4 it must be either 1, 2, 3, 5 or 6.

$$p(1, 2, 3, 5 \text{ or } 6) \quad = \frac{1}{6} + \frac{1}{6} + \frac{1}{6} + \frac{1}{6} + \frac{1}{6}$$
$$= \frac{5}{6}$$

Method 2
As the number must be *either* a 4 *or* not a 4, these two probabilities must add
up to 1. Hence

$$p(\text{not a } 4) = 1 - p(4)$$
$$= 1 - \frac{1}{6}$$
$$= \frac{5}{6} \text{ as before.}$$

In this example both methods are quite straightforward.

Example   What is the probability that when I am dealt a card, it is (a) an ace
(b) not an ace?

(a) $p(\text{ace}) = \frac{4}{52} = \frac{1}{13}$

(b)   It is easier to work out p(not an ace):

$$1 - p(\text{ace}) = 1 - \frac{1}{13}$$
$$= \frac{12}{13}$$

Exercise 9

1   Claire is a keen hockey player. The probability that she does not score a
goal in any game is 0.3. What is the probability that she scores at least one
goal in the next game?

2   When six dice are thrown, the probability that there are no 3's showing is
0.335. What is the probability that there is at least one 3 showing?

3   When four coins are thrown, the probability that all land 'heads' is $\frac{1}{16}$.
(a) What is the probability that they all land 'tails'? (b) What is the
probability that, in the four coins, there will be at least one 'head' and one
'tail'?

An American, Roy C. Sullivan has survived being hit by lightning seven times, in 1942, 1969, 1970, 1972, 1973, 1976 and 1977.

4 A box contains 18 coloured straws: ten are red, five are yellow and three are green. If one straw is selected, what is the probability that it is (a) yellow (b) not green (c) not red?

5 A bag contains a set of snooker balls. There are 15 reds, and one each of the colours white, yellow, green, brown, blue, pink and black. One ball is picked out at random. What is the probability that it is (a) white (b) not white (c) red (d) not red?

12.10 Repetition with or without replacement

Example   There are five 10p pieces and three 20p pieces in a box. I select two coins, one after the other.
What is the probability that *both* coins are 20p pieces, if (a) the first coin is replaced before the second selection (b) the first coin is *not* replaced?

(a) $p(20p) = \frac{3}{8}$ *There are 8 coins, 3 of which are 20p's.*

For the second selection,

$p(20p) = \frac{3}{8}.$ *The same as for the first selection.*

Hence, $p(\text{two } 20p) = \frac{3}{8} \times \frac{3}{8} = \frac{9}{64}$ (0.14...)

(b) $p(20p) = \frac{3}{8}$ *As in (a) above.*

For the second selection, however,

$p(20p) = \frac{2}{7}$ *Two 20p pieces.*
Two 20p and five 10p pieces.

Hence, $p(\text{two } 20p) = \frac{3}{8} \times \frac{2}{7}$
$= \frac{6}{56} (= \frac{3}{28} = 0.107...)$

Exercise 10

1 In her cupboard, Jane has six white socks and two blue socks. She takes two socks out one after the other. What is the probability that she has a pair of (a) white socks (b) blue socks?

2 Amanda picks a counter from a box which contains two green and two brown counters. Then Brenda picks a counter from the box.
What is the probability that both counters are green, if (a) Amanda returns her counter to the box (b) Amanda keeps her counter?

3 Of the eight teams left in the quarter finals of a Cup competition, five are Premier League teams. When the draw is made, what is the probability that the first two teams drawn out are both Premier League teams?

4 George has a 'full house' in a game of poker.
His five cards are three kings and two sevens.
He puts his cards face down on the table, and Harry picks one of his cards and then another.
What is the probability that both cards are kings?

5 A teacher says, 'Choose any letter from the word 'seven' and write it down.' What is the probability that both Tim and Jim write down the letter 'e'?

6 There are nine chocolates remaining in a box, of which two are coffee creams, Kathleen's favourites. If she eats two chocolates, what is the probability that they are both coffee creams?

7 To help to decide who wears which scarf, Michelle and Tracy each pick one of two dice and throw them. What is the probability that neither of them throws a 6?

8 There are six 'Chance' cards and four 'Community Chest' cards shuffled together. Angie picks a card, followed by Betty and then by Caroline. Daisy says that the probability of all three girls picking a 'Chance' card is $\frac{1}{6}$. Is she correct?

12.11 Tree diagrams

When we are considering two events, whether they are both different events or whether they are a repeat of the same event, a useful way of showing the probabilities is to draw a **tree diagram**.
The most straight forward example is to investigate the outcomes when two coins are thrown.

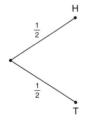

Example A 10p and a 50p piece are thrown. Draw a tree diagram to show all of the outcomes and their probabilities.

Firstly, the 10p coin has two outcomes: either heads (H) or tails (T). Each outcome has a probability of $\frac{1}{2}$; the first section of the diagram can be drawn:

Along each branch we write the probability of that outcome.

For each outcome (H or T) of the 10p coin, the 50p piece could land heads or tails, each again with a probability of $\frac{1}{2}$.
We draw another section on to each of the first set of outcomes.

From any starting point, the sum of the probabilities on the branches must add up to 1.

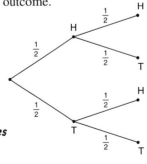

It is convenient to draw an 'Outcome/probability' table beside the diagram. In the 'Outcome' column we list all the possible outcomes that can be obtained by following all possible branches of the tree diagram.

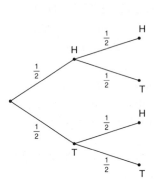

Outcome	Probability
HH	
HT	
TH	
TT	

To work out the probability of each outcome, we *multiply* the probabilities along the branches leading to each outcome. In this example the probability along each branch is $\frac{1}{2}$, so each combined outcome has a probability of $\frac{1}{4}$. The complete tree diagram and table is shown below.

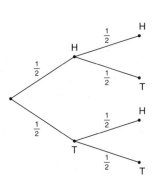

Outcome	Probability
HH	$\frac{1}{2} \times \frac{1}{2} = \frac{1}{4}$
HT	$\frac{1}{2} \times \frac{1}{2} = \frac{1}{4}$
TH	$\frac{1}{2} \times \frac{1}{2} = \frac{1}{4}$
TT	$\frac{1}{2} \times \frac{1}{2} = \frac{1}{4}$

In a random group of 25 people, the probability that two people have the same birthday (for example, 7th February) is better than evens.

Questions can then be answered, using the information in the table.

Example What is the probability of (a) two heads (b) two tails (c) a head and a tail?

(a) p(HH) = $\frac{1}{4}$ 　　　　　　　　(b) p(TT) = $\frac{1}{4}$

(c) There are two ways of getting a head and a tail: either HT or TH.

Each has a probability of $\frac{1}{4}$.

Therefore p(HT or TH) = $\frac{1}{4} + \frac{1}{4} = \frac{1}{2}$.

Note: The **sum** of the probabilities in the table *must* be 1, as we have listed *all* the possible outcomes. In this example, $\frac{1}{4} + \frac{1}{4} + \frac{1}{4} + \frac{1}{4} = 1$.

Example When I throw two dice, what is the probability that I get (a) a double 4 (b) one 4 (c) no 4's?

Although there are six outcomes for each of the dice, for the purposes of this question we are concerned only whether or not we get a 4.

$p(4) = \frac{1}{6}$,

then $p(\text{not }4) = 1 - \frac{1}{6} = \frac{5}{6}$ ***Using p(not A) = 1 – p(A).***

(We could have said $p(\text{not }4) = p(1, 2, 3, 5 \text{ or } 6) = \frac{1}{6} + \frac{1}{6} + \frac{1}{6} + \frac{1}{6} + \frac{1}{6} = \frac{5}{6}$: the first approach is much quicker, however.)

The tree diagram can now be drawn, followed by the table.

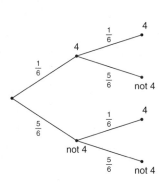

Outcome	Probability
4,4	$\frac{1}{6} \times \frac{1}{6} = \frac{1}{36}$
4, not 4	$\frac{1}{6} \times \frac{5}{6} = \frac{5}{36}$
not 4, 4	$\frac{5}{6} \times \frac{1}{6} = \frac{5}{36}$
not 4, not 4	$\frac{5}{6} \times \frac{5}{6} = \frac{25}{36}$

(a) $p(4 \text{ and } 4) = \frac{1}{36}$

(b) $p(\text{one } 4) = \frac{5}{36} + \frac{5}{36}$ ***The middle two outcomes both have one 4 (and one not 4).***

$\quad\quad\quad\quad = \frac{10}{36} = \frac{5}{18}$

(c) $p(\text{no } 4\text{'s}) = \frac{25}{36}$

(We can check that, as these are the only possible outcomes, the sum of their probabilities is 1: $\frac{1}{36} + \frac{10}{36} + \frac{25}{36} = \frac{36}{36} = 1$.)

Example Ivan has five medals for swimming, which he keeps in a drawer. Two are gold and three are silver. He picks two medals out of the drawer. Use a tree diagram to list all the possible outcomes.

(a) What is the probability that both medals are silver?

(b) What is the probability that at least one medal is gold?

In this case we must consider the selection of each medal separately, because Ivan is selecting **without replacement**: the second selection will depend upon the outcome of the first one, because there will be only four medals to choose from, instead of five.

The tree diagram for the first selection is shown.

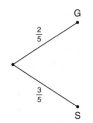

The probability of picking a gold medal on the *second* selection, assuming the *first* was gold, is $\frac{1}{4}$, as there would then be only one gold medal left out of the remaining four medals. Similarly, the probability that the *second* medal is gold, assuming that the *first* was silver is $\frac{2}{4}$, as there would be two gold medals left out of the remaining four.

The complete diagram, and table, will be:

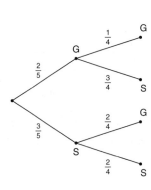

Outcome	Probability
GG	$\frac{2}{5} \times \frac{1}{4} = \frac{2}{20} \left(= \frac{1}{10}\right)$
GS	$\frac{2}{5} \times \frac{3}{4} = \frac{6}{20} \left(= \frac{3}{10}\right)$
SG	$\frac{3}{5} \times \frac{2}{4} = \frac{6}{20} \left(= \frac{3}{10}\right)$
SS	$\frac{3}{5} \times \frac{2}{4} = \frac{6}{20} \left(= \frac{3}{10}\right)$

(a)   p(two silver medals) $= \frac{3}{10}$.

(b)   For at least one medal to be gold, one of the outcomes GG, GS or SG must happen.

Hence p(at least one G) $= \frac{1}{10} + \frac{3}{10} + \frac{3}{10} = \frac{7}{10}$.

We could have said that any outcome, other than two silver medals, would contain at least one gold medal.

Hence p(at least one G) $\begin{aligned} &= 1 - \text{p(no G's)} \\ &= 1 - \text{p(SS)} \\ &= 1 - \frac{3}{10} \\ &= \frac{7}{10}, \text{ as before.} \end{aligned}$

Exercise II

1 Paul shuffles the four aces from a pack of cards, and asks Robert to pick one card, look at it, and return it to the three other aces. He then asks Gina to do the same. By copying and completing the tree diagram, work out the probability that, of the two aces:

(a) both are hearts,

(b) neither is a heart,

(c) only one is a heart.

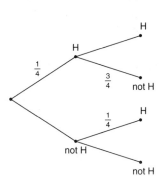

Outcome	Probability
HH	
H, not H	$\frac{1}{4} \times \frac{3}{4} = \frac{3}{16}$
not H not H	

2 On an island during July, the probability that it will rain on any day is 0.2. Copy and complete the tree diagram and table. What is the probability that on two consecutive days:

(a) it will be dry,

(b) it will rain on one of the days,

(c) it will rain on both days?

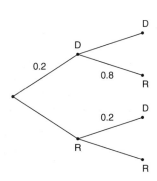

Outcome	Probability
DR	0.2 x 0.8 = 0.16
RR	

3 Out of a box of six eggs, two are rotten. Copy and complete the tree diagram and table. What is the probability that, when two eggs are picked from the box:

(a) both are good, (b) at least one is rotten?

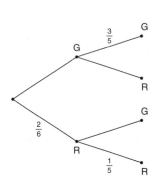

Outcome	Probability
GG	
RR	$\frac{2}{6} \times \frac{1}{5} = \frac{2}{30}$

4 Robin has a cassette holder which holds eight tapes. Five of these are Queen tapes.

Draw a tree diagram (use 'Q' and 'not Q') and a table.

When Robin picks out two cassettes, what is the probability that:

(a) both are Queen cassettes, (b) one is a Queen cassette,

(c) neither is a Queen cassette?

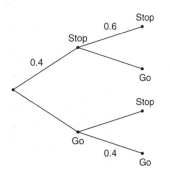

Outcome	Probability
SS	
SG	

5 As Tammy cycles to school, she passes through two sets of traffic lights. The probability of having to stop at the first set is 0.4, and at the second is 0.6. Copy and complete the tree diagram. What is the probability that Tammy:

(a) has to stop at both sets of lights,

(b) gets straight through both sets,

(c) has to stop at one set only?

6 The probability that Claire beats David at Scrabble is 0.7. They play two games, neither of which ends in a draw.

(a) Draw a tree diagram to show the possible outcomes.

(b) What is the probability that (i) Claire wins both games (ii) David wins at least one game?

7 Sally's spinner has one blue and four red sections.
She spins it twice.

(a) Draw a tree diagram to show the possible outcomes.

(b) What is the probability that Sally spins (i) two different colours
(ii) either two reds or two blues?

12.12   More than two events

*During spawning a
female salmon lays
10 000 eggs.*

Example   Three coins are thrown.

(a) Draw a tree diagram of the possible outcomes.

(b) What is the probability of (i) three heads (ii) one tail (iii) at
least one head?

(a) With three events, we continue the tree diagram to show all possibilities,
and their probabilities.

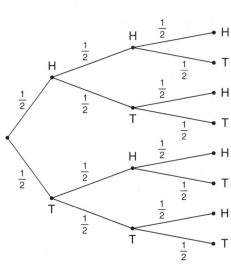

Outcome	Probability
HHH	$\frac{1}{2} \times \frac{1}{2} \times \frac{1}{2} = \frac{1}{8}$
HHT	$\frac{1}{2} \times \frac{1}{2} \times \frac{1}{2} = \frac{1}{8}$
HTH	$\frac{1}{2} \times \frac{1}{2} \times \frac{1}{2} = \frac{1}{8}$
HTT	$\frac{1}{2} \times \frac{1}{2} \times \frac{1}{2} = \frac{1}{8}$
THH	$\frac{1}{2} \times \frac{1}{2} \times \frac{1}{2} = \frac{1}{8}$
THT	$\frac{1}{2} \times \frac{1}{2} \times \frac{1}{2} = \frac{1}{8}$
TTH	$\frac{1}{2} \times \frac{1}{2} \times \frac{1}{2} = \frac{1}{8}$
TTT	$\frac{1}{2} \times \frac{1}{2} \times \frac{1}{2} = \frac{1}{8}$

(b)   (i) p(HHH) $= \frac{1}{8}$

(ii) p(one T) $=$ p(HHT + HTH + THH) $= \frac{3}{8}$

(iii) p(at least one H) $= 1 - $ p(no H)

$= 1 - $ p(TTT)

$= 1 - \frac{1}{8}$

$= \frac{7}{8}$

Exercise 12

1   Using the information from question 2 in exercise 11, the diagram is extended to three days.
What is the probability that the three consecutive days
(a) are all dry (b) have at least two wet days?

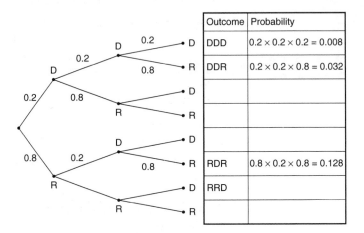

Outcome	Probability
DDD	$0.2 \times 0.2 \times 0.2 = 0.008$
DDR	$0.2 \times 0.2 \times 0.8 = 0.032$
RDR	$0.8 \times 0.2 \times 0.8 = 0.128$
RRD	

2   From question 4 in exercise 11, extend the tree diagram to show the outcomes if three cassettes are picked.
What is the probability that, of the three cassettes,

(a) all are Queen cassettes   (b) at least one is a Queen cassette
(c) none is a Queen cassette?

3   Looking back at question 6 in exercise 11, Claire and David play three games of Scrabble.

(a) Make up a new tree diagram, and outcome table.

(b) What is the probability that (i) David wins all three games (ii) Sally wins at least two games?

4   Sally spins her spinner three times (see question 7, exercise 11). Use a tree diagram to work out the probability that she spins (a) three reds (b) two reds (c) one red (d) no reds.

5   There are eight sandwiches remaining on a plate. Of these, six are cheese and two are cucumber.
Gerald ate three sandwiches.
By making up a tree diagram, what is the probability that Gerald ate

(a) three cheese sandwiches   (b) at least one of each?

Review

Exercise 13

1 I have six batteries for my walkman in a drawer. I know that four are new and two are old. If I pick one battery at random, what is the probability that it is (a) a new one (b) an old one?

2 Ian is in a hurry and grabs a handkerchief from a drawer which contains eight handkerchiefs, five of which are white and three coloured. What is the probability that the handkerchief is (a) white (b) coloured?

3 One person is selected at random from a class of nine girls and seven boys. What is the probability that the person is (a) a girl (b) a boy?

4 Judy has seven scarves on a shelf, three of which are red, two are blue and two are white. She picks one scarf from the shelf, without looking. What is the probability that it is (a) red (b) either white or red (c) not white (d) green?

5 A set of 16 pool balls is made up of seven 'spots', seven 'stripes', a white and a black. One ball drops on to the floor. What is the probability that it is (a) a 'stripe' (b) the black (c) not a 'spot'?

6 In a game of darts, Steve has scored 60 or more seven times in his last 20 throws of three darts. From this information, estimate the probability that his next throw will be 60 or more.

7 The seventh hole on a golf course is surrounded by bunkers. In her last 15 rounds of golf, Karen has landed in one of these bunkers 12 times. Estimate the probability that, during the next round she plays, Karen does *not* land in one of these bunkers.

8 The rules of indoor six-a-side cricket state that a batsman must retire, temporarily, once he has scored 25 runs. In the eight games so far this season, Pete has scored 25 six times, and Les has scored 25 on five occasions. For the next game, estimate the probability that (a) Pete will score 25 runs (b) Les will *not* score 25 runs.

9 A ball is rolled through a maze, and ends up in one of the slots A, B, C, D or E. Nathan has rolled the ball 20 times, and it has ended up as shown in the table.

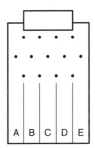

Slot	A	B	C	D	E
Number of times	1	5	9	3	2

From these figures, estimate the probability that the next ball Nathan rolls will end up in (a) slot B (b) either slot D or E (c) *not* slot C.

10 Chloe has a box which contains white, red and green beads. She picks one out, notes its colour, and puts it back. She repeats this ten times, and notes that the bead is white six times, red three times and green once.
What is the probability that the next time she picks a bead it will be (a) white (b) blue (c) not red?

11 In question 1, if my walkman needs two batteries, what is the probability that the first two I pick are both new?

12 In question 3, two people are chosen instead of one. What is the probability that they are both boys?

13 In question 4, Judy picks two scarves instead of one. What is the probability that both are red?

14 If two pool balls fall on to the floor in question 5, what is the probability that both are 'spots'?

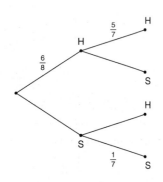

Outcome	Probability
HH	$\frac{6}{8} \times \frac{5}{7} =$
HS	
SH	
SS	$\times \frac{1}{7} =$

15 There are eight chocolates left in a box. Two have soft centres and six have hard centres. Joanna eats one chocolate, and then another.
Copy and complete the tree diagram and outcome table.
What is the probability that (a) both are soft centres (b) both are hard centres (c) Joanna picks one of each?

16 Alan shuffles the 13 hearts from a pack of cards. He deals out the top two cards, face up, noting whether or not they are picture cards.
By completing the tree diagram and outcome table, calculate the probability that (a) the cards are both picture cards (b) at least one of the cards is a picture card.

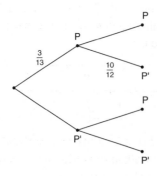

Outcome	Probability
PP	$\frac{3}{13} \times =$
PP'	$\times \frac{10}{12} =$
P'P	
P'P'	

17 A coin is spun three times.
Use a tree diagram and outcome table to calculate the probability of getting (a) three heads (b) only one head (c) at least two tails.

18 I have six black socks and four white socks in a drawer. I pick out one sock and then another. By drawing a tree diagram, or otherwise, work out the probability that I pick a matching pair of socks.

Exercise 14

The following questions are all taken from GCSE papers.

1 Ramondeep has a bag containing 12 beads. There are 5 red beads, 3 green beads and the rest are black. A bead is to be chosen at random from the bag. What is the probability, as a fraction, that

(a) the bead will be red, *(2 marks)*

(b) the bead will not be green, *(2 marks)*

(c) the bead will be white? *(2 marks)*

[LEAG]

2 A supermarket runs a prize draw. Each customer is given a card with two digits printed on it. The two digits are selected at random from the list 1, 2, 3, 4, 5, 6, 7, 8 and 9. Every day a number is displayed in the shop window. Each customer adds the two digits on her card. If this total is equal to the number in the window then she wins a prize.

(a) One day the number in the window is 14. Calculate the probability that a particular customer wins a prize. *(3 marks)*

(b) On another day the manager wants to ensure that very few customers win prizes. What number should he display in the window?

(1 mark)

(c) On another day, Mr Jones sees the number in the window. He calculates that the probability of winning a prize is $\frac{2}{81}$. What are the possible numbers in the window? *(2 marks)*

[SEG]

3 A spinner has the shape of an octagon. The eight sections of the spinner are numbered

1, 2, 1, 2, 1, 2, 1, 3.

When the spinner is used, it is equally likely to finish on any of its eight sides. Calculate the probability (as a fraction) that

(i) a score of 2 is obtained on the first spin, *(1 mark)*

(ii) a score of 3 is obtained on each of the first two spins. *(2 marks)*

[MEG]

4 John has constructed a toy which allows table tennis balls to drop down four separate routes with equal probability. A ball is placed in the top of the toy and released. It will come out of one of the four holes at the bottom marked A, B, C or D.

(a) Write down the probability that the table tennis ball will come out of the hole marked C. *(1 mark)*

(b) Calculate the probability that two successive table tennis balls will come out of the hole marked B. *(2 marks)*

(c) Calculate the probability that three successive tennis balls will come out of hole A or hole B. *(2 marks)*

[LEAG]

5 In a game two dice, one red and one blue, are thrown simultaneously. A score is found by adding together the numbers on the upper faces of the dice. Four players, Adam, Bethan, Christos and Dean, decide that
Adam will win if the red dice shows 6,
Bethan will win if the score is 5 or 6,
Christos will win if the score is 2 or 3 or 4,
Dean will win otherwise.

(a) Find the probability, expressed as a fraction , that

(i) Adam will win the game, *(2 marks)*

(ii) Bethan will win the game, *(2 marks)*

(iii) Christos will will the game, *(2 marks)*

(iv) Dean will win the game, *(2 marks)*

(b) Is the game fair? Explain your answer. *(2 marks)*

[LEAG]

6 On any day during the summer of 1979 the probability that it rained was $\frac{1}{6}$. In 1989, because of climatic changes, the probability that it rained on any day during the summer was only $\frac{1}{10}$.

(a) Calculate the probability that any 3 days chosen at random during the summer of 1979 were all wet. *(2 marks)*

(b) Calculate the probability that it rained on a particular date during the summer of 1979 and was dry on the same date in 1989. *(3 marks)*

[SEG]

7 Kim spun this pentagon spinner 30 times and recorded the results. She drew the diagram below to illustrate them.
Unfortunately she did not complete the diagram for the number 2.

(a) Complete the diagram. (*1 mark*)

(b) Use these results to suggest the probability that any given spin would result in a odd number.

(*2 marks*)

[MEG]

8 (a) A bag of sweets contains 4 toffees and 2 mints. David takes one sweet at random.

  (i) What is the probability that it is a mint? (*1 mark*)

  (ii) David eats the sweet, which is not a mint. Explain why the probability is $\frac{3}{5}$ that the next sweet chosen at random will be a toffee. (*2 marks*)

(b) Two sweets are chosen at random from another bag, which also contains 4 toffees and 2 mints. The first is not replaced.

  (i) Copy and complete this tree diagram.

  (ii) Find the probability that one of the sweets is a mint and the other a toffee. (*6 marks*)

[MEG]

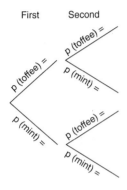

First   Second

Ideas for investigations

1 A pack of cards is shuffled and the cards are dealt out until the first heart appears.
The process is repeated a number of times.
Jack says that the most likely position of a heart is FIRST; Jill says that the most likely position of a heart is THIRD.
By performing the experiment a number of times, decide who you think is correct.
Which do you think is the most likely position for the first heart?

2 At one of the stalls at a village fête, you pay £1 to throw three dice.
If none of the dice show a '6' you lose your £1.
If one of the dice shows a '6' you get your £1 back.
If two of the dice show a '6' you get £2 back.
If all three dice show a '6' you get £10 back.

Investigate whether or not the game is fair.
Suggest how to alter the pay-outs, so that the organisers of the fête make a profit of about £2 for every ten attempts.
(A tree diagram may assist with the calculations.)

ANSWERS

1 Using numbers

Exercise 1
| **1** 20 | **2** 35 min | **3** 69 | **4** 34 | **5** 134 mm |
| **6** £1018 | **7** 2 | **8** 420 | | |

Exercise 2
| **1** £120 000 | **2** £2000 | **3** £20 | **4** 300 |
| **5** 1600 g | **6** 4000 g | **7** 40 litres | **8** 350 |

Exercise 3
| **1** 565 mm | **2** 2908 | **3** 49 | **4** 300 | **5** £82 |
| **6** 4 | **7** 15 264 | **8** 5856 | | |

Exercise 4
| **1** £6.20 | **2** £35.40 | **3** 90 | **4** £22 |
| **5** £350 | **6** £38 000 | **7** £395 | **8** £79.71 |

Exercise 5

1 £72.25 **2** 8th Dec.

3 (a) £9.80 (b) £15.30 (c) £18.70 **4** (a) £83.41 (b) £67.57

5 £3311

Exercise 6
| **1** 10 010 | **2** 1 105 400 | **3** 1 030 250 |
| **4** 410 006 | **5** 5 002 509 | **6** 4 805 078 |

7 Two hundred and five thousand, one hundred and three.

8 Four million, thirty thousand, one hundred and twenty.

9 Nine hundred and ninety thousand, and nine.

10 Eight million, seven hundred and fifty thousand, and three.

11 Seven million, six thousand, two hundred and seven.

12 Five million, one hundred thousand, five hundred and fifty.

13 605431, 609495, 631427, 649531, 650001, 650547

14 3600005, 3571453, 2837431, 2450401, 2435721, 2404321, 2314373

15 500250 **16** 1 million **17** 750 000

18 £50 000 **19** £22 750 **20** £35 750 000

Exercise 7
1 81	**2** 256	**3** 8	**4** 0	**5** 125
6 1	**7** 729	**8** 3125	**9** 64	**10** 3375
11 169	**12** 1	**13** 2	**14** 9	**15** 1296

16 16	**17** 6561	**18** 15625	**19** 2401	**20** 1
21 $\frac{1}{8}$	**22** $\frac{1}{6}$	**23** $\frac{1}{81}$	**24** $\frac{1}{1000}$	**25** 1
26 $\frac{1}{49}$	**27** $\frac{1}{243}$	**28** $\frac{1}{64}$	**29** $\frac{1}{27}$	**30** 1
31 3	**32** 3	**33** 6	**34** 3	**35** 5
36 3	**37** 3	**38** 3	**39** 10	**40** 3

Exercise 8

1 64	**2** 16	**3** 256	**4** 72	**5** 16
6 180	**7** 375	**8** 82 944	**9** 13 824	**10** 25

Exercise 9

1 $\frac{5}{8}$	**2** $\frac{9}{12} = \frac{3}{4}$	**3** $\frac{4}{6} = \frac{2}{3}$	**4** $\frac{6}{10} = \frac{3}{5}$
5 $\frac{2}{3} = \frac{6}{9}$	**6** $\frac{2}{5} = \frac{8}{20}$	**7** $\frac{1}{2} = \frac{2}{4}$	**8** $\frac{7}{10} = \frac{70}{100}$
9 $\frac{90}{100} = \frac{9}{10}$	**10** $\frac{15}{9} = \frac{135}{81}$	**11** $\frac{18}{21} = \frac{6}{7}$	**12** $\frac{4}{3} = \frac{16}{12}$
13 $\frac{24}{36} = \frac{6}{9}$	**14** $\frac{3}{8} = \frac{90}{240}$	**15** $\frac{7}{12} = \frac{84}{144}$	**16** $\frac{2}{3} = \frac{16}{24}$

Exercise 10

1 $\frac{11}{6}$	**2** $\frac{20}{3}$	**3** $\frac{47}{6}$	**4** $\frac{13}{6}$	**5** $\frac{41}{5}$
6 $\frac{23}{3}$	**7** $\frac{43}{5}$	**8** $\frac{57}{10}$	**9** $\frac{50}{9}$	**10** $\frac{31}{8}$

Exercise 11

1 $6\frac{1}{8}$	**2** $8\frac{5}{6}$	**3** $3\frac{3}{10}$	**4** $8\frac{5}{9}$	**5** $5\frac{3}{4}$
6 $7\frac{7}{11}$	**7** $5\frac{4}{5}$	**8** $5\frac{5}{11}$	**9** $4\frac{11}{12}$	**10** $5\frac{5}{7}$

Exercise 12

1 $\frac{2}{3}$	**2** $\frac{3}{4}$	**3** $\frac{2}{3}$	**4** $\frac{1}{6}$	**5** $\frac{2}{5}$
6 $\frac{3}{7}$	**7** $\frac{2}{3}$	**8** $\frac{3}{4}$	**9** $\frac{5}{8}$	**10** $\frac{2}{5}$

Exercise 13

1 $\frac{2}{3}$	**2** $\frac{1}{5}$	**3** $1\frac{1}{5}$	**4** $\frac{1}{4}$
5 $1\frac{3}{5}$	**6** $1\frac{3}{7}$	**7** $\frac{3}{16}$	**8** $\frac{1}{4}$
9 $\frac{3}{16}$	**10** $1\frac{1}{12}$	**11** $1\frac{1}{8}$	**12** $\frac{11}{16}$
13 $8\frac{1}{12}$	**14** $3\frac{1}{8}$	**15** $7\frac{7}{16}$	**16** $7\frac{9}{16}$

Exercise 14

1 $\frac{1}{10}$	**2** $\frac{5}{8}$	**3** $\frac{1}{15}$	**4** $\frac{4}{15}$	**5** $\frac{1}{20}$	**6** $\frac{1}{16}$
7 $\frac{4}{7}$	**8** $\frac{2}{7}$	**9** $2\frac{4}{5}$	**10** $1\frac{1}{5}$	**11** $\frac{3}{4}$	**12** 30

Exercise 15

1 $\frac{3}{4}$	**2** $1\frac{1}{2}$	**3** $1\frac{1}{5}$	**4** $\frac{5}{6}$
5 $6\frac{2}{3}$	**6** $4\frac{2}{3}$	**7** $17\frac{1}{3}$	**8** $1\frac{5}{6}$
9 $3\frac{3}{20}$	**10** $1\frac{7}{8}$	**11** $1\frac{1}{7}$	**12** $3\frac{1}{5}$

ANSWERS

Exercise 16

1 15	**2** 20	**3** (a) £4.50 (b) £3.00	
4 $\frac{3}{5}$ of 18 kg	**5** $\frac{1}{9}$	**6** 120	**7** £50.40 **8** 85

Exercise 17

1 $7\frac{5}{8}$ ft	**2** 27 bags	**3** $15\frac{1}{2}$ in
4 25	**5** $4\frac{11}{16}$ in	**6** $4\frac{3}{8}$ hands
7 7.5 cucumbers	**8** $18\frac{2}{3}$ hours	

Exercise 18

1 5.6	**2** 8.5	**3** 1.4	**4** 16.41	**5** 117.73
6 8.83	**7** 35.64	**8** 140.22	**9** 16.55	**10** 756.41

Exercise 19

1 0.48	**2** 7.38	**3** 17.5	**4** 340	**5** 12.1
6 1400	**7** 66.33	**8** 6.2	**9** 37.32	**10** 0.12
11 12.96	**12** 35.064			

Exercise 20

1 5	**2** 15	**3** 11	**4** 12
5 16	**6** 24	**7** 11	**8** 23
9 8	**10** 24	**11** 2	**12** 5

Exercise 21

1 (a) 41 000 (b) 41 300	**2** (a) 6000 (b) 5800
3 (a) 84 000 (b) 84 200	**4** (a) 67 000 (b) 66 700
5 (a) 8000 (b) 7600	**6** (a) 3000 (b) 3100
7 (a) 43 000 (b) 43 200	**8** (a) 5000 (b) 5100
9 (a) 47 000 (b) 47 200	**10** (a) 1000 (b) 1000
11 (a) 1000 (b) 1200	**12** (a) 1000 (b) 1100
13 24 000 **14** 12 800	**15** £19 000

Exercise 22

1 12	**2** 13	**3** 15	**4** 10
5 44	**6** 6	**7** 14	**8** (a) 5 (b) 7

Exercise 23

1 (a) 3.86 (b) 3.860	**2** (a) 9.42 (b) 9.419
3 (a) 29.83 (b) 29.831	**4** (a) 0.01 (b) 0.014
5 (a) 0.98 (b) 0.975	**6** (a) 6.41 (b) 6.407
7 (a) 50.91 (b) 50.914	**8** (a) 4.89 (b) 4.886
9 (a) 36.06 (b) 36.058	**10** (a) 9.09 (b) 9.094
11 7.22 **12** 95.8	**13** 68.9
14 29.97 **15** 0.7857	

Exercise 24

1 (a) 30 (b) 29.1	**2** (a) 6000 (b) 5650
3 (a) 70 000 (b) 73 400	**4** (a) 0.04 (b) 0.0375
5 (a) 20 (b) 23.5	**6** (a) 20 (b) 15.4

7 (a) 60   (b) 62.8   8 (a) 0.08   (b) 0.0810

9 (a) 500   (b) 468   10 (a) 4000   (b) 4090

11 0.126   12 10   13 0.66

14 290   15 4000

Exercise 25

1 0.000 75   2 0.0098   3 0.000 037 5   4 1 600 000

5 0.001 01   6 736 000   7 6200   8 70 000

9 0.009 21   10 9 830 000

Exercise 26

1 7.0×10^{-2} 2 4.5×10^{3} 3 3.5×10^{-1}

4 8.0×10^{5} 5 8.0×10^{-3} 6 2.7×10^{-2}

7 2.4×10^{4} 8 6.9×10^{-3} 9 4.0×10^{3}

10 1.4×10^{4} 11 8.5×10^{-6} 12 9.0×10^{-4}

Exercise 27

1 (a) 7.8×10^{-4} (b) 0.000 78   2 (a) 1.2×10^{9} (b) 1 200 000 000

3 (a) 2.4×10^{6} (b) 2 400 000   4 (a) 3.2×10^{-6} (b) 0.000 003 2

5 (a) 3.84×10^{0} (b) 3.84   6 (a) 1.2×10^{8} (b) 120 000 000

7 (a) 1.2×10^{3} (b) 1200   8 (a) 6.48×10^{-3} (b) 0.006 48

Exercise 28

Your own answers will be estimates. There are no unique answers to these estimates. The actual answers are provided below, for comparison.

1 £5.68   2 3335 g   3 383 mm   4 £728

5 638 kg   6 383 cm   7 Correct   8 Correct

9 Incorrect   10 Correct

Exercise 29

1 4.5   2 12.53   3 15.9   4 16.39   5 600

6 94.7   7 1300   8 20   9 52.2   10 600

11 20 m   12 1730 m^2 13 760 cm   14 7.4 m   15 534 m^2

Exercise 30

1 188 mm   2 £1069   3 6   4 51 g   5 1000

6 £8330   7 39   8 446 mm   9 412 mm   10 86 400

11 About £10 (£10.02)   12 About 50 000 (49 581.6)

13 About 10 (9.85)   14 About £32.50 (£32.39)

15 About 60 mg (62 mg)

Exercise 31

1 £535 500   2 3 408 005

3 (a) Five million, four hundred and seven thousand, eight hundred and ninety pounds

(b) (i) £5 408 000   (ii) £5 407 900   (iii) £5 408 000

ANSWERS

4 (a) 7776 (b) $\frac{1}{64}$ (c) 81 (d) 1 (e) 1600 (f) 243

5 (a) 21 (b) $\frac{7}{10}$ (c) $7\frac{5}{12}$ (d) $\frac{4}{21}$ (e) $1\frac{1}{6}$ (f) $1\frac{1}{4}$ (g) $12\frac{1}{4}$ (h) $\frac{4}{9}$

6 $8\frac{2}{3}$ inches   7 4   8 $\frac{5}{6}$ 9 $\frac{4}{5}$ of 35 kg

10 (a) 30.80   (b) 5.54   (c) 5.92   (d) 4.80

11 (a) 7290   (b) 620   (c) 63.6   (d) 3.50

12 (a) (i) 0.0256   (ii) 2.56×10^{-2}
    (b) (i) 21 440 000   (ii) 2.144×10^{7}
    (c) (i) 15 000   (ii) 1.5×10^{4}

Exercise 32

1 10004527, 10504125, 11509273, 21494731, 40425178, 40901079, 41239410, 41249372.

2 56 litres   3 £10.94

4 (a) Three hundred (b) Three-tenths

5 34 remainder   6 9 400 000 000 000

7 (a) (i) 125 (ii) $\frac{1}{125}$ (b) 6   8 £2.79

9 (a) 2 500 000   (b) Twenty thousand and twenty-two pounds

10 (a) 232   (b) £16.70 (c) £20.45 (d) £65   (e) £44.55

11 (a) Lara   (b) 19 years (c) 50 years old

12 (a) 64   (b) (i) 1   (ii) $\frac{1}{2}$

13 (a) 9.2×10^{-28} (b) (i) 2.76×10^{-27} (ii) 2.76×10^{-21}

14 (a) $3.021\,766\,32 \times 10^{8}$ (b) 302 000 000   (c) 8th Dec. 1999

15 480 000   16 (i) £60 (ii) £62.50 (iii) first

17 (a) 0.625 (b) (i) 0.0769 (ii) 0.7778 (iii) 0.454 545 454 545 5

18 (a) $1\frac{3}{4}$ yards (b) $2\frac{5}{8}$ yards (c) $4\frac{3}{8}$ yards

19 (a) 2.3×10^{8} (b) (i) 17 520 hours (ii) 10 000 km/h

20 2.95×10^{2} or 295 m

Investigations

The important thing with coursework is not necessarily the correct answer, but the evidence you provide to show the process you have followed in getting near to, or reaching the answer.

1 The maximum and minimum lengths can be expressed to one decimal place only, but will have a difference of just less than 0.1 in this instance. The difference will become greater when you calculate the area, since the difference between each of the lengths and widths is then multiplied by itself. When the figures are expressed to two decimal places, the difference in length is then 0.01, and the difference in the area is greater again.

2 The general rules are that if you multiply two powers of the same number, you add the powers. If you divide powers of the same number, you take away the powers:

$$2^{n} \times 2^{m} = 2^{n+m} \qquad\qquad 2^{n} \div 2^{m} = 2^{n-m}$$

3 $\frac{1}{2}x + \frac{1}{4}x + \frac{3}{16}x + 2 = \frac{15x}{16} + 2$ so 2 is $\frac{1}{16}$ of the apples
  The number of apples is therefore 32.

4 (a) One which works is G = 8, S = 27, B = 65 (b) G = 7, S = 49, B = 44

2 Percentages

Exercise I

1 (a) 0.4   (b) $\frac{3}{5}$ 2 (a) 0.35   (b) $\frac{7}{20}$ 3 (a) 0.15   (b) $\frac{3}{20}$

4 (a) 0.44   (b) $\frac{11}{25}$ 5 (a) 0.27   (b) $\frac{27}{100}$ 6 (a) 0.825   (b) $\frac{33}{40}$

7 (a) 0.325   (b) $\frac{13}{40}$ 8 (a) 0.175   (b) $\frac{3}{40}$ 9 (a) 0.075   (b) $\frac{19}{40}$

10 (a) 0.1525   (b) $\frac{61}{400}$

Exercise 2

1 30%   2 50%   3 35%   4 $37\frac{1}{2}$%   5 80%

6 132%   7 $31\frac{1}{4}$%   8 $31\frac{1}{4}$%   9 $58\frac{1}{3}$%   10 $93\frac{3}{4}$%

Exercise 3

1 75%   2 25%   3 25%   4 $66\frac{2}{3}$%

5 $16\frac{2}{3}$%   6 50%   7 50%   8 50%

Exercise 4

1 0.4, 50%, $\frac{3}{5}$ 2 $\frac{1}{5}$, 32%, 0.35   3 0.3, 33%, $\frac{1}{3}$ 4 70%, $\frac{3}{4}$, 0.80

5 0.25, 28%, $\frac{7}{20}$ 6 $\frac{3}{5}$, 63%, 0.65   7 $\frac{9}{20}$, 0.55, 59%   8 $\frac{5}{8}$, 0.7, 75%

Exercise 5

1 £8.00   2 £1.08   3 16 g   4 60 mm   5 9 kg

6 3 cm   7 15 t   8 £8.05   9 £0.72   10 40 m

Exercise 6

1 £777   2 £2312.5 g   3 708 g   4 £736   5 £325

6 112.8 m   7 420 ml   8 £2.93   9 £28.64   10 £8.88

Exercise 7

1 £31.50   2 53 000   3 £531.25   4 £242.65   5 130 people

6 1770 t   7 £2625   8 £104

Exercise 8

1 £13.27   2 £92.69   3 £144.67   4 £91.65   5 £149.49

Exercise 9

1 (a) £817   (b) £467   2 (a) £462   (b) £102

3 (a) £250   (b) £50   4 (a) £296.88   (b) £71.88

5 (a) £5905.80   (b) £955.80   6 (a) £626.25   (b) £51.25

Exercise 10

1 £487.50   2 £63.00   3 £11.93   4 £222.75

5 5 yr 8 m   6 2 yr 2 m   7 7.03%   8 £75

9 £166.67   10 2 yr 2 m

Exercise II

1 £630.50   2 £147.51   3 £270.10   4 £94.19

5 £88.36   6 £10.31

Exercise 12

1 £211.50	**2** £171.00	**3** £186.55	**4** £194.20
5 £3.96	**6** £4.08	**7** £26.80	**8** £21.60
9 £112.50	**10** £72.00	**11** £99.00	**12** £80.00
13 £104.00	**14** £28.25	**15** £37.18	**16** £85.14

Exercise 13

1 52.1% **2** $31\frac{1}{4}$% **3** $13\frac{1}{3}$% **4** $62\frac{1}{2}$%

5 15% **6** 57.2% **7** 9.7% **8** 34.2%

9 (a) $46\frac{2}{3}$% (b) $53\frac{1}{3}$% **10** (a) 54.1% (b) 45.8%

Exercise 14

1 £87.20 **2** £160 **3** £620 **4** £64 **5** £240

6 £2400 **7** 250 kg **8** £12800 **9** £3800 **10** £18.00

Exercise 15

1

Decimal	Fraction	Percentage
0.9	$\frac{9}{10}$	90%
0.375	$\frac{3}{8}$	$37\frac{1}{2}$%
0.45	$\frac{9}{20}$	45%
0.625	$\frac{5}{8}$	$62\frac{1}{2}$%
0.6666	$\frac{2}{3}$	$66\frac{2}{3}$%

2 $\frac{2}{3}$ of £139.53 **3** £8.05 **4** £1478.75

5 (a) £8694.25 (b) 394.25 **6** 1487.5 kg

7 £140 **8** £369.25 **9** £65.80

10 £172.42 **11** (a) £320 (b) £339.72

12 £68 **13** 20% **14** 16%

15 £120 **16** £77.40 **17** £283.75

18 (a) £15.00 (b) £30.50

Exercise 16

1 20% **2** £120

3 (a) £100 (b) £900 (c) £135 (d) £1035

4 (a) £637.20 (b) £557.55

5 1027, £45.19, £63.34, £9.50, £72.84

6 (a) 105, 356, 292 (b) 47.5% **7** (a) 138 cm (b) 182.5 cm

8 (a) 4250 (b) 3069 **9** 1.65 l, 1.875 l, bottle B

10 (a) (i) 0.111 11 (ii) 0. 222 22 (b) $\frac{8}{9}$

11 (a) 5p (b) 13.9%

12 (a) £189 billion (b) £220. 4496 billion

13 (a) 76p (b) (i) 2 (ii) £5.16 (c) 34: Sun, 36: Mirror, 38: Guardian

14 (a) £27.50 (b) £300 (c) £327.50 (d) £52.50

Investigations

1 Average weekly sales are 729 cases.
Piece rate: £120 ÷ 90 = £1.33 per document case produced
Time rate: £120 ÷ 36 = £3.33 per hour (0.4 hour per case)
Commission: £25 × 90 = £2250, £120 ÷ £2250 × 100 = 5% commission
An extra nine document cases are needed per week.
Piece rate: £1.33 × 9 = £12 extra
Time rate: 9 cases ÷ 0.4 hour = $22\frac{1}{2}$ hours extra at time and a quarter
= £93.66
Commission: 5% on 9 × £25 = £11.25 extra
Clearly the Time-rate figure may give the best profit for the workers, but the worst in terms of a deal for the manager. A compromise may be an arrangement which will pay by means of a combination of rates.

2 (a) 8 years   (b) $7\frac{1}{2}$ years   (c) $7\frac{1}{4}$ years

3 This investigation will give an opportunity for research into matters to do with the purchase of a house. Included in the calculations should be the cost of purchase, stamp duty, solicitor's fees, mortgage rates, insurance, etc. Monthly outgoings should include the mortgage repayments, building and contents insurance, local taxes and notional amounts for energy bills, repairs and maintenance.

3 Number relations

Exercise 1

1 1 : 4	**2** 1 : 2	**3** 3 : 2	**4** 1 : 3	**5** 1 : 4
6 2 : 3	**7** 2 : 5	**8** 6 : 7	**9** 2 : 1	**10** 1 : 2

Exercise 2

1 12 : 1	**2** 11 : 400	**3** 3 : 10	**4** 8 : 1	**5** 3 : 1
6 1 : 50	**7** 25 : 2	**8** 100 : 1	**9** 1 : 500	**10** 1 : 20
11 1 : 2	**12** 4 : 5			

Exercise 3

1 1 : 0.25	**2** 1 : 3	**3** 1 : 7.5	**4** 1 : 1.8	**5** 1 : 2.5
6 1 : 2.4	**7** 1 : 5	**8** 1 : 4	**9** 1 : 2.5	**10** 1 : 9

Exercise 4

1 $\frac{2}{7}$	**2** 0.2	**3** 25%	**4** 1.5	**5** $\frac{1}{3}$
6 40%	**7** 0.5	**8** 40%	**9** $\frac{7}{10}$	**10** $2\frac{1}{2}$

Exercise 5

1 30	**2** 15	**3** 4	**4** 3	**5** 12
6 7	**7** 4	**8** 9	**9** 7	**10** 20

Exercise 6

1 20 cm	**2** 3.33 kg	**3** 6 kg	**4** 12.5 cm	**5** 24 kg
6 22.5 km/h	**7** 3240	**8** 280		

Exercise 7	**1** £20 : £15	**2** 360 g : 240 g	**3** £4.26 : £10.65
	4 10.72 m : 37.52 m	**5** 12 cm : 20 cm	**6** 18 kg : 40 kg
	7 45 cm : 30 cm	**8** 32 boys, 40 girls	**9** 400 g flour, 200 g fat
	10 301		

Exercise 8	**1** 20.4 tonnes	**2** 55 kg	**3** 198.1 m	**4** 175.5 kg
	5 132 m	**6** £9144		

Exercise 9	**1** £3.71	**2** 40p	**3** $37\frac{1}{2}$ min	**4** £13.00
	5 70p	**6** 67.5 kg	**7** £8.40	**8** 420

Exercise 10	**1** $4\frac{1}{2}$ days	**2** 12 days	**3** 49 hours	**4** 4 days	**5** 3 hours
	6 6 hours	**7** 75 boxes	**8** 18 days		

Exercise 11	**1** £62.40	**2** £78.23	**3** £84.15	**4** £66.34
	5 £240.80 + £182.75 = £423.55			

Exercise 12	**1** (a) 800 miles (b) 1400 miles		**2** (a) $1\frac{1}{4}$ hours (b) $1\frac{1}{2}$ hours	
	3 40 m.p.h.	**4** $1\frac{1}{2}$ hours	**5** 37 m/s	**6** 84 km
	7 18 knots	**8** 3 km		

Exercise 13	**1** 39 km/h	**2** 14 km/h	**3** 73 km/h	**4** 37 km/h
	5 76 km/h	**6** 51 km/h	**7** 11 km/h	**8** 53 km/h

Exercise 14	**1** 782 schillings	**2** 136 500 lire	**3** 1339.20 marks	**4** 154.42 kroner
	5 7592 francs	**6** $1276.61	**7** 39072 peseta	**8** 140.92 punts
	9 £153.76	**10** £49.68	**11** £2.97	**12** £168.70
	13 £1.31	**14** £18.87	**15** £7.78	**16** £14.34
	17 £39.58	**18** £24.00	**19** 26 422.50 marks	**20** £35.00

Exercise 15	**1** −1°C	**2** −3°C	**3** −7°C	**4** −4°C	**5** 2°C
	6 5°C	**7** −6°C	**8** −3°C	**9** −1°C	**10** 3°C
	11 8°C	**12** 11°C	**13** 5°C	**14** 3°C	**15** 7°C

Exercise 16	**1** 3	**2** −4	**3** −8	**4** −4	**5** 0
	6 −9	**7** −3	**8** −5	**9** −12	

Exercise 17	**1** 1	**2** 4	**3** 6	**4** −9	**5** 1
	6 −13	**7** 7	**8** 15	**9** −7	

Exercise 18

1 20	**2** 4	**3** −12	**4** −2	**5** −30
6 7	**7** −32	**8** 64	**9** 9	**10** 42
11 4	**12** −54			

Exercise 19

1 2	**2** 9	**3** 1	**4** −15	**5** −21
6 −12	**7** −4	**8** 5	**9** 8	**10** −36
11 −40	**12** −6			

Exercise 20

1 1, 4, 9, 16, 25, 36, 49, 64, 81, 100, 121, 144, 169, 196, 225, 256, 289, 324, 361, 400

2 1, 8, 27, 64, 125, 216, 343, 512, 729, 1000, 1331, 1728, 2197, 2744, 3375, 4096, 4913, 5832, 6859, 8000

3 2, 3, 5, 7, 11, 13, 17, 19, 23, 29, 31, 37, 41, 43, 47, 53, 59, 61, 67, 71

4 2, 5, 10, 13, 17, 25

5 1, 121, 12321, 1234321, 123454321

6 9, 1089, 110889, 11108889, 1111088889

Exercise 21

1 $2 \times 2 \times 3 \times 3$	**2** $2 \times 2 \times 2 \times 2 \times 2 \times 3$
3 $2 \times 2 \times 2 \times 3 \times 3 \times 3 \times 5$	**4** $3 \times 3 \times 3$
5 $2 \times 2 \times 2 \times 3 \times 3$	**6** $2 \times 2 \times 2 \times 3 \times 3 \times 5$
7 $2 \times 2 \times 2 \times 3 \times 5$	**8** $2 \times 2 \times 5 \times 7 \times 7$
9 $3 \times 4 \times 5 \times 7 \times 7$	**10** $2 \times 2 \times 2 \times 2 \times 2 \times 5 \times 5 \times 5$
11 $2 \times 2 \times 2 \times 5 \times 5 \times 13$	**12** $2 \times 3 \times 167$
13 $3 \times 3 \times 3 \times 3 \times 3 \times 3$	**14** $2 \times 2 \times 2 \times 2 \times 3 \times 13$
15 $5 \times 5 \times 29$	

Exercise 22

1 5 : 2	**2** 1 : 8	**3** 2 : 7	**4** 1 : 13
5 3 : 20	**6** 3 : 5	**7** 12 : 5	**8** 10 : 3
9 5 : 1	**10** 1 : 0.25	**11** 1 : 0.2	**12** 1 : 0.625
13 1 : 0.0888	**14** 60%	**15** $\frac{3}{10}$	**16** $\frac{1}{4}$
17 75%	**18** 0.4	**19** $\frac{7}{15}$	**20** 0.9
21 8 kg	**22** 120 kg	**23** 30 cm	**24** 16 cm : 32 cm
25 £8.10 : £18.90		**26** 11.26 kg : 50.67 kg	
27 24 cm, 32 cm, 40 cm		**28** £96, £76.80, £67.20	
29 69p	**30** £59.60	**31** $5\frac{1}{4}$ h	**32** 980
33 £596.05	**34** £220.24	**35** 50 m.p.h.	**36** 7 miles
37 60 m.p.h.	**38** £64.29	**39** 1 134 000 pta	
40 (a) 4, 9, 25 (b) 8, 27 (c) 7, 11, 13, 29			

Exercise 23

1 (a) $267.00 (b) £23.67   **2** (a) −2 (b) Sun., Mon., Tue., Sat.

3 30 bricklayers   **4** 13.5 kg

5 (a) JML (b) (i) JMKL (ii) 16 km (iii) 48 min

6 (a) 0.288p (b) £1.44   **7** 2 pints

8 (a) 49.4pta (b) 81p (c) yes: 81p > 3 × 25p

9 (a) £2.25; £2.05 (i) French (ii) 20p (b) 10.22 francs

10 (a) £300 (b) £339.75 (c) £1653.75

11 49.583 kcals   **12** (a) 14 h 41 min (b) 8°C

13 (a) $\frac{157}{111}$, $\frac{379}{268}$ (b) Proof

14 (a) C (b) 29 (c) CA: −9, AB: +5, CB: −4, BC: +4

15 (a) (i) 190m − 195m (ii) 128m − 130m (b) $9.60

16 (a) 3:2 (b) 60% (c) 84

Investigations

1 1.618 to three decimal places.
The numbers make up the Fibonacci series: 1, 1, 2, 3, 5, 8, 13, ..., where each successive number is the sum of the two previous numbers.

2 $3^3 = 27 = 6^2 - 3^2$ $3^2 = 9 = 1 + 3 + 5$
$4^3 = 64 = 10^2 - 6^2$ $4^2 = 16 = 1 + 3 + 5 + 7$
$5^3 = 125 = 15^2 - 10^2$ $5^2 = 25 = 1 + 3 + 5 + 7 + 9$
............$21^2 - 15^2$ etc.   successive adding of odd numbers

3 Use the pound as the common currency to which others relate. The important factor, though, on world currency markets, is that each currency relates to others: the pound is itself not stable.

Commission is also an important consideration in buying and selling currencies. For this reason, when going abroad, you should only change that amount of currency which you feel you will need; to change too much money will mean you incur additional charges for changing this currency back.

4 Patterns and relationships

Exercise 1

1 21p   **2** 56p   **3** 98p

4 £2.66   **5** £14   **6** £70

Exercise 2

1 10   **2** 25   **3** 46

4 37   **5** 61   **6** 157

Exercise 3

1 (a) 40 cm^2 (b) 54 m^2 (c) 8.51 cm^2 (d) 30 000 km^2

2 (a) 26 cm (b) 33 m (c) 12 cm (d) 700 km

3 (a) 20 m/s   (b) 70 m/s   (c) 150 m/s   (d) 220 m/s
4 (a) 60°   (b) 45°   (c) 24°   (d) 90°
5 (a) £1.10   (b) £1.55   (c) £2.30   (d) £5.30
6 (a) 50 min   (b) 56 min   (c) 97 min   (d) 31 min
7 (a) 15 h   (b) 14 h   (c) 11 h   (d) $9\frac{1}{2}$ h

Exercise 4

1 (a) 15   (b) 50   (c) 80   **2** (a) 60   (b) 180   (c) 15
3 (a) 18   (b) 26   (c) 12   **4** (a) 5   (b) 2   (c) 15
5 (a) 90   (b) 75   (c) 390   **6** (a) 39   (b) 100
7 (a) 15   (b) 23   (c) 0

Exercise 5

1 (a) 0.39 m^2 (b) 3900 cm^2 **2** $27\,000 \text{ m}^2$
3 (a) 5.1 m^2 (b) yes; area of wall is 9.5 m^2 **4** £31.84
5 2160 cm^3 **6** 3.74 cm^3 **7** $6 (.084) \text{ m}^3$ **8** $17.4 (36) \text{ m}^2$

Exercise 6

1 multiply by 2   **2** subtract 1   **3** multiply by 3
4 add 5   **5** divide by 10   **6** subtract 3
7 multiply by 10, then add 1   **8** multiply by 2, then add 1
9 multiply by 4, then subtract 1   **10** multiply by itself (square)

Exercise 7

1 $y = 2x$ **2** $y = x - 1$ **3** $y = 3x$ **4** $y = x + 5$
5 $y = x/10$ **6** $y = x - 3$ **7** $y = 10x + 1$ **8** $y = 2x + 1$
9 $y = 4x - 1$ **10** $y = x^2$

Exercise 8

1 (a) $£C = £12 + £1.70 \times h$ (b) $£C = £12 + £(1.7 \times 10) = £29$
2 (a) $m - 30$ (b) $£C = £12 + £[(m - 30) \times 0.20]$
    (c) $£C = £12 + £(70 \times 0.20) = £12 + £14 = £26$
3 (a) $£H = £8.50 + £1.50 \times d$ (b) $£H = £8.50 + £(1.50 \times 9) = £22$
4 (a) $£M = £(2.50 \times h) + £(3.50 \times s)$
    (b) $£M = £(2.50 \times 6) + (3.50 \times 5) = £15 + £17.50 = £32.50$
5 (a) $£P = £240 + £45 \times c$ (b) $£P = £240 + £(45 \times 8) = £600$

Exercise 9

1 $G = 47.4$ **2** $m = 57.276$ **3** $r = 4.5$ **4** $Y = 4.8$
5 $h = 2.48$ **6** $J = 64$ **7** $A = 277.92$ **8** $t = 0.4$
9 $d = 322.7$ **10** $x = 3.802$

Exercise 10

1 (i) $T = 17.440\,164$ (ii) 17.4   **2** (i) $R = 288.808\,66$ (ii) 289
3 (a) (i) $w = 269.22$ (ii) 269 (b) (i) $w = 265.066\,32$ (ii) 265
    (c) (i) $w = 669.204$ (ii) 669   **4** (i) $b = 6.871\,435\,4$ (ii) 6.87
5 (a) (i) $d = 14.6$ (ii) 14.6 (b) (i) $d = 0.56$ (ii) 0.560
    (c) (i) $d = -1.6$ (ii) -1.60

Exercise 11

1 2^6 2 x^8 3 y^6 4 a^5 5 4^5

6 2^7 7 t^6 8 10^9 9 m^5 10 10^5

Exercise 12

1 $6a^2$ 2 $30t^2$ 3 $16b^6$ 4 $8p^3q^2$ 5 $28s^3t$

6 $8a^3b^3$ 7 m^6n^6 8 10^6 9 6×10^7

Exercise 13

1 4 2 5^2 3 r^3 4 S^4 5 $12x^5$

6 a^4 7 $2b$ 8 q^2 9 10^4

Exercise 14

1 $\frac{1}{y^3}$ 2 $\frac{5}{a^2}$ 3 $\frac{a}{b}$ 4 $\frac{5x}{y^3}$ 5 $\frac{1}{3pq}$

6 $2mn$ 7 $\frac{3}{y}$ 8 $\frac{d}{c}$ –

Exercise 15

1 $8x$ 2 $5 + y$ 3 $6b - 2a$ 4 $3w$ 5 $4g - 4h$

6 $c + 1$ 7 $6a - 2b$ 8 $4p - q$ 9 $x + 3$ 10 0

Exercise 16

1 $7c$ 2 $3m + 8$ 3 $5x$

4 $2v - 6$ 5 $18a - 3$ 6 $8 - 3a^2$

7 k^3 8 $6q^2 + 4p$ 9 $10x - 10y$

10 $4y - 4x$ 11 $4d^4$ 12 $5r^3 - 2r$

13 $3ab^2 + 2a^2b$ 14 $11t^3$ 15 $p^2 + 2pq - 15$

16 $4w^2$ 17 $9a$ 18 0

Exercise 17

1 $4c + 20$ 2 $5a - 10$ 3 $12x + 3$

4 $2r^2 + 2r - 12$ 5 $56 - 24h$ 6 $3x^3 + 6x$

7 $30t + 100$ 8 $7a + 4$ 9 12

Exercise 18

1 $b^2 - 5b$ 2 $t^2 + 3t$ 3 $m^3 + 4m^2$

4 $8h^2 - 9h$ 5 $3d^2 + 21d$ 6 $25x^4 + 5x^2$

7 $4v^4 - 12v^3 + 4v^2$ 8 $2pr^2 + 2prh$ 9 $15x^2y - 6xy^2$

Exercise 19

1 $7x + 6y$ 2 $3c - 2d$ 3 $23a - 24$

4 $5p - 23q$ 5 $7a^3 + 3b$ 6 $3ab - 2ac + 2bc$

7 $4 - 3x^2$ 8 $3b - 2a$

Exercise 20

1 $x^2 + 3x + 2$ 2 $x^2 + 11x + 30$ 3 $2x^2 + 7x - 4$

4 $a^2 + 6a + 9$ 5 $2y^2 - 17y - 30$ 6 $x^2 - 1$

7 $6t^2 - 19t + 15$ 8 $5m^2 + 26m + 5$ 9 $25c^2 + 60c + 36$

10 $100x^2 - 1$

Exercise 21

1 $2(a + 2b)$ **2** $2(3p - q)$ **3** $10(10x - y)$
4 $a(3 + 4b)$ **5** $r(pq + st)$ **6** $n(m - 4)$
7 $4t(2g + 3h)$ **8** $a(3b - 4c + 5d)$ **9** $x(2y - 3z)$
10 $t(u + 5t)$ **11** $cd(c - d)$ **12** $a(2b^2 - 6b + 1)$
13 $5(s^3 + 4)$ **14** $xyz(x + y + z)$ **15** $12d^2(3d - 1)$
16 $ap(2 + p^2)$ **17** $ax(a + x)$ **18** $y(3 - 2y^2)$
19 $a^3bc(a - b)$ **20** $2\pi r(r + h)$

Exercise 22

1 (a) 43, 48 (b) each term is 5 greater than the previous term

2 (a) 52, 49 (b) each term is 3 smaller than the previous term

3 (a) 162, 486 (b) each term is 3 times the previous term

4 (a) 6, 3 (b) each term is half of the previous term

5 (a) 25, 32 (b) the differences increase by 1 each time

6 (a) 56, 72 (b) the differences increase by 2 each time

7 (a) 55, 46 (b) each term is 9 smaller than the previous term

8 (a) 34, 55 (b) each term is the previous two terms added

9 (a) 12, 12 (b) two sequences written alternately: one increases by 1 each time, the other decreases by 2 each time.

10 (a) 53, 68 (b) the differences increase by 2 each time

Exercise 23

1 22, 25 **2** 32, 40 **3** 38, 45 **4** 24, 30 **5** 30, 26
6 42, 68 **7** 62, 78 **8** 24, 25 **9** 145, 185 **10** 106, 128

Exercise 24

1 (a) $2n + 1$ (b) 15, 101 **2** (a) $5n - 1$ (b) 34, 249
3 (a) $3n + 9$ (b) 30, 159 **4** (a) $n + 4$ (b) 11, 54
5 (a) $10n - 3$ (b) 67, 497 **6** (a) $4n + 2$ (b) 30, 202
7 (a) $2n + 8$ (b) 22, 108 **8** (a) $(0.5)n$ (b) 3.5, 25
9 (a) $n - 3$ (b) 4, 47

Exercise 25

1 (a) 50, 65 (b) $n^2 + 1$ **2** (a) 72, 98 (b) $2n^2$
3 (a) 35, 48 (b) $n^2 - 1$ **4** (a) 144, 196 (b) $4n^2$
5 (a) 75, 101 (b) $2n^2 + 3$

Exercise 26

1 (a) $\frac{1}{7}, \frac{1}{8}$ (b) $\dfrac{1}{n + 1}$ **2** (a) $\frac{1}{12}, \frac{1}{14}$ (b) $\dfrac{1}{2n}$

3 (a) $\frac{7}{10}, \frac{8}{11}$ (b) $\dfrac{n + 1}{n + 4}$ **4** (a) $\frac{11}{13}, \frac{13}{15}$ (b) $\dfrac{2n - 1}{2n + 1}$

5 (a) $\frac{8}{18}, \frac{9}{20}$ (b) $\dfrac{n + 2}{2n + 6}$ **6** (a) $\frac{11}{12}, \frac{13}{14}$ (b) $\dfrac{2n - 1}{2n}$

7 (a) $\frac{6}{14}, \frac{7}{16}$ (b) $\frac{n}{2n+2}$ **8** (a) $\frac{6}{17}, \frac{7}{20}$ (b) $\frac{n}{3n-1}$

9 (a) $\frac{9}{12}, \frac{10}{13}$ (b) $\frac{n+3}{n+6}$ **10** (a) $\frac{17}{18}, \frac{20}{21}$ (b) $\frac{2n-1}{3n}$

Exercise 27

1 63, 102, 165; each term is the sum of the two previous terms

2 47, 76, 123; each term is the sum of the two previous terms

3 81, 149, 274; each term is the sum of the three previous terms

4 105, 193, 355; each term is the sum of the three previous terms

5 896, 2448, 6688; each term is twice the sum of the two previous terms

6 109, 177, 287; each term is the sum of the two previous terms $+ 1$

Exercise 28

1 100, 81, 64, 49, 36, 25, 16, 9, 4, 1

2 2, 6, 12, 20, 30

3 16, 13, 10, 7, 4, 1

4 3, 6, 9, 12, 15, 18, 21, 24, 27, 30

5 24, 12, 8, 6, 4.8, 4, 3.42857, 3

6 0.5, 0.666.., 0.75, 0.8, 0.833.., 0.857142.., 0.875, 0.888.., 0.9

Exercise 29

Each flow diagram will need to be checked, as there are many possibilities.

Exercise 30

1 (a) £21   (b) £34.50   (c) £75

2 (a) 15   (b) 210   (c) 5050

3 (a) £36   (b) £78   (c) £252

4 (a) 4.2   (b) 65.4   (c) 0

5 (a) 33   (b) 9.416

6 (a) 66   (b) 66.05

7 $4x + 5y$ **8** $6p + 4$ **9** $3x + 2y$

10 $17 - 5x$ **11** $5x + 15$ **12** $7x - 20$

13 $8x - 12$ **14** $7x - 13$ **15** $2x + 19y$

16 $7x^2 + 11x - 31$ **17** $x^2 + 5x + 6$ **18** $2x^2 + 7x - 15$

19 $x^2 - 20x + 100$ **20** $x^2 - 100$ **21** 51, 66

22 25, 12.5   **23** $5x^6, 6x^7$ **24** 67, 131

25 50, 43

Exercise 31

1 (i) $A = \frac{1}{2}(10 + 12) \times 5 = 55 \text{ cm}^2$

    (ii) $A = \frac{1}{2}(2.5 + 3.5) \times 1.5 = 4.5 \text{ cm}^2$

2 Wages $= (40 \times £1.20) + £12 - £8.60 = £51.40$

3 (a)

Tower number (t)	1	2	3	4	5	6
Number of cubes (c)	1	3	6	10	15	21

(b) $c = \frac{1}{2} \times 20\,(20 + 1) = 210$ (c) (i) 36 (ii) 64 (iii) 400
(d) $t = 8$ and $b = 3$; both have 36 cubes

4 (a) $\frac{4}{5}$ (b) $\frac{10}{11}$ (c) $\frac{100}{101}$ (d) 1

5 (a) (i)

Diagram	Number of squares
1	2
2	6
3	12
4	20
5	30

(ii) $20 \times 21 = 420$ (iii) $n\,(n+1)$ (b) $n\,(n+2)$

6 (b) 175 feet (c) 315 feet

Investigations

1   3rd differences: 0 0 0 ...
Fourth, fifth, etc. differences will all be zeros.

(a) 6 7 9 12 16 21 27 ...
1st differences: 1 2 3 4 5 6 ...
2nd differences: 1 1 1 1 1 ...
3rd differences: 0 0 0 0 ...
4th differences: 0 0 0 ...
Third, and subsequent, differences are all zero.

(b) 2 8 18 32 50 72 98 ...
1st differences: 6 10 14 18 22 26
2nd differences: 4 4 4 4 4
Third, and subsequent, differences are all zero.

(c) 1 8 27 64 125 216 343 512 729 1000
1st differences: 7 19 37 61 91 127 169 217 271
2nd differences: 12 18 24 30 36 42 48 54
3rd differences: 6 6 6 6 6 6 6
Fourth, and subsequent, differences are all zero.

(d) 2 2 4 6 10 16 26 42 68 110 178
1st differences: 0 2 2 4 6 10 16 26 42 68
2nd differences: (2) 0 2 2 4 6 10 16 26
3rd differences: (–2 2) 0 2 2 4 6 10
4th differences: (4 –2 2) 0 2 2 4
5th differences: (–6 4 –2 2) 0 2
The differences are the same as the original sequence, moved along one term.

(e)

	2	3	5	9	17	33	65	129	257	513

1st differences: 1   2   4   8   16   32   64   128   256

2nd differences: 1   2   4   8   16   32   64   128

3rd differences: 1   2   4   8   16   32   64

All differences are the same, being increasing powers of 2.

The next two terms in each sequence are:

(a) 34, 42 (b) 128, 162 (c) 1331, 1728 (d) 288, 466 (e) 1025, 2049

2 **A** For any three consecutive numbers, x, y, z, from the sequence, the difference between $x \times z$ and y^2 is always 1.

B Dividing each term by the *previous* one gives a sequence which approaches the number 1.618 ...

Dividing each term by the *subsequent* one gives a sequence which approaches the number 0.618 ...

The ratio 1 : 1.618 is the same as the ratio 0.618 : 1; it is called the **golden ratio**, and appears much in classical art and sculpture.

5   Formulas, equations and inequalities

Exercise 1

1 121   **2** £414   **3** 28p   **4** 17

5 £1.74   **6** 26p   **7** 532

Exercise 2

1 $x = 3$ **2** $k = 6$ **3** $t = 22$ **4** $y = 10$

5 $x = 16$ **6** $r = 20$ **7** $y = 8$ **8** $p = 55$

9 $z = 0$

Exercise 3

1 $x = 16$ **2** $y = 30$ **3** $t = 18$ **4** $p = 16$

5 $m = 200$ **6** $s = 14$ **7** $x = 90$ **8** $t = 64$

9 $d = 0$ **10** $x = 30$

Exercise 4

1 $x = 2$ **2** $k = 5$ **3** $t = 4$ **4** $y = 12$

5 $y = 9$ **6** $p = 8$ **7** $x = 6$ **8** $y = 10$

9 $t = 14$ **10** $d = 6$ **11** $d = 60$ **12** $s = 0$

Exercise 5

1 $x = 2$ **2** $k = 3$ **3** $t = 1$ **4** $y = 5$

5 $x = 10$ **6** $r = 4$ **7** $y = 9$ **8** $p = 6$

9 $x = 20$

Exercise 6

1 $x = -3$ **2** $k = -4$ **3** $t = -1$ **4** $y = 7$

5 $x = -3$ **6** $r = 6\frac{2}{3}$ **7** $y = 4$ **8** $p = -4$

9 $x = -5$ **10** $z = -2\frac{1}{2}$ **11** $b = 1\frac{1}{2}$ **12** $c = -2$

13 $h = 10$ **14** $y = -1$ **15** $m = -6\frac{2}{3}$ **16** $r = -\frac{2}{5}$

17 $t = \frac{2}{3}$ **18** $g = 10$

Exercise 7

1 $t = 7$ **2** $H = 1$ **3** $n = 8$ **4** $c = 5$

5 $x = 8$ **6** $x = -1$ **7** $s = -2$ **8** $x = 2$

9 $b = 3$ **10** $w = -2$ **11** $r = 3\frac{1}{2}$ **12** $z = 1$

13 $x = 1$ **14** $y = 8$ **15** $x = -1\frac{1}{2}$ **16** $k = 1$

17 $p = 2$ **18** $v = 3$ **19** $g = 3\frac{1}{2}$ **20** $t = 4$

Exercise 8

1 $x = 4$ **2** $t = 2$ **3** $n = 5$ **4** $p = 5$

5 $x = 2$ **6** $t = 5$ **7** $s = 2$ **8** $x = 2$

Exercise 9

1 (a) £$(X + 12)$ (b) £$(2X + 12)$
  (c) $2X + 12 = 50$: $X = 19$. Jack has £19, Jill has £31

2 $9x + 20 = 177.5$: $x = 17.5$, each payment is £17.50

3 $c + (c + 1) = 37$: $c = 18$, Charles is 18 years old

4 $t + (t + 3) + t + (t + 3) = 46$ or $4t + 6 = 46$: $t = 10$ cm

5 $a + b + o = 2b + b + (23 + b) = 143$ or $4b + 23 = 143$: $b = 30$, the apple weighs 60 g, the banana weighs 30 g and the orange weighs 53 g

6 $3j + 3j + j = 14$: $j = 2$ kg, parents each pick 6 kg, Judy picks 2 kg

7 $s + 2s + 2s = 30$ m: $s = 6$ m, lengths are 12 m, 12 m and 6 m

8 $60t + (40 \times 2t) = 980$ or $140t = 980$: $t = 7$, she bought 7 tulips and 14 daffodils

Exercise 10

1 $x = \pm 5.48$ **2** $x = \pm 7.07$ **3** $x = 2.35$

4 $x = 3.91$ **5** $x = 3.29, -3.79$ **6** $x = \pm 7.07$

7 $x = 2.33$ **8** $x = 18.34, -16.34$

Exercise 11

1 $x = 1, y = 2$ **2** $a = 6, b = 2$ **3** $p = 5, q = 1$ **4** $x = 2, v = 7$

5 $m = 6, n = 8$ **6** $s = 3, t = 3$ **7** $a = 4, b = 5$ **8** $x = 10, y = 1$

9 $m = 4, n = 3$ **10** $y = 1, z = 0$

Exercise 12

1 $x = 4, y = 6$ **2** $a = 1, b = 2$ **3** $p = 5, q = 3$ **4** $u = 10, v = 3$

5 $x = 7, y = 1$ **6** $c = 4, d = 3$ **7** $x = 2, y = 8$ **8** $p = 1, q = 3$

9 $s = 5, t = 5$

Exercise 13

1 $d = 2, e = 5$ **2** $x = 10, y = 4$ **3** $p = 7, q = 6$ **4** $x = 12, y = 8$

5 $a = 13, b = 7$ **6** $u = 4, v = 5$ **7** $a = 3, b = 4$ **8** $s = 2, t = 3$

9 $x = 49, y = 1$

Exercise 14

1 $x = 5, y = -1$ **2** $a = 3, b = 7$ **3** $p = 9, q = 7$ **4** $a = 3, b = 2$

5 $u = 4, v = 5$ **6** $y = 9, z = 1$ **7** $d = 8, e = 2$ **8** $x = 2, y = 2$

9 $x = 5, y = 0$

Exercise 15

1 $x = 4, y = 2$ **2** $x = 5, y = 2$ **3** $x = 3, y = -1$ **4** $x = 7, y = 2$

5 $x = 4, y = -2$ **6** $x = -2, y = 5$ **7** $x = 1, y = 6$ **8** $x = 2, y = -3$

9 $x = 10, y = 5$ **10** $x = 5, y = -4$ **11** $x = \frac{1}{2}, y = 4$ **12** $x = 20, y = 3$

13 $x = 3, y = \frac{3}{2}$ **14** $x = 2, y = -5$ **15** $x = \frac{5}{2}, y = -1$

Exercise 16

1 $3b + s = 27, b + 2s = 24: b = 6p, s = 9p$

2 $4n + s = 28, 2n + 3s = 34: n = 5 \text{ g}, s = 8 \text{ g}$

3 $4A + 3B = 30, 3A + 6B = 30: A = 6 \text{ cm}, B = 2 \text{ cm}$

4 $5X + 4Y = 46, 2X - 3Y = 0: X = £6, Y = £4$

5 $3a + 2o = 88, a + 3o = 76: a = 16p, o = 20p$

Exercise 17

1 $d = c - 5$ **2** $n = 3m - 12$ **3** $x = y + 2$ **4** $s = 10 - 4r$

5 $p = \frac{t}{2}$ **6** $h = \frac{5g}{3}$ **7** $p = \frac{m + 5}{2}$ **8** $k = \frac{a - 4}{3}$

9 $V = \frac{k}{P}$ **10** $z = \frac{x}{m}$ **11** $v = \frac{330}{f}$ **12** $d = \frac{w}{6}$

Exercise 18

1 $R = \frac{V}{I}$ **2** $b = d - 3a$ **3** $q = \frac{2p}{3}$ **4** $r = \frac{C}{2\pi}$

5 $m = \frac{y - c}{x}$ **6** $x = \frac{z - 3}{2}$ **7** $v = at + u$ **8** $d = \frac{x}{3} + 4$

9 $C = \frac{5}{9}(F - 32)$ **10** $V = \frac{kT}{P}$

Exercise 19

1 $t = 40$ **2** $x = -0.6$ **3** $u = 20$ **4** $b = 6$

5 $p = 11$ **6** $m = 4$ **7** $p = 7$ **8** $C = 10$

9 $c = 2\frac{1}{2}$ **10** $u = 20$

Exercise 20

1 $x > 2$ **2** $k < 34$ **3** $t > 9$ **4** $y > 7$

5 $x < 7$ **6** $r > 10$ **7** $y < 6\frac{1}{2}$ **8** $p > -5$

9 $z < -3\frac{1}{4}$

Exercise 21

1 $x < 3$ **2** $k < 17$ **3** $t > 3$ **4** $y > -3$

5 $x < 8$ **6** $y < 1$ **7** $n < 3$ **8** $x < -\frac{20}{3}$

9 $z < 14$

Exercise 22

1 $t = 5, 6, 7, 8, 9$ **2** $x = 1, 2, 3, 4, 5, 6, 7, 8, 9$

3 $s = -4, -3, -2, -1, 0, 1,$ **4** $n = 2, 3, 4, 5, 6, 7, 8, 9, 10$

5 $x = 1, 2, 3, 4, 5$ **6** $t = -3, -2, -1, 0, 1, 2, 3$

7 $x = -9, -8, -7, -6, -5, -4, -3$

8 $m = 11, 12, 13, 14, 15, 16, 17, 18, 19, 20$

9 $n = 0, 1, 2, 3, 4, 5, 6, 7, 8, 9$

Exercise 23

1 $-3 < x < 3$ **2** $-5 < c < 5$ **3** $-6 \leqslant s \leqslant 6$ **4** $-8 < x < 8$

5 $-7 < x < 7$ **6** $-2 < k < 2$ **7** $-\frac{3}{2} \leqslant x \leqslant \frac{3}{2}$ **8** $-20 \leqslant n \leqslant 20$

9 $-\frac{1}{2} < d < \frac{1}{2}$ **10** $0.1 \leqslant x \leqslant 0.1$

Exercise 24

1 $x = 5$ **2** $x = 13$ **3** $x = 8$

4 $x = 6$ **5** $x = 7$ **6** $x = 11$

7 $x = 10$ **8** $x = 9$ **9** $x = 5$

10 $x = 8$ **11** $x = -4$ **12** $x = -8$

13 $x = 2\frac{1}{2}$ **14** $x = 1\frac{1}{4}$ **15** $x = 2$

16 $x = 3.61$ **17** $x = 4.22, (-5.22)$ **18** $x = 5.23, (-3.73)$

19 $x = 3.65$ **20** $x = 7.40, (-5.40)$ **21** $x = 4.07, (-10.1)$

22 $x = 13.44, (-7.44)$ **23** $x = 4.64$ **24** $x = 7, y = 5$

25 $x = 10, y = 7$ **26** $x = 2, y = 3$ **27** $x = 8, y = 2$

28 $x = 6, y = 1$ **29** $x = 8, y = 2\frac{1}{2}$ **30** $x = 7, y = -2$

31 $x = \frac{2}{3}, y = \frac{1}{3}$ **32** $y = \frac{x}{4}$ **33** $k = 3h + 5$

34 $k = \frac{h+5}{3}$ **35** $k = \frac{h}{3} + 5$ **36** $n = 3(m-2p)$

37 $F = \frac{9C}{5} + 32$ **38** $t = \sqrt{\frac{s}{10}}$ **39** $u = \sqrt{v^2 - 2as}$

40 $x > 7$ **41** $x < 5$ **42** $x < 19$

43 $x > 30$ **44** $x > 4$ **45** $x > 4$

46 $x > 2\frac{1}{2}$ **47** $x > 2$ **48** $-12 < x < 12$

49 $5 < x < 11$

Exercise 25

1 (a) $7x$ pence   (b) $(7x + 5y)$ pence   (c) $7x + 5y = 391$
   (d) $4x + 9y = 377$ (e) $x = 38, y = 25$ (f) $2(38p) + (25p) = 101p$

2 $x = 24$ **3** $3x + 11 = 5x - 7, x = 9$

4 $x + y = 50, 2x + 5y = 145$ (x = no. of 2p coins, y = no. of 5p coins)
   $y = 15, x = 35$ Hence: $35 \times$ 2p coins, $15 \times$ 5p coins.

5 (a) $v = 30 - 2(5) = 20$ (b) $0 = 30 - 2t \Rightarrow t = 15$

6 (a) $t = \frac{2(55) + 28}{3} = 46$ (b) $y = 3t - 2x$

7 (a) $x = 2\frac{1}{2}$ (b) $y = -2$ (c) $z = -1$

8 (a) $5x + 31$ (b) (i) $7x + 5 = 5x + 31$ (ii) $x = 13$, 96 balloons

9 (a) $x + 7$ (b) $2(x + 7)$ (c) (i) $2(x + 7) = 36$ (ii) $x = 11$ people

319

10 (a) $x = 17$ (b) $y = -5$

11 (a) $x + 15$ (b) (i) $x + 34$ (ii) $3x$ (c) $x + 34 = 3x; x = 17$

12 $x = 12, y = -7$

13 (i) $P = 2(2.4 + 4.8) = 14.4$ (ii) $y = \dfrac{P}{2} - x$

14 $1.5 = \dfrac{122.5 - m}{s}, 0.4 = \dfrac{106 - m}{s}; s = 15, m = 100$

15 (a) $y = 4x, y = x + 1; x = \frac{1}{3}, y = 1\frac{1}{3}$ (b) $x > \frac{1}{3}$

Investigations

1 (a) output is 3   (b) output is 7

In general, the output is the square root of x. There should be only 4 or 5 iterations before the desired accuracy is reached.

Each iteration improves the accuracy by at least 1, often 2 or more, decimal places

2 A (a) (i) no change   (ii) inequality sign has to be reversed

(b) (i) no change   (ii) inequality sign has to be reversed

B   If $\dfrac{1}{x} < k$, then $x > \dfrac{1}{k}$

C   If $\dfrac{-1}{x} < k$, then $x > \dfrac{-1}{k}$

---

6 Graphical representation

Exercise 1

1 H = (−2,4)
  I = (7,−3)
  J = (−5,−2)
  K = (0,−4)
  L = (−4,1)

2

Exercise 2

1

2
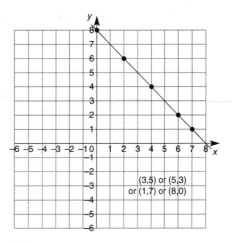

(3,5) or (5,3)
or (1,7) or (8,0)

3
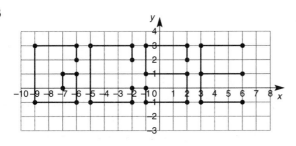

Exercise 3

1

x				−3	−2	−1	0	1	2	3	4
$x+2$				−1	0	1	2	3	4	5	6

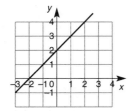

2

x				−3	−2	−1	0	1	2	3	4
$x-1$				−4	−3	−2	−1	0	1	2	3

3

x				−3	−2	−1	0	1	2	3	4
$2x+5$				−1	1	3	5	7	9	11	13

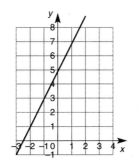

4

x				−3	−2	−1	0	1	2	3	4
$5-x$				8	7	6	5	4	3	2	1

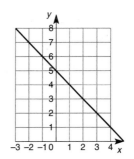

ANSWERS

5

x			-3	-2	-1	0	1	2	3	4
$3x - 5$			-14	-11	-8	-5	-2	1	4	7

6

x			-3	-2	-1	0	1	2	3	4
$\frac{x}{2} + 7$			$5\frac{1}{2}$	6	$6\frac{1}{2}$	7	$7\frac{1}{2}$	8	$8\frac{1}{2}$	9

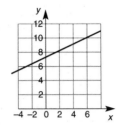

7

x			-3	-2	-1	0	1	2	3	4
$\frac{x}{2} - 1$			$-2\frac{1}{2}$	-2	$-1\frac{1}{2}$	-1	$-\frac{1}{2}$	0	$\frac{1}{2}$	1

8

x		0	1	2	3	4	5	6	7	8
$15 - 2x$		15	13	11	9	7	5	3	1	-1

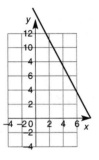

9

x		0	1	2	3	4	5	6	7	8	9	10	11	12
$10 - x$		10	9	8	7	6	5	4	3	2	1	0	-1	-2

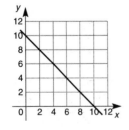

10

x			-3	-2	-1	0	1	2	3	4
$2x - 2$			-8	-6	-4	-2	0	2	4	6

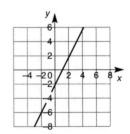

Exercise 4

1

x		−3	−2	−1	0	1	2	3	4
y = 8−x		11	10	9	8	7	6	5	4

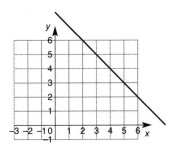

2

x		−3	−2	−1	0	1	2	3	4
y = 2x −3		−9	−7	−5	−3	−1	1	3	5

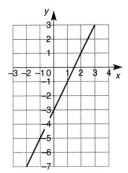

3

x		−3	−2	−1	0	1	2	3	4
y = x + 2		−1	0	1	2	3	4	5	6

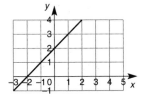

4

x		−3	−2	−1	0	1	2	3	4
y = 12 − x		15	14	13	12	11	10	9	8

5

x		−3	−2	−1	0	1	2	3	4
y = x + 4		1	2	3	4	5	6	7	8

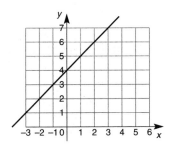

6

x		−3	−2	−1	0	1	2	3	4
y = 2x + 4		−2	0	− 2	4	6	8	10	12

7

x					−3	−2	−1	0	1	2	3	4
$y = 2x + \frac{5}{2}$					$-3\frac{1}{2}$	$-1\frac{1}{2}$	$\frac{1}{2}$	$2\frac{1}{2}$	$4\frac{1}{2}$	$6\frac{1}{2}$	$8\frac{1}{2}$	$10\frac{1}{2}$

8

x					−3	−2	−1	0	1	2	3	4
$y = 2x + 3$					−3	−1	1	3	5	7	9	11

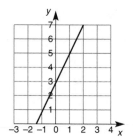

9

x					−3	−2	−1	0	1	2	3	4
$y = 2x - \frac{2}{3}$					$-6\frac{2}{3}$	$-4\frac{2}{3}$	$-2\frac{2}{3}$	$-\frac{2}{3}$	$1\frac{1}{3}$	$3\frac{1}{3}$	$5\frac{1}{3}$	$7\frac{1}{3}$

10

x					−3	−2	−1	0	1	2	3	4
$y = \frac{x}{2} + 4$					$2\frac{1}{2}$	3	$3\frac{1}{2}$	4	$4\frac{1}{2}$	5	$5\frac{1}{2}$	6

Exercise 5

1 (0,3), (1,4),(2,5),(3,6) etc.

2 (0,−1), (1,1),(2,3),(3,5) etc.

3 (0,2), (1,3),(2,4),(3,5) etc.

4 (1,0), (4,1),(7,2),(10,3) etc.

5 (0,4), (2,5),(4,6),(6,7) etc.

6 (0,−1), (1,2),(2,5),(3,8) etc.

7 (3,9), (4,8),(5,7),(6,6) etc.

8 (0,2), (1,4),(2,6),(3,8) etc.

9 (4,0), (5,1),(6,2),(7,3) etc.

10 (1,9), (2,8),(3,7),(4,6) etc.

11 (4,0), (6,1),(8,2),(10,3) etc.

12 (0,16), (1,14),(2,12),(3,10) etc.

13 (0,3), (3,2),(6,1),(9,0) etc.

14 (0,8), (3,6),(6,4),(9,2) etc.

15 (4,0), (5,4),(6,8),(7,12) etc.

Exercise 6

1 (0,1) **2** (0,−4) **3** (0,−3) **4** (0,5) **5** (0,−2)

6 (0,3) **7** (0,−1) **8** (0,$\frac{3}{4}$) **9** (0,$\frac{1}{2}$)

Exercise 7

1 (a) 2 (b) −1 **2** (a) 3 (b) 4 **3** (a) 5 (b) 2

4 (a) 1 (b) −7 **5** (a) $\frac{1}{2}$ (b) 2 **6** (a) $\frac{2}{3}$ (b) −2

7 (a) −1 (b) 3 **8** (a) −2 (b) 0 **9** (a) −3 (b) 10

Exercise 8

1 1, 2; $y = x + 2$ **2** $\frac{1}{2}$, 1; $y = \frac{x}{2} + 1$ $(2y = x + 2)$

3 2,−2; $y = 2x − 2$ **4** −1, 4; $y = −x + 4$ $(x + y = 4)$

5 −2, 6; $y = −2x + 6$ $(2x + y = 6)$ **6** $\frac{1}{2}$, −2; $y = \frac{x}{2} − 2$ $(2y = x − 4)$

Exercise 9

1 $x = 2, y = 3$ **2** $x = 4, y = 1$ **3** $x = 3, y = −2$

4 $x = −2, y = 4$ **5** $x = −1, y = −3$ **6** $x = 0, y = 4$

Exercise 10

1

$x = 3, y = 1$

2

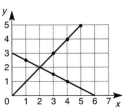

$x = 2, y = 2$

3

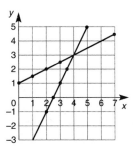

$x = 4, y = 3$

4

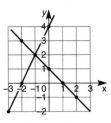

$x = −1, y = 2$

5

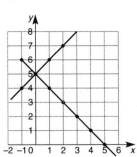

$x = 0, y = 5$

6

$x = 2, y = −2$

Exercise II

1

2

3

4

5

6

7

8

9

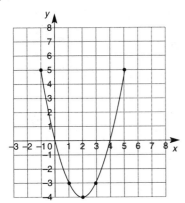

ANSWERS

Exercise 12

1

2

3

4

5

6

7

8

9

Exercise 13

1

2

3

4

5

6

7

8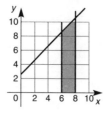

328

Exercise 14

1 (a) 1400   (b) 60 km/h   (c) 1 h   (d) 10 km

   (e) 1 h   (f) 1.5 h   (g) 46.7 km/h

2 (a) 1000   (b) $\frac{1}{2}$ h   (c) 70 km   (d) 1 h

   (e) third   (f) 60 km/h

3 (a) 20 cm   (b) 1.15 p.m.   (c) 200 cm/h

   (d) 1.15 p.m. and 1.30 p.m.   (e) 160 cm/h

   (f) 1.33 p.m.   (g) 15 min   (h) 100 cm/h

4 (a) 66.7 km/h   (b) 100 km/h   (c) 4.30 p.m.   (d) 5.00 p.m.

5 (a) $\frac{1}{2}$ h   (b) 10.00 p.m.   (c) 50 km   (d) 10.42 a.m.

   (e) Steve's   (f) $\frac{1}{2}$ h

Exercise 15

1 (a) $(-2,10),(5,10)$ (b) $(-2,-6),(5,-6)$ (c) $(1,6),(1,-2)$

2 (a)

x	0	1	2	3	4
y	12	9	6	3	0

(b)

x	-4	-3	-2	-1	0
y	0	3	6	9	12

(c) Area of triangle = 48 sq. units.

3 (a) $(0, 16), (16, 0)$

   (b) $(0, 10), (20, 0)$

   (c) $(12, 4)$

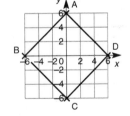

4 AB: $y = x + 6$

   BC: $x + y = -6$

   CD: $y = x - 6$

   DA: $x + y = 6$

5

x	-4	-3	-2	-1	0	1	2	3	4
y	20	13	8	5	4	5	8	13	20

(a) $y = 4$

(b) $-3 < x < 3$

6

x	0	1	2	3	4	5	6	7	8
y	15	10	7.5	6	5	4.3	3.75	3.3	3

(a) $y = 4$

(b) $x = 3.5$

(c) $y = 0.1$ $(\frac{30}{300})$

As x becomes larger and larger, y becomes smaller and smaller, getting nearer and nearer to zero, but never quite reaching zero.

7

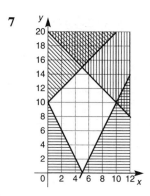

Shape is a kite

Exercise 16

1 (a) $x \times y = 120$; $y = \frac{120}{x}$

(b)

x	4	8	12	16	20	24	30
y	30	15	10	7.5	6	5	4

(d) $y = 6\frac{2}{3}$ (e) $x^2 = 120$; $x = \sqrt{120} = 10.95$ m

2 $y < x, x < 4, y > 1$

3 (a)

Distance (miles)	Tariff A cost	Tariff B cost
0	£20	£0
20	£23.00	£8
50	£27.50	£20
70	£30.50	£28
100	£35.00	£40

(c) 80 miles

4 (a) 1000 m (b) 4 min

5 (a) 10 cm (b) tank filling (c) tank emptying (d) tank empty

6 (b) $x = 2.4, y = 5.8$

7 (a) R is $(1,-1)$ (b) S is $(-1,2)$

8 (a) $x = 5, y = 2.4$ (b) $k = 12$

9 (a)

x	2	4	6	8
y	3	2	1	0

(b)

x	2	4	6	8
y	0	1	2	3

(d) $x = 5, y = 1\frac{1}{2}$

10 (a)   nothing, the coach stopped   (b) 12.30   (c) $2\frac{1}{2}$ hours
(d)   (i) 100 miles   (ii) $1\frac{1}{2}$ hours   (iii) $66\frac{2}{3}$ m.p.h.

11 (a)

V	1	2	3	4	5	6
P	10	5	3.33	2.5	2	1.7

(c) $P = 2.7$

(d) P is never zero. As V increases, P decreases but is always

$$\frac{10}{(\text{something})}$$, which gets smaller and smaller.

12 (i) $x = 2$ (ii) $x > 2$ or $y > 0$

Investigations   **1** (i)

x	-4	-3	-2	-1	0	1	2	3	4
y	16	9	4	1	0	1	4	9	16

(ii)

x	-4	-3	-2	-1	0	1	2	3	4
y	19	12	7	4	3	4	7	12	19

(iii)

x	-4	-3	-2	-1	0	1	2	3	4
y	9	2	-3	-6	-7	-6	-3	2	9

All three graphs are identical in shape, but moved vertically.

Extension

(i)

x	-4	-3	-2	-1	0	1	2	3	4
y	9	4	1	0	1	4	9	16	25

(ii)

x	-6	-5	-4	-3	-2	-1	0	1	2
y	9	4	1	0	1	4	9	16	25

(iii)

x	2	3	4	5	6	7	8	9	10
y	25	16	9	4	1	0	1	4	9

All three graphs are identical in shape, but moved horizontally.

2 All such lines are parallel with those shown in the diagram.

Extension
All such lines are parallel with those shown in the diagram.
As K increases, the lines move further away from the origin.
If $K = 0$, the line passes through origin.

(i)

(ii)

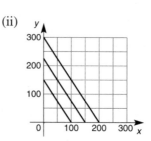

---

7 Measures

Exercise 1

1 70 mm	**2** 400 cm	**3** 0.043 km	**4** 6.25 cm	**5** 1.25 kg
6 310 ml	**7** 1370 g	**8** 130 cl	**9** 3000 m	**10** 3.51 m
11 30 ml	**12** 2000 kg	**13** 0.2 g	**14** 0.4 *l*	**15** 0.7 t
16 0.003 kg	**17** 49.8 cm	**18** 70 ml	**19** 113.2 mm	**20** 963 cm

Exercise 2

1 1.05 litres **2** 2550 metres **3** 1500 bags **4** 48.6 kg
5 25 **6** 4 kg 225 g **7** 10.5 kg
8 750 mm, 35 m, 0.072 km, 78 m, 0.3 km, 0.4 km, 550 m, 1.5 km
9 0.012 *l*, 0.02 *l*, 0.14 *l*, 1.3 *l*, 270 cl, 400 cl, 600 cl, 750 cl
10 112 kg, 0.2 t, 300 kg, 0.8 t, 0.85 t, 875 kg, 1.4 t, 1500 kg

Exercise 3

1 $6\,\text{ft}\,11\frac{1}{2}\,\text{in}$	**2** 14 pints	**3** 8 st 13 lb	**4** 12 oz	**5** 5 ft 5 in
6 110 yd	**7** 10 ft	**8** 35 oz	**9** 7 yd 1 ft	**10** 5 fl. oz
11 $6\frac{1}{2}\,\text{cwt}$	**12** $2\,\text{ft}\,7\frac{1}{4}\,\text{in}$

Exercise 4

1 9 in	**2** 7 ft 2 in	**3** 6 gal 5 pt	**4** 660 yd	**5** $1\frac{3}{4}$ tons
6 $13\frac{1}{8}$ gal	**7** 11 st	**8** 16 st	**9** $4\frac{3}{4}$ oz	**10** 48

Exercise 5

1 22 lb	**2** 15 cm	**3** 24 km	**4** 7 kg	**5** 10.29 l
6 $33\frac{3}{4}$ miles	**7** 7 pt	**8** 20 kg	**9** 60 cm	**10** 40 km
11 237.5 cm	**12** 1.19 kg	**13** $4\frac{1}{2}$ m	**14** 40 ft	**15** 60 miles

Exercise 6

1 6.14 kg	**2** 85 cm	**3** $207\frac{1}{2}$ miles	**4** 6.6 lb	**5** 14 oz
6 12 m	**7** 6.56 gal	**8** 17.6 lb	**9** 8 m	**10** 6 ft

Exercise 7

1 kg	**2** cm	**3** km	**4** cm
5 litres	**6** cm	**7** cm	**8** ml
9 litres	**10** km	**11** ml	**12** mm

Exercise 8

1 (a) 17 cm (b) $17.5\,\text{cm}^2$	**2** (a) 17 cm (b) $18\,\text{cm}^2$
3 (a) 28 m (b) $24\,\text{m}^2$	**4** (a) 25 m (b) $19\,\text{m}^2$
5 (a) 28 cm (b) $28.75\,\text{cm}^2$	**6** (a) 28 cm (b) $24\,\text{cm}^2$
7 (a) 30 cm (b) $38.5\,\text{cm}^2$	

Exercise 9

1 $9\,\text{cm}^2$	**2** $20\,\text{cm}^2$	**3** $20\,\text{m}^2$	**4** $20\,\text{m}^2$	**5** $27\,\text{cm}^2$
6 $42\,\text{cm}^2$	**7** $30\,\text{m}^2$	**8** $6.75\,\text{m}^2$		

Exercise 10

	Rectangles					Triangles		
	Length	Breadth	Area	Perimeter		Base	Height	Area
1	3 m	2 m	$6\,\text{m}^2$	10 m	**9**	4 m	3 m	$6\,\text{m}^2$
2	9 m	5 m	$45\,\text{m}^2$	28 m	**10**	10 m	14 m	$70\,\text{m}^2$
3	4 cm	3 cm	$12\,\text{cm}^2$	14 cm	**11**	18 cm	12.5 cm	$112.5\,\text{cm}^2$
4	6 cm	4 cm	$24\,\text{cm}^2$	20 cm	**12**	24 cm	16 cm	$192\,\text{cm}^2$
5	10 m	7.5 m	$75\,\text{m}^2$	35 m				
6	18 cm	4.5 cm	$81\,\text{cm}^2$	45 cm				
7	40 cm	12.5 cm	$500\,\text{cm}^2$	105 cm				
8	30 cm	25 cm	$750\,\text{cm}^2$	110 cm				

ANSWERS

Exercise 11

1 24 cm^2	2 22 cm^2	3 24 cm^2	4 24 cm^2
5 53.4 cm^2	6 25.6 cm^2	7 26.25 cm^2	8 8.4 m^2
9 21.875 cm^2			

Exercise 12

1 37.70 cm	2 69.11 cm	3 25.13 cm	4 40.84 cm
5 9.42 cm	6 34.56 cm	7 163.36 cm	8 31.42 cm
9 23.88 m	10 87.96 cm	11 6.37 cm	12 13.53 m
13 38.20 m	14 23.87 mm	15 14.32 cm	16 10.03 m

Exercise 13

1 188.5 cm	2 34.5 mm	3 204.2 cm	4 40 023.89 km
5 942.48 cm	6 21.36 m		

Exercise 14

1 78.5 m^2	2 201.06 m^2	3 113.10 cm^2
4 38.48 m^2	5 19.63 cm^2	6 132.73 cm^2
7 18.86 cm^2	8 45.36 cm^2	9 50.27 m^2
10 78.54 cm^2	11 4.55 cm	12 5.64 m
13 7.57 mm	14 5.47 cm	15 2.52 m

Exercise 15

1 201.06 m^2	2 113 m^2	3 9.62 m^2	4 4.52 m^2
5 1.60 m	6 4.6 m	7 706.19 cm^2	8 138.54 cm^2
9 38.48 cm^2	10 17.36 m^2		

Exercise 16

1 54 cm^3	2 40 cm^3	3 330 cm^3
4 141.37 cm^3	5 603.19 cm^3	6 200 cm^3
7 96.21 cm^3	8 48 cm^3	9 15 cm^3
10 60 cm^3	11 112.5 cm^3	12 150 cm^3

Exercise 17

1 2.5 cm	2 1.78 cm	3 7.08 m	4 4.58 mm
5 1.99 m	6 3.5 m	7 3 cm	8 1.27 m

Exercise 18

1 132 m^2	2 132 cm^2	3 26 cm^2	4 30 cm^2
5 156 cm^2	6 84 cm^2	7 42 cm^2	8 30 cm^2
9 3600 cm^2	10 660 cm^2	11 620 cm^2	12 960 cm^2

Exercise 19

1 030°	2 300°	3 310°	4 110°	5 225°
6 025°	7 115°	8 S20°E	9 S5°W	10 N30°W
11 S22°E	12 N25°E	13 N75°E	14 N65°W	15 S70°E

Exercise 20 Check the compass directions and 3-figures bearings you have drawn.

Exercise 21

1 (a) 100 km (b) 132 km (c) 276 km (d) 288 km
2 (a) 7.5 km (b) 14 km (c) 41.5 km (d) 42 km
3 (a) 87.5 km (b) 30 km (c) 242.5 km (d) 169.25 km
4 (a) 3 km (b) 8.4 km (c) 60.6 km (d) 72.6 km
5 (a) 175 km (b) 42 km (c) 532 km (d) 616 km

Exercise 22

Bearings should be ±2° of those shown below, and distances ±0.5 km.

1 (a) 033° (b) 32.4 km   2 (a) 277° (b) 9.6 km
3 (a) 052° (b) 15 km   4 (a) 187° (b) 10.5 km
5 (a) 242° (b) 23.1 km   6 (a) 062° (b) 23. km
7 (a) 213° (b) 32.4 km   8 (a) 350° (b) 16.5 km
9 (a) 072° (b) 26.7 km   10 (a) 232° (b) 37.8 km
11 (a) 016° (b) 15.6 km   12 (a) 080° (b) 16.5 km

Exercise 23

1 30 m   2 5 km   3 200 m   4 400 m   5 1.25 km
6 8.75 km   7 1.25 km   8 600 m   9 4.8 km   10 2.175 km

Exercise 24

1 1.65 cm and 1.749 cm   2 8.25 m and 8.34 m
3 10.35 km and 10.449 km   4 9.5 cm and 9.149 cm
5 4.45 m and 4.549 m   6 7.95 m and 8.049 m
7 2.95 cm and 3.049 cm   8 4.845 cm and 4.8549 cm
9 2.125 mm and 2.1349 mm   10 7.245 cm and 7.2549 cm
11 8.945 cm and 8.9549 cm   12 2.05 mm and 2.149 mm
13 14.505 m and 14.5149 m   14 8.385 m and 8.3949 m
15 7.115 cm and 7.12489 cm

Exercise 25

1 50 mm   2 40 ml   3 3500 kg   4 2 kg   5 752 cm
6 0.7 m   7 17   8 45 kg   9 30 pt   10 4 yd
11 24 oz   12 4 ft 8 in   13 90 cm   14 5.71 l 15 64 km
16 (a) 15.4 cm (b) 14.4 cm^2 17 (a) 27 cm (b) 35.5 cm^2
18 (a) 40 cm (b) 64 cm^2 19 40 cm^2 20 60 cm^2
21 136 cm^2 22 8.75 cm^2 23 (a) 31.42 cm (b) 78.54 cm^2
24 (a) 37.70 cm (b) 113.10 cm^2 25 (a) 9.42 cm (b) 7.07 cm^2
26 (a) 22.0 cm (b) 38.48 cm^2 27 48 cm^3 28 157.1 cm^3
29 432 cm^3 30 166 cm^2 31 39 cm^2 32 468 cm^2
33 (a) N44°E (b) 044°   34 (a) S44°W (b) 224°
35 (a) N45°W (b) 315°   36 (a) S65°E (b) 115°

Exercise 26

1 (a) metres   (b) millimetres

2 (a) (i) 250 000 cm   (ii) 2500 m   (iii) 2.5 km   (b) 30 minutes

3 (a) $100 \, \text{cm}^2$ (b) $78.5 \, \text{cm}^2$ (c) $21.46 \, \text{cm}^2$

4 (b) $290°$ 5   (b) 24.3 km

6 (i) $55 \, \text{cm}^2$ (ii) $4.5 \, \text{cm}^2$ 7 (a) 28 cm   (b) $40 \, \text{cm}^2$

8 (a) $75 \, 398 \, \text{cm}^3$ (b) $45 \, 239 \, \text{cm}^3$ (c) 125

9 (a) (i) 800 m   (ii) $39 \, 991 \, \text{m}^2$ (b) 4 hectares

10 (a) 125.66 cm   (b) 268.5 cm

11 (a) 9.54 cm   (b) $52.47 \, \text{cm}^2$

12 (a) (i) 94.24 cm   (ii) 94.24 cm by 80 cm   (iii) $56548.7 \, \text{cm}^3$ (b) 26.59 cm

13 (a) $392 \, \text{cm}^2$ (b) 765

Investigations

1

Year	Value	Error
1700 BC	3.160 493 8	0.6%
250 BC max	3.845 070 4	22.4%
250 BC min	3.142 857 1	0.04%
AD 100	3.162 277 7	0.65%
AD 300	3.155 555 5	0.4%
AD 500	3.141 592 9	0.000 008 4%

All values of π shown are *greater* than today's value of π, 3.1415927. The most accurate value used throughout Europe was the Greek maximum value (250 BC) of $\frac{22}{7}$. Indeed, this approximation continued to be in common use until calculators were introduced into schools and colleges in the 1980s: $\frac{22}{7}$ was easy to remember, and both numbers were small and, therefore, easy to handle in calculations done by hand. Although the Chinese value (AD 500) was more accurate, these two 3-digit numbers were not easy to handle.

2 The area is maximised when the sides are all at their maximum value, that is, all the same length.

$$16 \div 3 = 5.3333, \qquad 5.3333^2 = 28.44 \, \text{ft}^2$$

For a length x of fencing, the maximum area of the pen will, therefore, be

$$\left(\tfrac{x}{3}\right)^2 = \tfrac{x^2}{9}$$

3 This investigation uses the idea that if the dimensions are increased to a percentage P, then the volume will be increased to a percentage P^3.
An increase of 10% takes the percentage to 110%, or 1.10. The volume will be increased by a factor of $(1.10)^3 = 1.331$, or 33.1%.
An increase of 100% (doubling) takes the percentage to 200%, or 2.0. The volume will increased by a factor of $(2.0)^3 = 8$, or an increase of 700%.

8 Geometry and trigonometry

Exercise 1

1 Not congruent 2 Congruent 3 Congruent 4 Not congruent
5 Congruent 6 Not congruent 7 Congruent 8 B,C
9 A,D 10 A,C 11 B,D 12 A,D
13 B,C 14 B,D 15 C,D

Exercise 2

1 (a) 102° (b) Obtuse 2 (a) 39° (b) Acute
3 (a) 82° (b) Acute 4 (a) 105° (b) Obtuse
5 (a) 68° (b) Acute 6 (a) 39° (b) Acute
7 (a) 142° (b) Obtuse 8 (a) 150° (b) Obtuse
9 (a) 120° (b) Obtuse 10 (a) 205° (b) Reflex
11 (a) 48° (b) Acute 12 (a) 278° (b) Reflex

Exercise 3

1 104° 2 67° 3 57° 4 87° 5 100°
6 70° 7 70° 8 113°

Exercise 4

1 (a) 36° (b) Isosceles 2 (a) 50° (b) Isosceles
3 (a) 60° (b) Equilateral 4 (a) 60° (b) Right-angled
5 (a) 65° (b) Isosceles 6 (a) 120° (b) Equilateral
7 (a) 45° (b) Right-angled and isosceles
8 (a) 90° (b) Isosceles and right-angled

Exercise 5

1 $a = 60°, b = 70°$ 2 $c = 65°, d = 70°$ 3 $e = 75°, f = 40°$
4 $g = 10°, h = 42°$ 5 $i = 100°, j = 55°$ 6 $k = 70°, l = 40°$
7 $m = 40°, n = 40°$ 8 $p = 80°, q = 60°$

Exercise 6

1   2   3

4   5 $a = 55°, b = 50°$ 6 108°
7 $e = 22\frac{1}{2}°, d = 22\frac{1}{2}°$ 8 60°
9 $g = 50°, h = 60°$ 10 $i = 65°, j = 115°, k = 50°$
11 $l = 90°$ 12 $m = 65°, n = 75°, p = 40°$

Exercise 7

1 114° 2 57° 3 47° 4 88°

Exercise 8

1 Square, rhombus   2 Trapezium   3 Square

4 Square, rectangle   5 Parallelogram, rhombus

6 Trapezium   7 Square, rectangle, rhombus

8 Trapezium   9 Square   10 Square

Exercise 9

1

	Cube	Cuboid	Pyramid	Tetrahedron	Cylinder	Cone
Faces	6	6	5	4	2	1
Vertices	8	8	5	4	0	1
Edges	12	12	8	6	0	0

2 Faces + Vertices = Edges + 2

3 (a) Cuboid   (b) Cuboid   (c) Cylinder

Exercise 10

1 Tetrahedron   2 Pentagonal prism   3 Cylinder

4

5

6

7

8

9

10

11

12 GE, BHD, IKA, MO, QS, ZX

Exercise 11 Check diagrams have been drawn correctly.

Exercise 12

1 Divide lengths by 5   2 Divide lengths by 10   3 Divide lengths by 20

4 Divide lengths by 12   5 Divide lengths by 100   6 Divide lengths by 8

Exercise 13

1

2

3

4

5

A ◄──►─► B
Equal
distance

6

7

Exercise 14

1 6.7 cm	2 13.1 cm	3 11.7 cm	4 12.3 cm	5 7.7 cm
6 9.0 m	7 8.35 m	8 4.8 m	9 6.9 cm	10 6.5 m

Exercise 15

1 5.63 cm	2 3.94 m	3 66.2 mm	4 4.08 cm
5 10.4 m	6 6.16 cm	7 22.0 cm	8 154 mm
9 4.78 cm	10 3.86 m	11 5.56 m	12 6.01 cm
13 25.9 m	14 5.77 m	15 6.16 m × 7.88 m	

Exercise 16

1 45.6°	2 63.6°	3 67.6°	4 46.2°
5 41.8°	6 22.9°	7 44.4°	8 52.4°
9 50.0°	10 39.3°	11 48.6°	12 1.9°
13 20.5°	14 33.7°	15 67.4°, 112.6°	

Exercise 17

1 10.7 cm	2 12.9 m	3 349 mm	4 212 mm
5 4.53 m	6 54.0 cm	7 40.6 cm	8 4.90 m

Exercise 18

1 50°	2 70°	3 120°
4 10°	5 84°	6 50°
7 $x = 75°$, $y = 75°$	8 $x = 68°$, $y = 58°$	9 $x = 65°$, $y = 55°$
10 $x = 70°$, $y = 55°$	11 99°	12 18
13 Trapezium	14 Square, rhombus	15 Cylinder
16 Cone		

17

18

or alternative

19 Tetrahedron

20–22: Check the accuracy of the drawings.

23

24 5.32 cm	25 7.68 cm
26 8.43 cm	27 10.8 cm
28 31.4°	29 5.33 cm
30 9.23 cm	31 13.4 cm
32 53.9°	

339

Exercise 19

1 (a) 52° ±2°   (b) Mark point D   (c) (i) 2.8 cm   (ii) 28 mm

2 (a) Scale drawing   (b) 3.6 cm   (c) 1.8 m

3 (a)

(b) 80 cm^3

4 (a) $\frac{2}{3}$ (b) 2   5 (a) Drawing   (b) 4.97 m

6 (a) 131°   (b) 49°   (c) 82°   7 4.21 m

8 (a)

(b) $x + y = 90°$

9 11.67 m   10 (a) 6.32 cm   (b) 18.97 cm^2

11 (a) Triangular prism (b) 9   (c) 60°

12 (a) (i) $x = 110°$ (ii) $y = 70°$ (b) Any pair such that $s + t = 110°$

13 (a)

(b) BCE = DEC, ABE = ADE

14 (a) 40 m   (b) 2800 m^2

15

16 (a) 53.6 miles   (b) 45.0 miles   (c) 183.6 miles

    (d) 76.2°   (e) 190 miles

Investigations

1 Diagram

Diagram	1	2	3	4	5	10
Number of interconnectors	4	10	19	31	46	166

The formula for the series is:

Number of interconnectors $= 1 + \dfrac{3n}{2}\,(n + 1)$

2 There are many Pythagorean triplets. Four triplets with small numbers
   are: 3, 4, 5; 8, 15, 17; 5, 12, 13; 7, 24, 25

Other triplets can be formed by creating multiples of these, e.g:
$(3, 4, 5) \times 5 = 15, 20, 25$

3 There is no unique answer to this practical investigation. Your work should show evidence of a variety of strategies attempted, in order that a wide range of different envelopes can be produced. Some conclusions can be reached depending on the range of envelopes produced.

9 Symmetry

Exercise 1

Exercise 2

Exercise 3

Exercise 4

1 9	**2** 3	**3** 4	**4** 6	**5** 4	**6** 3
7 2	**8** 3	**9** 4			

Exercise 5

1 8	**2** 5	**3** 3	**4** 5
5 2	**6** 4	**7** 6	**8** 4

9   **10**   **11**   **12**

Exercise 6

1 Rotation, clockwise, 90°   **2** Rotation, clockwise, 135°

3 Rotation, 180°   **4** Rotation, clockwise, 90°

5 Rotation, clockwise, 90°   **6** Rotation, anticlockwise, 135°

7 Rotation, anticlockwise, 90°   **8** Rotation, clockwise, 90°

Exercise 7

Exercise 8

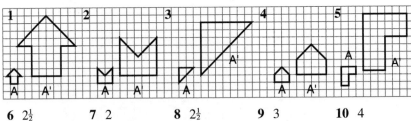

6 $2\frac{1}{2}$	**7** 2	**8** $2\frac{1}{2}$	**9** 3	**10** 4

Exercise 9

1 Enlargement s.f. 2, point of enlargement (0,0)

2 Enlargement s.f. 2, point of enlargement (3,0)

3 Enlargement s.f. 2, point of enlargement (0,1)

4 Enlargement s.f. 3, point of enlargement (1,1)

5 Enlargement s.f. 2, point of enlargement (0,0)

6 Enlargement s.f. 2, point of enlargement (0,4)

7 Enlargement s.f. 3, point of enlargement (0,3)

8 Enlargement s.f. 2, point of enlargement (2,6)

9

10

11

12

Exercise 10	**1** 8	**2** 9	**3** 144	**4** 64
	5 6	**6** 5	**7** (a) 3 (b) 9	**8** (a) 4 (b) 64

Exercise 11	**1** 54 cm	**2** 18 cm^2	**3** 4500 cm^2	**4** 664 cm^3
	5 55.3 cm	**6** 16 cm	**7** 15 cm^2	**8** 9.45 cm^2
	9 7680 cm^2	**10** 126 cm		

Exercise 12	**1** 8	**2** 5	**3** 9	**4** 12
	5 10	**6** 15	**7** 20	**8** 18
	9 2520	**10** 4140°	**11** 5400°	**12** 6120°
	13 (a) Yes 18	(b) No	(c) Yes 24	
	14 (a) Yes 10	(b) Yes 9	(c) No	

Exercise 13

Regular polygon	No. of sides	Sum of interior angles	Size of interior angle	Size of exterior angle
Triangle	3	180°	60°	120°
Quadrilateral	4	360°	90°	90°
Pentagon	5	540°	108°	72°
Hexagon	6	720°	120°	60°
Heptagon	7	900°	128.57°	51.42°
Octagon	8	1080°	135°	45°
Nonagon	9	1260°	140°	40°
Decagon	10	1440°	144°	36°
Undecagon	11	1620°	147.27°	32.72°
Dodecagon	12	1800°	150°	30°

Exercise 14

1

squares tessellate

triangles tessellate

hexagons tessellate

2 The following tessellate: (b), (c), (d), (g), (j), (k)

Exercise 15

1 $\begin{pmatrix} 6 \\ 0 \end{pmatrix}$ 2 $\begin{pmatrix} 3 \\ 2 \end{pmatrix}$ 3 $\begin{pmatrix} -3 \\ -2 \end{pmatrix}$ 4 $\begin{pmatrix} 3 \\ -2 \end{pmatrix}$ 5 $\begin{pmatrix} -6 \\ 0 \end{pmatrix}$

6 $\begin{pmatrix} -3 \\ 2 \end{pmatrix}$ 7 $\begin{pmatrix} 5 \\ 2 \end{pmatrix}$ 8 $\begin{pmatrix} -2 \\ -1 \end{pmatrix}$ 9 $\begin{pmatrix} -5 \\ 0 \end{pmatrix}$ 10 $\begin{pmatrix} -4 \\ -3 \end{pmatrix}$

11 $\begin{pmatrix} 4 \\ 3 \end{pmatrix}$ 12 $\begin{pmatrix} -4 \\ 2 \end{pmatrix}$ 13 $\begin{pmatrix} 1 \\ 4 \end{pmatrix}$ 14 $\begin{pmatrix} -8 \\ -1 \end{pmatrix}$

15

16

Exercise 16

1 F   2 T   3 T   4 F   5 F   6 F

7 T   8 F   9 T   10 F   11 T   12 F

13 a = $\begin{pmatrix} 2 \\ 2 \end{pmatrix}$ b = $\begin{pmatrix} -3 \\ 0 \end{pmatrix}$ c = $\begin{pmatrix} 2 \\ -1 \end{pmatrix}$ d = $\begin{pmatrix} -1 \\ 3 \end{pmatrix}$ e = $\begin{pmatrix} -3 \\ 1 \end{pmatrix}$ f = $\begin{pmatrix} 4 \\ -2 \end{pmatrix}$ g = $\begin{pmatrix} 4 \\ -1 \end{pmatrix}$

h = $\begin{pmatrix} -1 \\ -2 \end{pmatrix}$ i = $\begin{pmatrix} -2 \\ 2 \end{pmatrix}$ j = $\begin{pmatrix} 1 \\ 3 \end{pmatrix}$ k = $\begin{pmatrix} -1 \\ -1 \end{pmatrix}$ l = $\begin{pmatrix} -3 \\ -2 \end{pmatrix}$ m = $\begin{pmatrix} 4 \\ 0 \end{pmatrix}$

14

Exercise 17

1 (a) (0,0,0), (0,0,3), (0,5,0), (0,5,3), (4,0,0), (4,0,4), (4,5,0), (4,5,3)
   (b) 3×4×3   (c) 36 cube units

2 (a) (0,0,0), (0,0,3), (0,4,0), (0,4,3), (2,0,0), (2,0,3), (2,4,0), (2,4,3)
   (b) 2×3×4   (c) 24 cube units

3 (a) (0,0,0), (0,0,2), (0,5,0), (0,5,2), (4,0,0), (4,5,0), (4,5,0), (4,0,2), (4,5,2)
   (b) 4×5×2   (c) 40 cube units

4 (a) (0,1,0), (0,1,3), (0,4,0), (0,4,3), (4,1,0), (4,4,0), (4,1,3), (4,4,3)
   (b) 3×3×4   (c) 36 cube units

5 (a) (0,0,2), (0,3,2), (0,0,5), (0,3,5), (5,0,2), (5,3,2), (5,0,5), (5,3,5)
   (b) 3×5×3   (c) 45 cube units

6 (a) (2,2,0), (2,5,0), (4,2,0), (4,5,0), (4,2,5), (4,5,5), (2,5,5), (2,2,5)
   (b) 3×2×5   (c) 30 cube units

7–10 Various cuboids can be drawn.

11

12

13

14

Exercise 18

1

2

3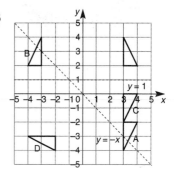

4 (a) 1   (b) 4   5 (a) 3   (b) 2   (c) 3   (d) 0

6

135° clockwise

7

180°

8

45° anticlockwise

9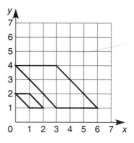

10 No   11 24   12 8

13 (a) $\begin{pmatrix} 5 \\ 1 \end{pmatrix}$ (b) $\begin{pmatrix} 0 \\ -4 \end{pmatrix}$ (c) $\begin{pmatrix} -4 \\ 1 \end{pmatrix}$ (d) $\begin{pmatrix} 4 \\ -1 \end{pmatrix}$

14

15

16 648 cm^2

17 36 cm

Exercise 19

1 3

2

3 (i) Rotation of 90° about the origin
  (ii) Translation of $\begin{pmatrix} 3 \\ -3 \end{pmatrix}$ (iii) Reflection in the line $y=x$

4 128.6°

5 (a) 150°   (b)

6 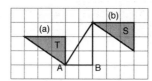   (c) Translation of $\binom{5}{1}$

7 (a) Reflection in the x-axis

   (b) Rotation of 90° clockwise about the origin

8 (a) $360 \div 5 = 72°$ (b) 54°   (c)

9 (b) parallelogram

10

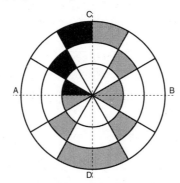

11 (a) Rotation 90° anticlockwise about the origin

   (b) Reflection in the line $y = -1$

Investigations

1 Scale factor area = (scale factor length)^2
Scale factor volume = (scale factor length)^3

2 It is easier if the scale diagram is drawn on squared paper. There are many extensions to this investigation, such as: What is the maximum possible number of rebounds? Try different sizes of snooker table.

3 The rule is: Total of interior angles = $180° \times (n-2)$ where n is the number of sides of the polygon.

---

10 Collecting and processing

Exercise I

1 Heading could be 'number of occupants', and easier to summarise if there were columns with headings:

Number of occupants					
1	2	3	4	5	6

2 There are no questions about the quality of each meal, the available choice, or other meals which could be provided and which may prove popular. You could have two recording sheets:

(a) Meal   Number eaten   (b)

Questionnaire
Meal eaten: _____
Was your meal:
(i) satisfactory? [_____]
(ii) good value? [_____]
Was there enough choice? <u>YES/NO</u>
If not, what other meals would you
like to see on the menu?

3 There may need to be a column for 'Second choice', for when the first choice of newspaper is sold out.

4 It is easier to count the cars coming in, and going out, as, while you are counting empty spaces, there may be a large influx or exodus of cars.

Exercise 2

1 (a) There are no criteria for deciding an order of preference.

  (b) It is not clear whether (i) the numbers 1, 2, 3, 4, 5 are to be entered, one in each box (ii) any number from 1 to 5 can be entered in any of the boxes.

For each of the three criteria, put ONE tick against EACH name.
Which lecturer, in your opinion:

	Knows the subject?			Maintains interest?			Helps Learning?		
	a lot	some	not much	a lot	some	not much	a lot	some	not much
Mr James									
Mr Anderson									
Mrs Robson									
Mr Islam									
Mrs Oates									

You could ask about knowledge of the subject, maintaining interest, and helping you to learn, as three criteria. Also, it may help to allow, say, three levels of response, to questions.

2 The question does not ask how often any meal is eaten.

1 Do you eat at the College canteen regularly?

YES [____]   NO [____]   (please tick)

2 If YES, over an average two-week period, (i.e. 10 days), write in the number of times you have eaten one of the following meals.

Number of times

Sausage
Pizza
Stir-fry
Roast meat
Vegetarian
Baked potato
Hamburger
Other

3 What other meals of about the same cost would you eat, if they were available? (List up to three.)
  (i) _____
  (ii) _____
  (iii) _____

> Please tick which of these countries you visited on your main holiday for the three years shown.
>
> | | 1991 | 1992 | 1993 |
> |---|---|---|---|
> | France | | | |
> | Spain | | | |
> | Belgium | | | |
> | Germany | | | |
> | Greece | | | |
> | U.S.A. | | | |
> | Other: please state | | | |

3 The time of year is not asked for; it would be better to ask for the main holiday, possibly over the last three years.

4 Instead of 'What are you intending to do?', give alternatives, e.g. 'Do you intend to
(a) continue studying
(b) seek employment
(c) have a break?'

Exercise 3

1 (a) 961°C (b) 2570°C (c) copper, gold, lead and silver
(d) Magnesium (e) gold (f) more (8.18 g/cm^3)

2 (a) 2015 (b) 1600 (c) 3 h 15 min (d) 2 h 41 min (e) 0023

3 (a) £159.34 (b) £194.61 (c) £2000 (d) £143.13

4 (a) £59.99 (b) £4.00 (c) 78 × 78 (d) £9.50 (e) £5.50

Exercise 4

The column showing the tally marks has been omitted.

1

Mark	Frequency
0	3
1	2
2	3
3	2
4	4
5	3
6	7
7	5
8	5
9	4
10	2
	40

2

Fruit	Frequency
apple	8
banana	2
grape	2
kiwi	1
melon	3
orange	5
pear	3
	24

3

Minutes late	Frequency
0	12
1	6
2	5
3	3
4	4
5	2
6	0
7	1
8	1
9	1
	35

4

Level	Frequency
5	6
6	22
7	19
8	8
9	5
	60

Exercise 5

1

Number of tomatoes	Frequency
0–4	0
5–9	1
10–14	1
15–19	6
20–24	6
25–29	5
30–34	5
	24

2

Number of words	Frequency
0–2	2
3–5	4
6–8	8
9–11	15
12–14	9
15–17	2
	40

3

Number of books	Frequency
21–25	1
26–30	7
31–35	6
36–40	7
41–45	6
	27

Exercise 6

The column showing the tally marks has been omitted.

1

Amount (£)	Frequency
0–9.99	4
10–19.99	15
20–29.99	8
30–39.99	7
40–49.99	4
50–59.99	2
	40

2

Weight (kg)	Frequency
0.50–0.99	5
1.00–1.49	12
1.50–1.99	14
2.00–2.49	5
2.50–2.99	4
	40

3

Duration (min)	Frequency
80–89	7
90–99	13
100–109	9
110–119	7
120–129	4
	40

Exercise 7

1 mode = 4, median = 5   **2** mode = 13, median = 15

3 mode = 7, median = 6   **4** mode = 51, median = 52

5 mode = 8, median = 6   **6** mode = 24, median = 28

7 mode = 11, median = 11   **8** (a) 13 m   (b) 14 m

9 (a) 16   (b) 15   **10** 3, 4, 4, 6, 7, 8, 9

Exercise 8

1 modal group = 200 − 299 mm, median height (estimate) = 258 mm

2 modal group = 2 − 3.99 m, median length (estimate) = 3.33 m

3 modal group = 60 − 79 points, median score (estimate) = 65 points

4 modal group = £60 − £89.99, median amount (estimate) = £79.50

Exercise 9

1

3

2

4

42 did
not fail

5

Exercise 10

1

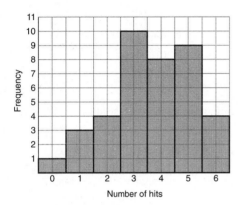

mode = 3 hits,
median (estimate) = 3.75 hits

2

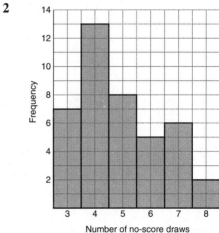

mode = 4 draws (0–0),
median (estimate) = 4.63 draws (0–0)

3

mode = 8 GCSE's,
median (estimate) = 7.71 GCSE's

4

mode = 0 packets,
median (estimate) = 2.1/2.2 packets

Exercise II

1

2

3

Exercise I2

1 £118.43

2 99.75 kg

3 Sandra (58.17; Tracey's mean score is 56.43)

4 14°C

5 $\frac{30}{24} = 1.25$ winners

6 (a) $\frac{54}{20} = 2.7$ min   (b) No

7 $\frac{350}{23} = 15.22$ pigeons

8 $\frac{299}{20} = 14.95$ students

Exercise I3

1 $\frac{385}{30} = 12.83$ m

2 $\frac{766}{33} = 23.21$ eggs

3 $\frac{349.5}{11} = 31.77$ points

4 $\frac{52.5}{17} = 3.09$ faulty components

Exercise I4

1 £399.99 − £293.23 = £106.76

2 (a) Dean: range = 126 − 2 = 124; Ian: range = 133 − 1 = 132
(b) Dean: mean = 54.1;   Ian: mean = 60.7; Ian's is better.

3 (a) Betty: mean = 81; Moira: mean = 81
(b) Betty: range = 7 (84 − 77); Moira: range = 20 (93 − 73)
(c) Betty is more consistent.
(d) Could choose either; there are arguments for both.

4 Total for 5 days = 743 × 5 = 3715. Total for 6 days = 750 × 6 = 4500.
Attendance on day 6 = 4500 − 3715 = 785.

5 (a) £52.32 × 2 = £104.64
(b) Edwin's takings = £45.62 × 3 = £136.86. Total takings = £241.50;
hence mean takings = £48.30.
(c) They need to take £330 (£55 × 6) − £241.50 = £88.50.

Exercise I5

1

Mark	0	1	2	3	4	5	6	7	8	9	10
Frequency	1	3	1	3	7	9	7	4	2	0	3

(a) 5 (b) 9 (c) 8

2

Mark	1–10	11–20	21–30	31–40	41–50
Frequency	6	8	12	11	8

(a)

(b) $11 + 8 = 19$

(c) $6 + 4 = 10$

3

Letter	Frequency
T	1
X	1
Y	2
A	2
B	2
C	1
D	6
E	2
F	3
G	3
H	3
J	2
K	2
Total	30

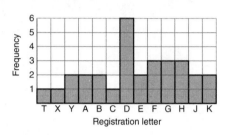

(a) D

(b) T

(c) 20

4

Wicket	Frequency
0	2
1	3
2	4
3	6
4	10
5	3
6	5
7	1
8	1
Total	35

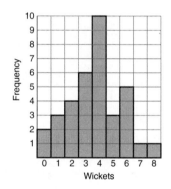

(a) 2   (b) 4   (c) 10   (d) $3 + 8 + 18 + 40 + 15 + 30 + 7 + 8 = 129$

(e) $129 \div 35 = 3.69$

5 mode = 9, median = 8, mean = 7.5, range = 4

6 mode = 30, median = 31, mean = 33, range = 15

7 mode = 18, median = 18, mean = 19, range = 16

8 mean = $(775 + 1320 + 3500 + 2960 = 2145) \div 60 = 178(.3)$ cm.

9 (a)

10 (a)

(b) 46 trees   (b) 40–50 hours

(c) 13 trees   (c) 40 hours

(d) mean $= \frac{458}{46} = 9.96$ kg   (d) 34.3 hours (2060 ÷ 60)

Exercise 16

1   mean $= 215 \div 20 = 10.75$ piglets per litter

2   (a) mean $= 27.32 \div 21 = 1.3$ m   (b) mode $= 1.25$ m
     (c) median $= 1.26$ m

3   (a) modal rate $= £3.50$ (b) median rate $= £3.70$
     (c) mean rate $= £3.65$ (d) range $= £3.90 - £3.20 = 70$p

4   (a) mode $= 6$ (b) median $= 5$

5   (a) £33.00   (b) £59 + £15 = £74
     (c) £22 + £25 + £6.50 = £53.50

6   (a) Ela's average time $= 177 \div 6 = 29.5$ s
       Sharon's average time $= 147.5 \div 5 = 29.5$ s
     (b) Ela's range $= 32 - 27 = 5$ s, Sharon's range $= 30.5 - 27.5 = 3$ s
     (c) Sharon: she is more consistent.

7   (a) Clothing   7   (b)
       Electrical   4
       Stationery   3
       Shoe   6
       Toy   5

8   (a) mode $= 2$
     (b) mean 2.63

9   (a) $528 \div 20 = 26.4$ cm

     (b) Volume: $\pi \times (13.2)^2 \times 500 \times 20 = 5\ 475\ 000$ cm^3

     (c) Trailer can carry 5000 kg which is $\dfrac{5000 \times 1000}{0.5} = 10\ 000\ 000$ cm^3.

       Volume of log $= \pi\ (13.2)^2 \times 500$ cm^3.

       Maximum number of logs $= \dfrac{10\ 000\ 000}{\pi\ (13.2)^2 \times 500} = 36$

10   (a) 17, 4, 0

     (b) Grange Mount School chess team is much better than most opponents.

     (c) 1989   (d) 77   (e) $77 \div 5 = 15.4$ matches/year

     (f) p(win in 1985) $= \frac{9}{12} = \frac{3}{4} (= 0.75)$

11   $8\frac{1}{2}$

12   (a) $(\frac{28}{7} =) 4$ (b) £8.96

13 (i)

Number of tomatoes per plant	Frequency
18	1
19	1
20	3
21	1
22	3
23	6
24	3
25	3
26	1
27	2

(ii)

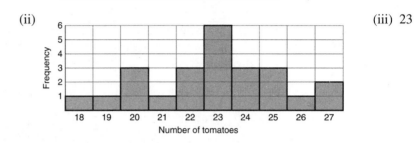

(iii) 23

14 (i) 3   (ii) 12   (iii) 18

15 (i)

Number of newspapers	0	1	2	3	4	5	6
Frequency	4	3	1	2	0	2	5

(ii) 2   (iii) 6   (iv) 51

Investigations

1 There is likely to be only a relatively minor change in mean value, or in the general appearance of a bar graph.

2 The more uniform ('normal') the spread of results, the better the rule works.

11 Representing and interpreting

Exercise 1

1 (a) T   (b) S   (c) V   2 (a) F   (b) E   (c) H

3 (a) WINGS   (b) WHITEBURN   (c) OLD TOWN

4 (a) C   (b) F   (c) D   (d) B   5 (a) F   (b) H   (c) B   (d) J

Exercise 2

1 (a) 1788, on Monday   (b) Tuesday   (c) 12 (Wed–Thur)   (d) 1795.6

2

(a) Wednesday is half-day, Thursday is late-night opening

(b) More people do not work on Saturdays.

(c) 18.7 customers

3 (a)

(b) 1200–1300

(c) 1100

(d) 2 hours

4

(a) August

(b) £69

(c) Feb, Mar, Aug, Dec

Exercise 3

1

E	A	S	T
152	92	76	40

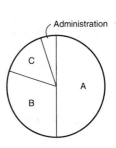

2

Fish	Sausage	Pie	Fishcake	Spring Roll
72	78	51	96	63

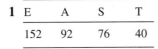

3

A	B	C	Admin.
180	108	54	18

4 (a) plain

(b) plain, salt and vinegar

(c) 1st week 35, 2nd week 30

5 BBC1 217, BBC2 83, ITV 250, C4 50

6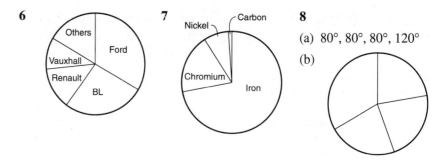

7

8 (a) 80°, 80°, 80°, 120°

(b)

Exercise 4

1

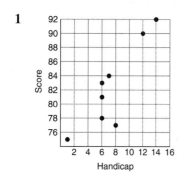

Higher handicap
means higher score.

2

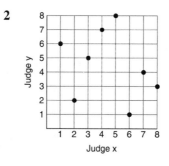

No evidence of
similar opinions.

3

There is evidence of a link;
higher science scores mean
higher technology scores.

4

Yes, taller means higher.

Exercise 5
(All answers are approximate, as they are read from graphs.)

1

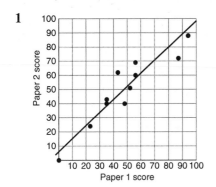

(c) 60 marks   (d) 56/57 marks

2

(b) 276 g   (c) 96 pages

3

(b) 5 m

4

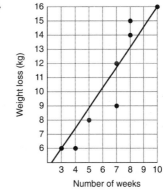

(b) Yes   (c) 8 weeks

Exercise 6

1

Cumulative frequencies:
1   5   16   43   81   93   97   100

2

Cumulative frequencies:
4   12   27   49   67   81

3

Cumulative frequencies:

5   15   37   55   66

4

Cumulative frequencies:

4   11   29   41   48   51

Exercise 7   **1** 41 km/h   **2** 6.7 ft   **3** 593 g   **4** £14.50

Exercise 8   **1** 10.3 cm, 12.7 cm, 2.4 cm   **2** £64 000, £108 000, £44 000

3 100p, 168p, 68p

5 2.8 min, 6.2 min, 3.4 min

4 2.07 kg, 2.4 kg, 0.33 kg

Exercise 9   **1** (a) Group A   (b) Group E   (c) Group C

2 (a) Saturday   (b) £60   (c) Tue, Thu, Fri, Sat   (d) £375

3 (a)

(b) 240 copies

(c) Wed

(d) 720 copies

4 A:4, B:7, C:12, D:8, E:5

5 Day	M	Tu	W	Th	F	Total
Copies	138	154	86	208	134	720
Angle	69°	77°	43°	104°	67°	360°

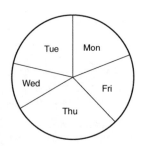

6

Age	19	20	21	22	23	24
Number	6	3	2	4	4	5
Angle	90°	45°	30°	60°	60°	75°

(a)

(b) $\frac{1}{3}$

7

(c) 73 kg

(d) 183 cm

8 (a)

(b) $32\frac{1}{2}$ cm

(c) 245 cm

9 Cumulative frequency   1 4 8 14 24 32 38 43 47 50

(a)

(b) 51/52

(c) lower quartile = 37/38

upper quartile = 68

10 Cumulative frequency   5 23 56 108 150 176 184

(a)

(b) 73–75 kg

(c) lower quartile = 53 kg

upper quartile = 92 kg

interquartile range = 39 kg

ANSWERS

Exercise 10

1 (a) mode = 14   (b) (i) 84°   (ii) Number of size $10 = \frac{84}{360} \times 150 = 35$

2

Grade	Number	Angle
C	5	$5 \times 360° \div 24 = 75°$
D	12	$12 \times 360° \div 24 = 180°$
E	5	$5 \times 360° \div 24 = 75°$
F	2	$2 \times 360° \div 24 = 30°$
	24	360°

3 (a) $4 \rightarrow 32$ (b) $4 \rightarrow 11 \rightarrow 22$ (c) $4 \rightarrow 8 \rightarrow 16 \rightarrow 32 \rightarrow 64 \rightarrow 128$

4 (a)

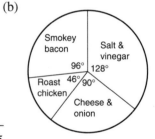

(b) In general, a high N.E score means a low H.I. score.
[N.E. + H.I. = 10, approximately]

5 (a) type 1   (b) type 2   (c) type 3

6 (a)

Variety	Number of packets	Angle
Salt & Vinegar	64	128°
Smokey Bacon	48	96°
Cheese & Onion	45	90°
Roast Chicken	23	46°
	180	360°

(b)

7 (a)

Age	1–2	2–3	3–4	4–5
Frequency	0	17	18	5

(b) mean age $= 128 \div 40 = 3.2$ years

(c) angle is $\frac{18}{40} \times 360° = 162°$

8 (a)

	Frequency
26.5 – 27.5	2
27.5 – 28.5	4
28.5 – 29.5	5
29.5 – 30.5	6
30.5 – 31.5	5
31.5 – 32.5	4
32.5 – 33.5	2
33.5 – 34.5	2
	30

(b)

(c) 30 g   (d) $\frac{11}{30}$ (e) 201 g

9 (a)

Cumulative frequency vs Solving time (mm)

(b) (i) 127 mins

(ii) 12

(iii) 24

(c) 110 mins

(d) (i)

Solving time (minutes)	Mid value	Frequency	Total
0 – under 30	15	0	0
30 – under 60	45	10	450
60 – under 90	75	26	1950
90 – under 120	105	34	3570
120 – under 150	135	36	4860
150 – under 180	165	30	4950
180 – under 210	195	18	3510
210 – under 240	225	6	1350
Total		160	20640

(ii) 129 min

10 (i) 6 (ii)

(iii) u.q. = 8.8; l.q. = 6.2

(iv) 50%

(v) mean $\dfrac{290.10}{34} = 8.53$

11 (i) 216°,108°, 36° (ii)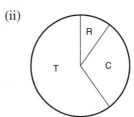

12 (a) (i) 120°   (b)
      (ii) 84°
      (iii) 60°
      (iv) 24°
      (v) 72°

13 (a) 5° (b) (i) 100° (ii) 20 packets (c) 72

Investigations

1 (There are other advantages/disadvantages than those stated here.)
   Bar chart
   Advantages: • easy to compare heights of bars in a diagram
                    • easy to draw
                    • can display easily a wide range of values
   Disadvantages: • applying different ways of grouping can alter the
                      bar chart
   Pie chart
   Advantages: • can be rotated, hence gives equal weighting to all
                      sectors
                    • easy to compare two or more pie charts
   Disadvantages: • angles need to be calculated
                    • awkward to distinguish small sectors
                    • less clear, if there are many sectors

2 (a) Estimate the distances of each point from the line, and check that the
      sum of the distances of points *above* the line is equal to the sum of the
      distances *below* the line.
  (b) Alter the position of the line slightly, and repeat.
  (c) Check that the total of the distances of *all* points from the line is small.

---

12 Probability

Exercise 1

1 (a) P = 0.5 or 50%, Q = 0.25 or 25%, R is almost 1 or 100%,
      S is about 0.03 or 3%, T = 0.01 or 1%

  (b)
```
  TS              Q              P                          R
  ↓↓              ↓              ↓                          ↓
 ┌─────────────────────────────────────────────────────────┐
 │  0   0.1  0.2  0.3  0.4  0.5  0.6  0.7  0.8  0.9   1      │
 │                                                          │
 │  0  10%  20%  30%  40%  50%  60%  70%  80%  90%  100%    │
 │     |    |    |    |    |    |    |    |    |    |        │
 └─────────────────────────────────────────────────────────┘
```

Exercise 2

1 (a) $\frac{2}{3}$ (b) $\frac{1}{3}$

2 (a) $\frac{1}{7}$ (b) $\frac{2}{7}$ (c) $\frac{5}{7}$

3 (a) $\frac{1}{6}$ (b) $\frac{2}{6} = \frac{1}{3}$ (c) $\frac{3}{6} = \frac{1}{2}$ (d) $\frac{5}{6}$

4 (a) $\frac{5}{12}$ (b) $\frac{7}{12}$ (c) 0 $(\frac{0}{12})$ – impossible (d) $\frac{12}{12}=1$ – certain

5 (a) $\frac{5}{12}$ (b) $\frac{4}{12}=\frac{1}{3}$ (c) $\frac{8}{12}=\frac{2}{3}$ (d) $\frac{9}{12}=\frac{3}{4}$ (e) 0 $(\frac{0}{12})$ – impossible

6 $\frac{10}{200}=\frac{1}{20}$ (b) 51 tickets

7 (a) $\frac{1}{37}$ (b) $\frac{2}{37}$ (c) $\frac{4}{37}$ (d) $\frac{7}{37}$ (e) $\frac{12}{37}$ (f) $\frac{18}{37}$

Exercise 3   1 $\frac{3}{23}$ 2 $\frac{22}{30}$

3 (a) $\frac{6}{12}=\frac{1}{2}$

(b) four hearts, two clubs, a diamond and a spade

4 (a) (i) $\frac{3}{20}$ (ii) $\frac{5}{20}=\frac{1}{4}$ (iii) $\frac{12}{20}=\frac{3}{5}$ (iv) 0 $(\frac{0}{20})$

(b) (i) 9 (ii) 15 (iii) 36 (iv) none

Exercise 4   1 (i) $\frac{8}{20}=0.4$ (ii) $\frac{6}{14}=0.428$; (ii) is more likely

2 (i) $\frac{3}{8}=0.375$ (ii) $\frac{2}{5}=0.4$; (ii) is more likely

3 (i) $\frac{13}{52}=0.25$ (ii) $\frac{1}{5}=0.2$; (i) is more likely

4 (i) $\frac{5}{7}=0.71$ (ii) $\frac{3}{4}=0.75$; (ii) is more likely

5 (i) $\frac{4}{100}=0.04$ (ii) $\frac{15}{350}=0.0428$; (ii) is more likely

Exercise 5   1 $\frac{5}{36}$ 2 $\frac{6}{36}=\frac{1}{6}$ 3 $\frac{18}{36}=\frac{1}{2}$ 4 $\frac{5}{36}$ 5 0

Exercise 6   1 $\frac{1}{4}$ 2 $\frac{1}{8}$ 3 (a) $\frac{8}{10}\times\frac{8}{10}=\frac{64}{100}=\frac{16}{25}$ (b) $\frac{2}{10}\times\frac{2}{10}=\frac{4}{100}=\frac{1}{25}$

4 (a) $\frac{4}{5}$ (b) $\frac{4}{5}\times\frac{4}{5}=\frac{16}{25}$ 5 $\frac{3}{4}\times\frac{2}{3}=\frac{6}{12}=\frac{1}{2}$

Exercise 7   1 (a) 0.5   (b) 0.7   (c) 0.5

2 (a) 0.28   (b) 0.12   (c) 0.28

3   (a) 0.45   (b) 0.2   (c) 0.3

4 (a)

Age	0–19	20–29	30–39	40–49	50–
Number	27	13	6	3	1
Relative frequency	0.54	0.26	0.12	0.06	0.02

(b) (i) 0.54 (ii) 0.2 (iii) 0.98

Exercise 8

1 (a) $\frac{9}{12} = \frac{3}{4}$ (b) $\frac{8}{12} = \frac{2}{3}$

2 (a) $\frac{5}{6}$ (b) $\frac{4}{6} = \frac{2}{3}$

3 (a) $\frac{7}{12}$ (b) $\frac{5}{12}$

4 (a) $\frac{6}{16} = \frac{3}{8}$ (b) $\frac{4}{16} = \frac{1}{4}$ (c) $\frac{11}{16}$

5 (a) $\frac{8}{13}$ (b) $\frac{5}{13}$ (c) $\frac{9}{13}$

Exercise 9

1 0.7

2 0.665

3 (a) $\frac{1}{16}$ (b) $\frac{14}{16} = \frac{7}{8}$

4 (a) $\frac{5}{18}$ (b) $\frac{15}{18} = \frac{5}{6}$ (c) $\frac{8}{18} = \frac{4}{9}$

5 (a) $\frac{1}{22}$ (b) $\frac{21}{22}$ (c) $\frac{15}{22}$ (d) $\frac{7}{22}$

Exercise 10

1 (a) $\frac{6}{8} \times \frac{5}{7} = \frac{30}{56} = \frac{15}{28}$

(b) $\frac{2}{8} \times \frac{1}{7} = \frac{2}{56} = \frac{1}{28}$

2 (a) $\frac{2}{4} \times \frac{2}{4} = \frac{4}{16} = \frac{1}{4}$

(b) $\frac{2}{4} \times \frac{1}{3} = \frac{2}{12} = \frac{1}{6}$

3 $\frac{5}{8} \times \frac{4}{7} = \frac{20}{56} = \frac{5}{14}$

4 $\frac{3}{5} \times \frac{2}{4} = \frac{6}{20} = \frac{3}{10}$

5 $\frac{2}{5} \times \frac{2}{5} = \frac{4}{25}$

6 $\frac{2}{9} \times \frac{1}{8} = \frac{2}{72} = \frac{1}{36}$

7 $\frac{5}{6} \times \frac{5}{6} = \frac{25}{36}$

8 $\frac{6}{10} \times \frac{5}{9} \times \frac{4}{8} = \frac{120}{720} = \frac{1}{6}$; yes

Exercise 11

1

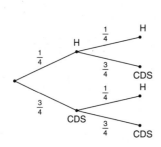

Outcome	Probability
HH	$\frac{1}{4} \times \frac{1}{4} = \frac{1}{16}$
H (CDS)	$\frac{1}{4} \times \frac{3}{4} = \frac{3}{16}$
(CDS) H	$\frac{3}{4} \times \frac{1}{4} = \frac{3}{16}$
(CDS) (CDS)	$\frac{3}{4} \times \frac{3}{4} = \frac{9}{16}$

(a) $\frac{1}{16}$

(b) $\frac{9}{16}$

(c) $\frac{6}{16} = \frac{3}{8}$

2 (a) 0.64 (b) 0.32 (c) 0.04

3 (a) $\frac{2}{5}$ (b) $\frac{3}{5}$

4

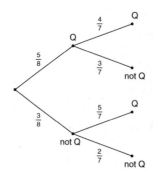

Outcome	Probability
Q, Q	$\frac{5}{8} \times \frac{4}{7} = \frac{5}{14}$
Q, not Q	$\frac{5}{8} \times \frac{3}{7} = \frac{15}{56}$
not Q, Q	$\frac{3}{8} \times \frac{5}{7} = \frac{15}{56}$
not Q, not Q	$\frac{3}{8} \times \frac{2}{7} = \frac{3}{28}$

(a) $\frac{5}{14}$

(b) $\frac{15}{28}$

(c) $\frac{3}{28}$

5

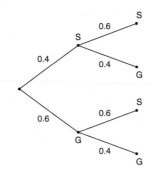

Outcome	Probability
SS	$0.4 \times 0.6 = 0.24$
SG	$0.4 \times 0.4 = 0.16$
GS	$0.6 \times 0.6 = 0.36$
GG	$0.6 \times 0.4 = 0.24$

(a) 0.24

(b) 0.24

(c) 0.52

6

Outcome	Probability
CW, CW	$0.7 \times 0.7 = 0.49$
CW, DW	$0.7 \times 0.3 = 0.21$
DW, CW	$0.3 \times 0.7 = 0.21$
DW, DW	$0.3 \times 0.3 = 0.09$

(b) (i) 0.49

(ii) 0.51

7

Outcome	Probability
BB	$\frac{1}{5} \times \frac{1}{5} = \frac{1}{25}$
BR	$\frac{1}{5} \times \frac{4}{5} = \frac{4}{25}$
RB	$\frac{4}{5} \times \frac{1}{5} = \frac{4}{25}$
RR	$\frac{4}{5} \times \frac{4}{5} = \frac{16}{25}$

(b) (i) $\frac{8}{25}$

(ii) $\frac{17}{25}$

Exercise 12

1 (a) 0.008 (b) 0.896   **2** (a) $\frac{5}{28}$ (b) $\frac{55}{56}$ (c) $\frac{1}{56}$

3

Outcome	Probability
CCC	$0.7 \times 0.7 \times 0.7 = 0.343$
CCD	$0.7 \times 0.7 \times 0.3 = 0.147$
CDC	$0.7 \times 0.3 \times 0.7 = 0.147$
CDD	$0.7 \times 0.3 \times 0.3 = 0.063$
DCC	$0.3 \times 0.7 \times 0.7 = 0.147$
DCD	$0.3 \times 0.7 \times 0.3 = 0.063$
DDC	$0.3 \times 0.3 \times 0.7 = 0.063$
DDD	$0.3 \times 0.3 \times 0.3 = 0.027$

(b) (i) 0.027

(ii) 0.784

4

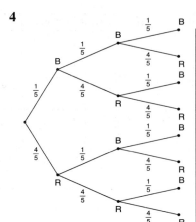

Outcome	Probability
BBB	$\frac{1}{5} \times \frac{1}{5} \times \frac{1}{5} = \frac{1}{125}$
BBR	$\frac{1}{5} \times \frac{1}{5} \times \frac{4}{5} = \frac{4}{125}$
BRB	$\frac{1}{5} \times \frac{4}{5} \times \frac{1}{5} = \frac{4}{125}$
BRR	$\frac{1}{5} \times \frac{4}{5} \times \frac{4}{5} = \frac{16}{125}$
RBB	$\frac{4}{5} \times \frac{1}{5} \times \frac{1}{5} = \frac{4}{125}$
RBR	$\frac{4}{5} \times \frac{1}{5} \times \frac{4}{5} = \frac{16}{125}$
RRB	$\frac{4}{5} \times \frac{4}{5} \times \frac{1}{5} = \frac{16}{125}$
RRR	$\frac{4}{5} \times \frac{4}{5} \times \frac{4}{5} = \frac{64}{125}$

(a) $\frac{64}{125}$

(0.512)

(b) $\frac{48}{125}$

(0.384)

(c) $\frac{12}{125}$

(0.096)

(d) $\frac{1}{125}$

5

Outcome	Probability
Ch Ch Ch	$\frac{6}{8} \times \frac{5}{7} \times \frac{4}{6} = \frac{5}{14}$
Ch Ch Cu	$\frac{6}{8} \times \frac{5}{7} \times \frac{2}{6} = \frac{5}{28}$
Ch Cu Ch	$\frac{6}{8} \times \frac{2}{7} \times \frac{5}{6} = \frac{5}{28}$
Ch Cu Cu	$\frac{6}{8} \times \frac{2}{7} \times \frac{1}{6} = \frac{1}{28}$
Cu Ch Ch	$\frac{2}{8} \times \frac{6}{7} \times \frac{5}{6} = \frac{5}{28}$
Cu Ch Cu	$\frac{2}{8} \times \frac{6}{7} \times \frac{1}{6} = \frac{1}{28}$
Cu Cu Ch	$\frac{2}{8} \times \frac{1}{7} \times \frac{6}{6} = \frac{1}{28}$
Cu Cu Cu	$\frac{2}{8} \times \frac{1}{7} \times \frac{0}{6} = 0$

(a) $\frac{5}{14}$

(b) $\frac{9}{14}$

Exercise 13

1 (a) $\frac{4}{6} \left(= \frac{2}{3}\right)$ (b) $\frac{2}{6} \left(= \frac{1}{3}\right)$ **2** (a) $\frac{5}{8}$ (b) $\frac{3}{8}$

3 (a) $\frac{9}{16}$ (b) $\frac{7}{16}$

4 (a) $\frac{3}{7}$ (b) $\frac{5}{7}$ (c) $\frac{5}{7}$ (d) 0

5 (a) $\frac{7}{16}$ (b) $\frac{1}{16}$ (c) $\frac{9}{16}$

6 $\frac{7}{20}$ **7** $\frac{3}{15} \left(= \frac{1}{5}\right)$ **8** (a) $\frac{6}{8} \left(= \frac{3}{4}\right)$ (b) $\frac{3}{8}$

9 (a) $\frac{5}{20} \left(= \frac{1}{4}\right)$ (b) $\frac{5}{20} \left(= \frac{1}{4}\right)$ (c) $\frac{11}{20}$

10 (a) $\frac{6}{10} \left(= \frac{3}{5}\right)$ (b) 0   (c) $\frac{7}{10}$

11 $\frac{4}{6} \times \frac{3}{5} = \frac{12}{30} \left(= \frac{2}{5}\right)$ **12** $\frac{7}{16} \times \frac{6}{15} = \frac{42}{240} \left(= \frac{7}{40}\right)$

13 $\frac{3}{7} \times \frac{2}{6} = \frac{6}{42} \left(= \frac{1}{7}\right)$ **14** $\frac{7}{16} \times \frac{6}{15} = \frac{42}{240} \left(= \frac{7}{40}\right)$

15

Outcome	Probability
HH	$\frac{6}{8} \times \frac{5}{7} = \frac{30}{56}$
HS	$\frac{6}{8} \times \frac{2}{7} = \frac{12}{56}$
SH	$\frac{2}{8} \times \frac{6}{7} = \frac{12}{56}$
SS	$\frac{2}{8} \times \frac{1}{7} = \frac{2}{56}$

(a) $p(SS) = \frac{2}{56} \ (= \frac{1}{28})$

(b) $p(HH) = \frac{30}{56} \ (= \frac{15}{28})$

(c) $p(HS \text{ or} SH) = \frac{24}{56} (= \frac{3}{7})$

16

Outcome	Probability
PP	$\frac{3}{13} \times \frac{2}{12} = \frac{6}{156}$
PP^1	$\frac{3}{13} \times \frac{10}{12} = \frac{30}{156}$
P^{1}P	$\frac{10}{13} \times \frac{3}{12} = \frac{30}{156}$
P^{1}P^1	$\frac{10}{13} \times \frac{9}{12} = \frac{90}{156}$

(a) $p(PP) = \frac{6}{156} \ (= \frac{1}{26})$

(b) $p(\text{at least one P})$

$= 1 - \frac{90}{156}$

$= \frac{66}{156} \ (= \frac{11}{26})$

17 (a) $\frac{1}{8}$

(b) $\frac{3}{8}$

(c) $\frac{4}{8} \ (= \frac{1}{2})$

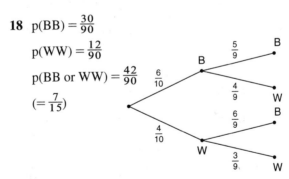

Outcome	Probability
HHH	$\frac{1}{2} \times \frac{1}{2} \times \frac{1}{2} = \frac{1}{8}$
HHT	$\frac{1}{2} \times \frac{1}{2} \times \frac{1}{2} = \frac{1}{8}$
HTH	$\frac{1}{2} \times \frac{1}{2} \times \frac{1}{2} = \frac{1}{8}$
HTT	$\frac{1}{2} \times \frac{1}{2} \times \frac{1}{2} = \frac{1}{8}$
THH	$\frac{1}{2} \times \frac{1}{2} \times \frac{1}{2} = \frac{1}{8}$
THT	$\frac{1}{2} \times \frac{1}{2} \times \frac{1}{2} = \frac{1}{8}$
TTH	$\frac{1}{2} \times \frac{1}{2} \times \frac{1}{2} = \frac{1}{8}$
TTT	$\frac{1}{2} \times \frac{1}{2} \times \frac{1}{2} = \frac{1}{8}$

18 $p(BB) = \frac{30}{90}$

$p(WW) = \frac{12}{90}$

$p(BB \text{ or } WW) = \frac{42}{90}$

$(= \frac{7}{15})$

Outcome	Probability
BB	$\frac{6}{10} \times \frac{5}{9} = \frac{30}{90}$
BW	$\frac{6}{10} \times \frac{4}{9} = \frac{24}{90}$
WB	$\frac{4}{10} \times \frac{6}{9} = \frac{24}{90}$
WW	$\frac{4}{10} \times \frac{3}{9} = \frac{12}{90}$

Exercise 14

1 (a) $p(R) = \frac{5}{12}$ (b) $p(\text{not G}) = \frac{9}{12} = \frac{3}{4}$ (c) $p(W) = 0$

2 (a) $14 = 5 + 9, 6 + 8, 7 + 7, 8 + 6, 9 + 5; p(14) = \frac{5}{81}$ (81 possibilities)
   (b) either 2 or 18   (c) 3 or 17

3 (i) $\frac{3}{8}$ (ii) $\frac{1}{8} \times \frac{1}{8} = \frac{1}{64}$

4 (a) $\frac{1}{4}$ (b) $\frac{1}{4} \times \frac{1}{4} = \frac{1}{16}$ (c) $\frac{1}{2} \times \frac{1}{2} \times \frac{1}{2} = \frac{1}{8}$

5 (a) (i) p(Adam wins) $= \frac{1}{6}$ (ii) p(Bethan wins) $= \frac{9}{36} = \frac{1}{4}$

(iii) p(Christos wins) $= \frac{6}{36} = \frac{1}{6}$ (iv) p(Dean wins) $= \frac{5}{12}$

(b) The game is not fair as Dean is more likely to win. All probabilities need to be $\frac{1}{4}$ for the game to be fair.

6 (a) $\frac{1}{6} \times \frac{1}{6} \times \frac{1}{6} = \frac{1}{216}$ (b) $\frac{1}{6} \times \frac{9}{10} = \frac{9}{60} = \frac{3}{20}$

7 (a) Frequency for 2 is 8

(b) p(odd number) $= \dfrac{10 + 6 + 5}{30} = \frac{21}{30} = \frac{7}{10}$ $(= 0.7)$

8 (a) (i) p(mint) $= \frac{1}{3}$

(ii) David has eaten a toffee leaving 3 toffees and 2 mints, hence p(toffee) $= \frac{3}{5}$, (total of 5 sweets).

(b) (i)

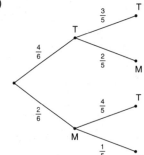

(ii) p(one of each)
$= (\frac{4}{6} \times \frac{2}{5}) + (\frac{2}{6} \times \frac{4}{5}) = \frac{8}{15}$

Investigations

1 The theoretical probabilities are:
p(heart first) $= 0.25$
p(heart third) $= 0.145$ $(2941 \ldots)$

The most likely position is *first*.
(p(H first) $= 0.25$, p(H second) $= 0.19$,
p(H third) $= 0.145$, p(H fourth) $= 0.11$)

2

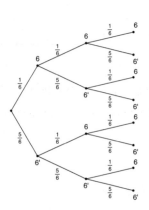

Outcome	Probability
666	$\frac{1}{6} \times \frac{1}{6} \times \frac{1}{6} = \frac{1}{216}$
666'	$\frac{1}{6} \times \frac{1}{6} \times \frac{5}{6} = \frac{5}{216}$
66'6	$\frac{1}{6} \times \frac{5}{6} \times \frac{1}{6} = \frac{5}{216}$
66'6'	$\frac{1}{6} \times \frac{5}{6} \times \frac{5}{6} = \frac{25}{216}$
6'66	$\frac{5}{6} \times \frac{1}{6} \times \frac{1}{6} = \frac{5}{216}$
6'66'	$\frac{5}{6} \times \frac{1}{6} \times \frac{5}{6} = \frac{25}{216}$
6'6'6	$\frac{5}{6} \times \frac{5}{6} \times \frac{1}{6} = \frac{25}{216}$
6'6'6'	$\frac{5}{6} \times \frac{5}{6} \times \frac{5}{6} = \frac{125}{216}$

From the diagram:

p(no 6's) $= \frac{125}{216} = 0.579$

p(one 6) $= \frac{75}{216} = 0.347$

p(two 6's) $= \frac{15}{216} = 0.069$

p(three 6's) $= \frac{1}{216} = 0.0046$

On average, every set of 216 throws will pay out:
$(75 \times £1) + (15 \times £2) + (1 \times £10) = £75 + £30 + £10 = £115$
The total money taken in will be £216. The game is *not* fair, and is weighted in favour of the stallholder, who makes on average £101 on every 216 throws (or 47p each throw).
(This may well be satisfactory in so far as a village fête is concerned.)

Here are two ways of making a profit of about £2 every ten throws (there are many others):

(a) If 50p is paid out for no 6's, then the total pay-out for 216 throws, on average, will be: $(125 \times 50p) + £115 = £177.50$.
Profit will be $£216 - £177.50 = £38.50$

This is $\frac{£38.50}{216} = 17.8p$ per throw $= £1.78$ for 10 throws.

(b) If, instead, the payments are: £1 for one 6, £5 for two 6's and £24 for three 6's, then the pay-out for 216 throws, on average, will be:
$(75 \times £1) + (15 \times £5) + (1 \times £24) = £174$.
Profit on 216 throws is $£216 - £174 = £42$

This is $\frac{£42}{216} = 19.4p$ per throw $= £1.94$ for 10 throws

(If the pay-out for throwing three 6's was lowered to £22.80, the average takings would be exactly £2 for every ten throws.)

INDEX